# New Applications
# of Lasers to Chemistry

# New Applications of Lasers to Chemistry

Gary M. Hieftje, EDITOR

*Indiana University*

Based on a symposium

sponsored by the

ACS Division of Analytical

Chemistry at the 175th

Meeting of the American

Chemical Society, Anaheim,

California, March 14–15, 1978.

ACS SYMPOSIUM SERIES 85

AMERICAN CHEMICAL SOCIETY

WASHINGTON, D. C.    1978

Library of Congress CIP Data

New applications of lasers to chemistry.
 (ACS symposium series; 85 ISSN 0097-6156)

 Includes bibliographies and index.

 1. Lasers in chemistry—Congresses.
 I. Hieftje, Gary M. II. American Chemical Society.
Division of Analytical Chemistry. III. Series: American
Chemical Society. ACS symposium series; 85.

QD715.N48          543               78-22032
ISBN 0-8412-0459-4     ASCMC 8     85 1–242 1978

# ACS Symposium Series

## Robert F. Gould, *Editor*

# FOREWORD

The ACS Symposium Series was founded in 1974 to provide a medium for publishing symposia quickly in book form. The format of the Series parallels that of the continuing Advances in Chemistry Series except that in order to save time the papers are not typeset but are reproduced as they are submitted by the authors in camera-ready form. Papers are reviewed under the supervision of the Editors with the assistance of the Series Advisory Board and are selected to maintain the integrity of the symposia; however, verbatim reproductions of previously published papers are not accepted. Both reviews and reports of research are acceptable since symposia may embrace both types of presentation.

# CONTENTS

# PREFACE

The papers collected in this volume reflect the content of the two-day invited symposium which was organized under the auspices of the Analytical Division of the American Chemical Society; however, because the presentations contained subject matter not ordinarily associated directly with chemical analysis, a more general symposium title was chosen. This same title is born by the present volume.

A rather general title seems especially appropriate here. It is clear that the present and future impact of lasers in analytical chemistry can only be assessed from the broader perspective of the laser's overall application to chemistry. By its very nature, analytical chemistry relies heavily on advances in measurement technology and, consequently, on developments in physics and engineering. Accordingly, symposium speakers were invited who addressed the subject of laser application from several vantage points. Physicists, engineers, and chemists all participated and represented not only academic laboratories but government agencies and industrial organizations as well. Consequently, subject material ranged from new developments in laser technology and measurement systems to the use of lasers in the detection of single atoms and molecules.

This volume is organized in essentially the same way as the Anaheim Symposium. Although no well-delineated separation among topics occurs, the first portion of the volume deals principally with the subject of high-resolution spectroscopy, the second with high-sensitivity analysis, the third with time-resolved or kinetic spectroscopy, and the last with new techniques in laser Raman spectrometry. To a large extent, these divisions represent areas of chemistry in which the laser has had greatest impact. The high spectroscopic resolution afforded by modern lasers makes possible the more accurate identification of molecular and atomic energy levels, affords the specificity necessary to spectroscopically resolve components in a mixture, and permits isotope analysis and separation. Similarly, the high power available from some lasers, coupled with new measurement techniques, has extended analytical sensitivities to the single atom and molecule limit, as indicated earlier. Moreover, the brief pulses emitted by mode-locked lasers provides time resolution below the picosecond regime. Finally, new linear and nonlinear Raman methods made possible by high-power, monochromatic laser sources have extended the range of applicability of Raman techniques, their specificity, and sensitivity.

Unfortunately, not all individuals who participated in the Anaheim Symposium have contributed to this volume. However, an excellent cross section of topics and authors appears and serves to represent the scope of current applications of lasers to chemistry and the potential importance of lasers in the future of chemistry and chemical analysis.

Indiana University GARY M. HIEFTJE
Bloomington, Indiana
August 7, 1978

# Selective Excitation of Probe Ion Luminescence (SEPIL)

JOHN C. WRIGHT, FREDERICK J. GUSTAFSON, and LAURA C. PORTER

Department of Chemistry, University of Wisconsin, Madison, WI 53706

There have been numerous studies that illustrate the excellent detection limits obtained when a laser excitation source generates optical emission from a sample (1-7). When working at such low concentration levels, one must battle the new problems of contamination and impurities. The laser can provide a potential advantage here as well because of the very narrow spectral bandpasses of modern lasers. If the analytical system has sharp line optical transitions whose wavelength depends upon the particular analyte, the narrow bandwidth can provide a high degree of selectivity for the analyte of interest. A common method of providing the narrow transitions is to convert the analytical sample to a gas as is commonly done in atomic absorption and atomic fluorescence experiments (7). The techniques for accomplishing this transformation have a long history in the field and there can be little doubt about the eventual success.

We have been studying the feasibility of a very different method of achieving narrow transitions that are characteristic of an analyte. The lanthanide ions have narrow line transitions, even in condensed phases, as a result of shielding of the optically active $4f^n$ electron shell by the outer $5s^2 5p^6$ orbitals (8,9). A small crystal field splitting is produced by the immediate surroundings. This splitting can be used as a short range spectroscopic probe of the condensed phase. In particular if analyte ions are also present in the condensed phase near a lanthanide probe ion, a crystal field splitting will be produced that is characteristic of the presence of that analyte.

0-8412-0459-4/78/47-085-001$05.00/0

In an arbitrary condensed phase, lanthanide ions will
encounter a number of different surroundings either because of
different ways the ions of the phase can be ordered around the
lanthanide ion or because other ions (analytes) have also entered
the phase. The absorption and fluorescence spectra can therefore
become quite complex because of the different splittings of the
lanthanide ions in different surroundings. This complexity may
be simplified if a tuneable laser is used to excite at a wavelength that matches an absorption line of a lanthanide ion with a
particular surroundings (10). Since the lanthanide ions with
different surroundings have different crystal field splittings,
these ions will not be excited. The fluorescence spectrum then
contains only lines from a lanthanide with one type of surroundings. This process is called selective laser excitation or
site selective spectroscopy. Similarly, an excitation spectrum
of one site may be obtained by monitoring a specific fluorescence
line while scanning the dye laser excitation wavelength. Thus a
high selectivity for a particular analyte may be obtained by
either exciting or monitoring spectral transitions of the lanthanide ion that has the analyte of interest in the immediate surroundings.

In order to make this idea practical, one must solve the
chemical problem of bringing about an association between an
analyte ion and a lanthanide ion. There are a number of methods
that can be used to accomplish this. The simplest method is to
make the condensed phase itself from lanthanide ions, i.e. a pure
lanthanide compound. Any foreign ion that enters the crystalline
lattice of such a compound will have to perturb a lanthanide ion.
In a second method, the presence of analyte ions could lead to
the establishment of a second crystalline phase which will parti-
cipate in the partitioning of trace amounts of lanthanide ions.
If two phases are present, one containing the analyte and the
other an innocuous diluent, the lanthanide spectra will reflect
the presence of both phases. A third method introduces both the
lanthanide and analyte ions at trace concentrations in a host
compound and relies upon interactions between them to form associates or complexes. The interactions can be the result of
chemical bonding or of differences in ionic radii or charge state
between analyte and lanthanide. For example, substitution of a
trivalent lanthanide for a divalent cadmium in cadmium molybdate
produces a charge imbalance which could be compensated by
replacing the hexavalent molybdenum by a quadravalent niobium.
The effective positive charge of the lanthanide ion (relative to
the lattice) and the effective negative charge of the niobium

will cause Coulombic attractions which will favor formation of a
lanthanide-niobium complex in the lattice. The perturbations of
the local crystal fields by the niobium will produce crystal field
splittings on the lanthanide ion that are unique and permit the
use of selective laser techniques to excite only lanthanide ions
that have nearby niobium ions. The intensity is proportional to
the number of niobium ions.

Any of the lanthanide ions which are fluorescent can be used
for these procedures. In a practical analysis, it would be best
to choose the lanthanide ion and the specific transitions that
gave the best selectivity and sensitivity. In order to limit the
number of variables that need to be optimized, we have chosen to
use europium as the lanthanide ion in all of our studies because
of several unique properties that make Eu particularly suitable
for preliminary work. The Eu energy level structure is shown in
Figure 1 (8). The ground state $^7F_0$ and the most fluorescent
excited state $^5D_0$ are both singlet levels (a J=0 state can have
only an $M_J$ = 0) and therefore fluorescent transitions from $^5D_0 \rightarrow ^7F_0$
or absorption transitions from $^7F_0 \rightarrow ^5D_0$ have only one transition.
Thus, when one monitors the $^5D_0 \rightarrow ^7F_2$ fluorescence transitions
with an instrument of sufficiently large bandpass to include transitions from the Eu ions in all possible crystallographic sites as
one scans a tuneable laser over the region of $^7F_0 \rightarrow ^5D_0$ transitions,
the resulting spectrum will contain only one line for each type of
crystallographic environment that Eu encounters in the sample.
This procedure permits a rapid characterization of the sites
present in a sample by taking a single scan. The advantage is
partially offset because the position of the $^7F_0 \rightarrow ^5D_0$ transition
results only from a second order perturbation and its intensity is
lower because it is forbidden in first order. There is also a
possibility of having the line from a Eu with a nearby analyte
accidentally overlapping lines from Eu ions in other sites. These
problems can be eliminated by using the other Eu transitions such
as $^7F_0 \rightarrow ^5D_2$ or by using other lanthanide ions.

LANTHANIDE ANALYSIS

Our research into the feasibility of implementing these ideas
as an analytical methodology has been divided into two sections -
development of trace methods for lanthanide ion analysis where the
association with an analyte is not a factor (the lanthanide ion
itself is the analyte) and development of methods for other ions
where the analyte ion must be associated with the lanthanide. The
over-all problem can then be approached in smaller sections while
simultaneously providing new analytical methods.

The procedure for performing a lanthanide analysis consists
of adding $Ca(NO_3)_2$ to the solution containing unknown amounts of
lanthanide ions and precipitating with the addition of $NH_4F$ (11).
The lanthanide ions co-precipitate with a very favorable

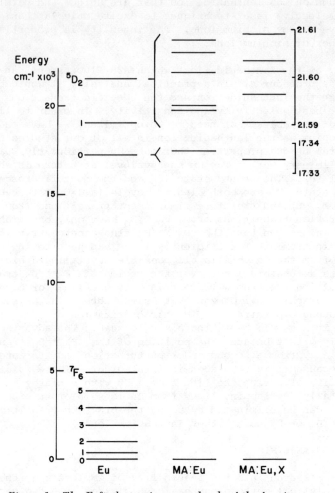

*Figure 1.  The $Eu^{3+}$ electronic energy levels of the free ion are shown on the left. The splittings and shifts that occur when the $Eu^{3+}$ ion is placed within two different crystal fields is shown on the right for the $^5D_2$ and $^5D_0$ manifolds. Note the scale expansion required to see the crystal field splittings. The MA:Eu represents Eu doped in a lattice MA and the MA:Eu,X represents Eu and an analyte X in association in the MA lattice.*

distribution coefficient in the $CaF_2$.   This step serves both as
an extraction, separation, and pre-concentration.   The precipitate
is filtered, washed, and ignited.   The ignition step converts the
fluoride interstitial charge compensation of the co-precipitated
lanthanide ions to an oxygen charge compensation.   This conversion
also reduces the number of different sites present and increases
the oscillator strengths of the optical transitions.   The procedure works quite well.   No separation steps are required for iso-
lating individual lanthanide ions, linear calibration curves are
obtained up to concentrations of 1 ppm, and detection limits of
200 parts in $10^{15}$ are possible.   The latter limit is expected to
be lowered by at least an order of magnitude because of several
improvements in our detection electronics.

ANALYTES ASSOCIATED WITH LANTHANIDES

     The simplest method of establishing an association between
the lanthanide ion and an analyte was by forming an ordered structure of a lanthanide compound in the presence of an analyte.   This
method is illustrated in Figure 2 for $Eu_2(SO_4)_3$ which has been
produced by rapid evaporation of solution containing 0.5 mole %
$Na_3PO_4$ relative to $SO_4^=$.   The spectrum in Figure 2 was obtained by
scanning a dye laser over the excitation region of the $^7F_0 \rightarrow {}^5D_0$
transition while monitoring the $^5D_0 \rightarrow {}^7F_2$ fluorescence with a very
wide bandpass.   Each peak represents a single Eu site.   The two
small peaks to the left of the main intrinsic peak are only
obtained with $PO_4^=$ in the original solution and they have an
intensity which is proportional to the $PO_4^=$ concentration.   The
same behavior is obtained if $AsO_4^=$ is present although the two
$AsO_4^=$ peaks occur at different wavelengths from those of $PO_4^=$.
Although the analyte peaks do not look very significant in comparison with the main intrinsic peak and would seem susceptible to
being lost in the main line at lower concentrations, their absolute intensity is considerable.   In fact, the interference from
the main peak can be eliminated either by tuning the laser to
either of the excitation wavelengths of the $PO_4^=$ peaks and selectively exciting fluorescence from only the Eu sites with $PO_4^=$
nearby or by setting a monochromator with a narrower bandpass to
monitor a fluorescence transition of Eu sites with nearby $PO_4^=$ and
obtaining a single site excitation spectrum.   Either method produces spectra completely free of the main intrinsic lines and permits one to follow the $PO_4^=$ peaks to much lower concentrations.

     Association between the lanthanide and analyte ions can also
be achieved if the two ions provide a mutual charge compensation
for each other in a lattice of ions with different valences (12).
This method is more complex than the previous example because
several additional factors become important.   The Coulombic interactions within the charge compensating pair that promote their
association are opposed by the lattice distortions that might

result if the pair becomes associated and by entropy considerations which favor randomization of the ions. If these associates have favorable free energies, they will cause an increase in the distribution coefficients for the partitioning of the ions into the crystal lattice. Additionally, both ions can be compensated by native defects that are present in the lattice giving rise to intrinsic sites that comprise the spectra in the absence of analytes. One can again have associates of either lanthanide or analyte ions with the native defects in a number of different arrangements. A lanthanide ion will be involved in a competition between association with an analyte, association with a native defect, and dissociation. Each of the possible equilibria will also affect the native defect equilibria of the host lattice. This situation can be compared directly with the familiar equilibria that a chemist considers for complexation of EDTA with a transition metal in an ammonia buffer solution. A conditional formation constant can be assigned for particular values of pH and ammonia ligand concentration. In the same way, success of this method requires favorable "conditional formation constants" for the lanthanide-analyte associates. There are different limiting cases that can be encountered for different values of the equilibria constants.

1.  Analyte-lanthanide association is strong.

2.  Lanthanide-native defect association is strong while analyte-native defect association and analyte-lanthanide association are weak.

3.  Both lanthanide-native defect association and analyte-native defect association are strong.

4.  Lanthanide association with either analyte or native defects is weak.

Each of the different cases has a distinctive influence on the observed spectra. The first case is the analytically useful one in which new lines appear in the spectra that are directly related to the presence of an analyte. This case is shown in Figure 3 for $CdMoO_4$ with Eu and Nb present in trace quantities. These spectra were obtained by monitoring the $^5D_0 \rightarrow {}^7F_2$ transition with a very broad bandpass while scanning the wavelength of a dye laser over the possible $^7F_0 \rightarrow {}^5D_0$ transitions. The lines characteristic of Nb can be selectively excited or monitored to obtain spectra of only those Eu ions with nearby Nb.

For case 2, the addition of analyte to a material can cause marked changes in the spectrum of a Eu doped system because of the disturbance in native defect concentrations. The addition of analyte is accompanied by an increase in the native defect concentration required to charge compensate that analyte. If there is little association between the analyte and its native defect, the concentration of the unassociated native defect will become large

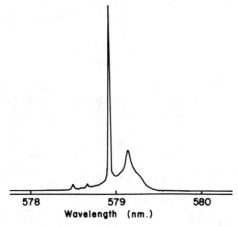

578    579    580
**Wavelength (nm.)**

*Figure 2. The excitation spectrum of the $^7F_0 \rightarrow {}^5D_0$ transition in $Eu_2(SO_4)_3$ with $PO_4^{3-}$ added obtained by monitoring the fluorescence from $^5D_0 \rightarrow {}^7F_2$ with a broad bandpass instrument. The two small peaks on the left are characteristic of the presence of $PO_4^{3-}$.*

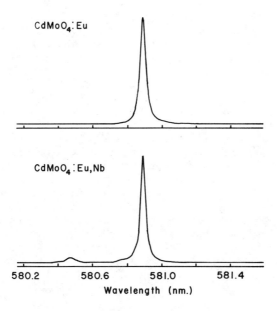

$CdMoO_4$ : Eu

$CdMoO_4$ : Eu, Nb

580.2    580.6    581.0    581.4
**Wavelength (nm.)**

*Figure 3. The excitation spectra of the $^7F_0 \rightarrow {}^5D_0$ transition in $CdMoO_4$ with europium alone and with europium and niobium added in trace quantities. This spectra was obtained by monitoring the $^5D_0 \rightarrow {}^7F_2$ fluorescence with a broad bandpass instrument. The additional line associated with the niobium is readily observed. The niobium concentration is 1 mol%.*

thus depressing the concentration of the native defects compensating the Eu ion. This lowered concentration can be partially restored by dissociation of Eu-native defect associates which is reflected by the loss of line intensity from these associated Eu sites. An example of this is shown in Figure 4 for $PbMoO_4$ with Eu and As present in trace amounts. No new lines appear that can be related to As but there is a strong influence of As on the spectrum. It should be emphasized at this point that the explanation given above can only be classified as highly speculative at this point because of the lack of research in this area in our laboratory and others.

The spectra that are observed in the third case are not well defined. The addition of analyte can have no affect on the Eu spectra if the association of analyte and its native defect is strong enough that the previously existing equilibria of native defects is not affected. In general however, the association cannot be that strong and changes are expected although not as marked as case 2. No new lines appear that are characteristic of the analyte.

The final case corresponds to no changes in the Eu spectra because of the addition of an analyte species. The Eu is isolated and not interacting with either analyte nor native defect compensations.

The model presented above is an idealized one in many respects that is meant only to focus attention on the important aspects of this method of analysis. It neglects many variables such as several competing equilibria with other native defects or impurities, equilibria with the surrounding atmosphere, and the changes that occur in distribution coefficients because of the addition of an analyte species. It does point out the possibility of controlling the important defect equilibria for optimizing an analysis procedure by analogy to the EDTA equilibria where the pH controls the analytically important equilibria. For crystalline lattices, it may be possible to control the native defect concentrations to increase "conditional formation constants" for the lanthanide-analyte associates making a particular procedure feasible or optimal.

CONCLUSIONS

These methods represent a departure from conventional fluorescence approaches that become feasible with the addition of the laser to the line of analytical instruments. The approach is very promising for several reasons. It is inherently a method with very low detection limits and can be used over a wide dynamic range of concentrations as demonstrated in the experiments on trace lanthanide analysis. If the preparation step involves a

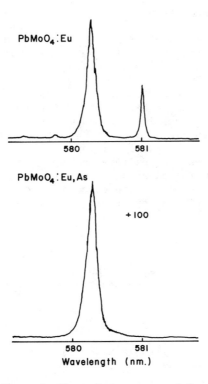

*Figure 4. The excitation spectra of the $^7F_0 \to {}^5D_0$ transition in $PbMoO_4$ with europium alone and with europium and arsenic added in trace quantities. This spectrum was obtained by monitoring the $^5D_0 \to {}^7F_2$ fluorescence with a broad bandpass instrument. It can be seen that the addition of the arsenic analyte does not produce any useful lines but it does have a marked effect on the intrinsic europium sites. The arsenic concentration is 1 mol%.*

precipitation, this step will serve as a method of preconcentration of the solution into the lattice.  There are two steps in the method that provide a high selectivity for particular analytes thus potentially eliminating the need for prior separation steps.

- The preparation will exclude other ions with ionic radii and charges incompatible with the crystal lattice.

- The narrow line-widths of spectral transitions permit the selective excitation of only the Eu ions with the analyte of interest nearby.

We have examined a number of different chemical systems to determine the range of applicability of such methods. Thus far, we have shown analytically useful lines can be found in 15 of the elements as well as the lanthanide ions and we believe the method can be extended to include a majority if not all of the ions in the periodic table.  We thus believe the method is widely applicable and has some powerful advantages but considerably more work is required before the method can be considered an addition to the analytical chemist's bag of tricks.

ACKNOWLEDGMENTS

We would like to thank the National Science Foundation for the support of this research under grant number MPS74-24394.

LITERATURE CITED

1.  Steinfeld, J.I., Tunable Lasers and Their Application in Analytical Chemistry, C.R.C. Crit. Rev. Anal. Chem. (1975) 5, 225-241.

2.  Fairbank, W.M., Hänsch, R.W. and Schawlow, A.L., Absolute Measurement of Very Low Sodium-Vapor Densities Using Laser Resonance Fluorescence, J. Opt. Soc. Am. (1975) 65, 199-204.

3.  Hurst, G.S., Nayfeh, M.H. and Young, J.P., A Demonstration of One-Atom Detection, Appl. Phys. Lett. (1977) 30, 229-231.

4.  Lytle, F.E. and Kelsey, M.S., Cavity Dumped Argon-Ion Laser as an Excitation Source in Time-Resolved Fluorimetry, Anal. Chem. (1974) 46, 855-860.

5.  Richardson, J.H., Wallin, B.W., Johnson, D.C. and Hrubesh, L.W., Sub-Part-Per-Trillion Detection of Riboflavin by Laser Induced Fluorescence, Anal. Chem. (1976) 98, 620-621.

6.   Bradley, A.B. and Zare, R.N., Laser Fluorimetry. Sub-Part-
     Per Trillion Detection of Solutes, J. Am. Chem. Soc. (1976)
     98, 620-621.

7.   Fraser, L.M. and Windfordner, J.D., Laser-Excited Atomic
     Fluorescence Flame Spectrometry, Anal. Chem. (1971) 43,
     1693-1696.

8.   Dieke, G.H., "Spectra and Energy Levels of Rare Earth Ions
     in Crystals", Interscience Publishers, New York (1968).

9.   Wybourne, B.G., "Spectroscopic Properties of Rare Earths",
     Interscience Publishers, New York (1965).

10.  Tallant, D.R. and Wright, J.C., Selective Laser Excitation
     of Charge Compensated Sites in $CaF_2:Er^{3+}$, J. Chem. Phys.
     (1975) 63, 2074-2085.

11.  Gustafson, F.J. and Wright, J.C., Ultratrace Method for
     Lanthanide Ion Determination by Selective Laser Excitation,
     Anal. Chem. (1977) 49, 1680-1689.

12.  Wright, J.C., Trace Analysis of Nonfluorescent Ions by
     Selective Laser Excitation of Lanthanide Ions, Anal. Chem.
     (1977) 49, 1690-1701.

RECEIVED August 24, 1978.

# 2

# Applications of Tunable-Diode-Laser IR Spectroscopy to Chemical Analysis

J. F. BUTLER, K. W. NILL, A. W. MANTZ, and R. S. ENG

Laser Analytics, Inc., 38 Hartwell Ave., Lexington, MA 02173

Tunable diode laser spectroscopy has become a widely used and important technique for ultra-high resolution infrared measurements (1). A resolution in the order of $10^{-4}$ cm$^{-1}$ makes it possible, for example, to study fully resolved lineshapes of Doppler broadened lines of low pressure molecular gases. Such measurements, which can be made rapidly and easily with a tunable diode laser spectrometer, are virtually impossible by other techniques. Tunable diode lasers are also being used in sensitive air pollution monitors in both point (2) and long-path configurations (3).

The purpose of the present paper is to review and discuss new applications of tunable diode laser spectroscopy in several areas relating specifically to chemical analysis and measurement, including nonlinear spectroscopy and photochemistry. These lasers have a number of unique features of particular interest in chemical analysis. Some of these features and their general uses are summarized in Table I.

## Low Level Detection

Concentrations of molecular gases can be measured to exceptionally low levels using tunable diode laser IR absorption spectroscopy. As one example of this application, a group at McMaster University has constructed a highly sensitive air pollution monitor using the apparatus diagrammed in Figure 1 (2). The air sample flows into the multi-traversal absorption cell at reduced pressures. An AC modulation superimposed on the DC bias current induces a small repetitive scan of the laser emission frequency, allowing the use of derivative spectroscopy. The McMaster group was able to measure absorbance levels as low as $\alpha = 10^{-5}$ by using the second derivative. Figure 2 illustrates the use of this apparatus for the detection of atmospheric $SO_2$. The McMaster group reported sensitivity levels as low as 3 ppb

0-8412-0459-4/78/47-085-012$05.00/0

TABLE I

TUNABLE DIODE LASER FEATURES RELEVANT
TO ANALYTICAL INSTRUMENTATION

High Spectral Purity ($10^{-4}$ $cm^{-1}$)

    High specificity eliminates or greatly reduces errors due to interfering absorption lines and the complexity of algorithms required to compensate for background absorptions.

Spectral Region

    3-30 µm region contains absorption spectra of nearly all molecular substances.

Tunability

    Precise spectral lines or regions may be selected.
Information in the lineshape can be utilized.

Ease of Rapid Modulation

    High frequency operation reduces turbulence and particulate noise.
Novel signal processing techniques can be employed.

High Brightness

    Nearly opaque substances can be analyzed.
Transmission over long optical path is feasible.

Small Emitting Area (5 x $10^{-6}$ $cm^2$)

    Small, constrained regions can be probed.
Long-path measurements are facilitated.

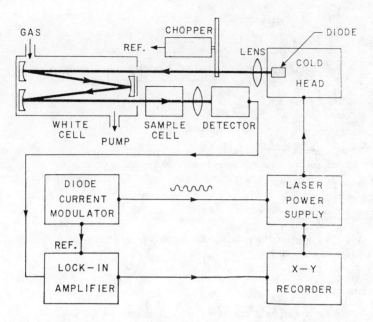

*Figure 1. Diagram of a tunable-diode-laser pollution monitoring system. Sensitivity is enhanced by the use of a multi-traversal, low-pressure cell and second-derivative detection.*

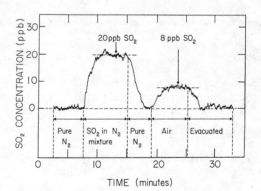

*Figure 2. Typical measurement data for the tunable-diode-laser instrument diagrammed in Figure 1. A calibration measurement of 20 ppb of SO$_2$ in N$_2$ is followed by a measurement of air containing 8 ppb of SO$_2$.*

for $SO_2$. Their predicted sensitivity levels for other pollutants measured by this technique are summarized in Table II.

As another illustration of the potential low level detection capability of tunable diode laser spectroscopy, consider the measurement of $^{14}CO_2$ concentration. Researchers from Laser Analytics and the New York State Department of Health (4,5) have shown that the isotopic shifts in $CO_2$ absorption lines are easily resolved with diode lasers (Figure 3) and have experimentally verified an absorption strength for strong lines of about $S = 2.1 \times 10^{-18} cm^{-1} \text{-} molecule^{-1} cm^2$. From the AFGL line listings (6), it is found that the optimum $^{14}CO_2$ line for detection purposes is the P(18) line at 2210.885 $cm^{-1}$, and that the principal interfering species in air is $N_2O$. Assume a detection system incorporating a 6-liter multitraversal cell, a 200 m optical path, and $\alpha \ell = 10^{-5}$. In a background of 7.6 Torr of air, the minimum detectable concentration of $^{14}CO_2$ is found to be $2.6 \times 10^4$ molecules/$cm^3$. This corresponds to a total mass of $1.16 \times 10^{-2}$ picograms in the cell, or $1.73 \times 10^{-2}$ picocuries in equivalent units of radioactivity. In pure $CO_2$ without a background of air, concentration as low as 975 molecules/$cm^3$ corresponding to a total mass of $4.36 \times 10^{-4}$ picograms or $6.48 \times 10^{-4}$ picocuries can, in principle, be detected.

## Partial Pressure Determination

Laser spectroscopic analysis offers a direct, non-perturbing and general method of determining partial pressures in gaseous mixtures. As illustrated in the $H_2SO_4$ study discussed below, partial pressures can be measured by this new technique to much lower levels and under more severe conditions (e.g., 200°C hot sulfuric acid) than would be possible by other methods.

A Laser Analytics group has investigated partial pressures of $H_2O$, $SO_3$ and $H_2SO_4$ vapors over azeotropic aqueous solution of $H_2SO_4$ under a program sponsored by the U.S. Environmental Protection Agency (7). The partial pressures were determined by measuring absorption line strengths of $SO_3$ and $H_2O$ above the solution and comparing them with line strengths of calibration samples. The $H_2SO_4$ pressure was then deduced from a total pressure measurement using a U-tube manometer filled with liquid sulfuric acid.

Figure 4 shows a diode laser scan of the vapor over an $H_2SO_4$ bath near 1416 $cm^{-1}$ for a sample temperature of 165°C. The broad absorption dip in the center is due to atmospheric water vapor in the 2.2 m unpurged optical path external to the sample cell. One low pressure water line is apparent at the center of this dip; the other lines are due to $SO_3$. The use of diode laser spectroscopy allows single lines of $SO_3$ or $H_2O$ to be selected and their strengths measured.

Partial pressures of $SO_3$, $H_2O$ and $H_2SO_4$ obtained in this study are summarized in Table III. The dissociation constant $K_p$ was calculated from the data of Table III and is included in

TABLE II

MINIMUM DETECTABLE CONCENTRATION FOR
A TUNABLE DIODE LASER SYSTEM

| Pollutant | Approximate Frequency ($cm^{-1}$) | Sensitivity (ppb) |
|---|---|---|
| $SO_2$ | 1140 | 3 |
| $O_3$ | 1050 | 0.5 |
| $N_2O$ | 1150 | 2 |
| $CO_2$ | 1075 | 300 |
| $H_2O$ | 1135 | 50 |
| $NH_3$ | 1050 | 0.05 |
| PAN | 1150 | ~0.3 |
| $CH_4$ | 1300 | 0.03 |
| $SO_2$ | 1370 | 0.3 |
| $NO_2$ | 1600 | 0.02 |
| NO | 1880 | 0.03 |
| CO | 2120 | 0.01 |
| $CO_2$ | 2350 | 0.001 |

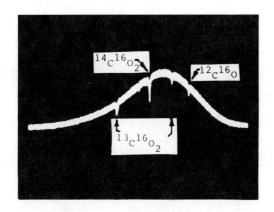

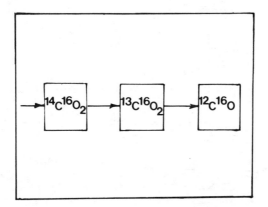

*Figure 3. Tunable-diode-laser transmission spectrum near 4.5 μm showing the $^{12}C^{16}O_2$ 1–0 band R(23) absorption line at 2224.713 cm$^{-1}$, the $^{13}C^{16}O_2$ $\nu_3$ band P(62) line at 224.033 cm$^{-1}$, the $^{13}C^{16}O_2$ [01$^1$1 ← 01$^1$0] band P(51C) line at 2224.514 cm$^{-1}$, and the $^{14}C^{16}O_2$ $\nu_3$ band P(2) line at 2224.257 cm$^{-1}$. The lower figure illustrates that three different, low pressure gas cells in series were used for the measurement.*

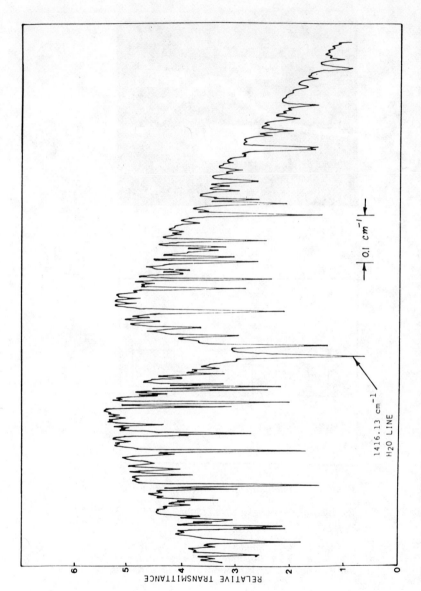

Figure 4. Tunable-diode-laser transmission spectrum of the vapor above a hot (~165°C) H₂SO₄ solution. A large dip attributable to atmospheric water vapor in the unpurged optical path external to the sample cell is evident.

Table III. The data in Table III are in good agreement with an extrapolation of higher temperature data obtained by other methods (8).

TABLE III

PARTIAL VAPOR PRESSURES ABOVE A HOT $H_2SO_4$ AZEOTROPIC SOLUTION

| a. Temp. (°C) | Partial Pressure (Torr) | | | Dissociation Constant $K_p$ (Torr) |
|---|---|---|---|---|
| | $H_2O$ | $SO_3$ | $H_2SO_4$ | |
| 107 | 0.024 + 0.002 | 0.022 + 0.002 | 0.034 + 0.02 | 0.0155 |
| 150 | 0.23 + 0.02 | 0.21 + 0.02 | 0.32 + 0.08 | 0.151 |
| 180 | | 0.90 + 0.09 | | |
| 200 | 2.3 + 0.2 | 2.0 + 0.2 | 3.5 + 0.8 | 1.31 |

a. Azeotropic solution temperature, cell body is 20°C hotter in each case.

## IR Spectral Analysis of Aqueous Solutions

Infrared spectroscopy of aqueous solutions is potentially a powerful analytical tool in, for example, blood analysis, biological studies and many areas of chemistry. However, it has not been widely used in the past because water samples of useful thickness are essentially opaque to IR radiation at the intensity provided by conventional spectrometers. The availability of IR lasers with their much higher intensity now makes it possible to realistically consider IR spectroscopy of aqueous solutions.

To further pursue this possibility, researchers at Laser Analytics have measured the transmission of liquid water as a function of thickness. Laboratory, deionized water was inserted into a sample cell with microadjustable length. A Laser Analytics LS-3 spectrometer equipped with a 4.8 μm diode laser was used for the measurement. Results are summarized in Figure 5, which shows absorbance plotted as a function of thickness. Signal-to-noise ratios in excess of two were obtained for absorbances as high as 5.2 ($\alpha\ell = 12$), in samples more than 0.3 mm thick. This is a sufficient thickness to allow a variety of important IR analysis techniques to be employed.

## Nonlinear Spectroscopy and IR Photochemistry

Tunable diode lasers have been used in a number of recent experiments involving nonlinear absorption and photochemical excitation. Figure 6, for example, illustrates an arrangement used by a group at MIT Lincoln Laboratory to study double resonance absorption in $SF_6$ (9). The crossbeam geometry minimized scatter of pump beam radiation into the probe beam detection sys-

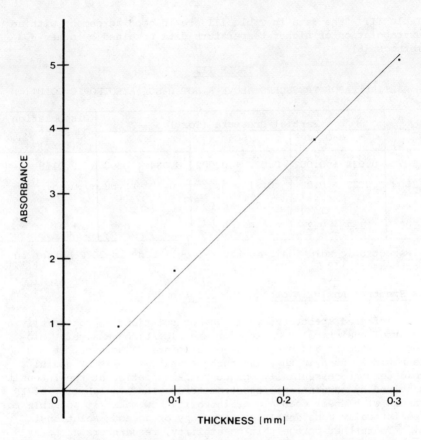

Figure 5.  Tunable-diode-laser measurement of the absorbance of liquid water as a function of thickness at a frequency of 2080 cm⁻¹.  A signal-to-noise ratio greater than two was observed for thickness greater than 0.3 mm.

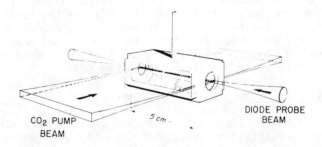

Figure 6.  Experimental arrangement for double resonance absorption studies of $SF_6$.  The crossed-beam geometry was used to minimize scatter of pump radiation into the detection system.

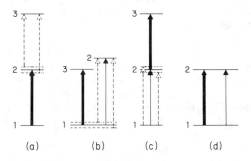

*Figure 7. Excitation diagrams for the four DR processes observed in $SF_6$. Thick arrows represent pump radiation, thin arrows, probe radiation. The pump induces Rabi-split levels and associated transitions, which are indicated by dashed lines and arrows.*

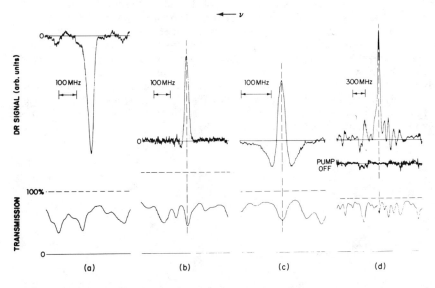

*Figure 8. Four representative transient DR signals, each with corresponding and simultaneously-measured, average transmission spectra shown below. Main peaks of DR signals in (a), (b), (c), and (d) occur at 944.91, 945.69, 943.59, and 951.19 $cm^{-1}$, respectively, found using $CO_2$ pump lines P(18), P(16), P(22), and P(12), respectively. Gas pressure was 0.2 Torr in (a), (b), and (d), and 0.3 Torr in (c). Dotted lines connect DR signals with associated absorption lines. In (d), DR signal is shown with pump laser off, to indicate system noise.*

tem. The peak intensity of the $CO_2$ laser pump was about 1 kW/cm$^2$, while the CW probe beam intensity was less than 5 mW/cm$^2$. The CW probe beam was mechanically chopped and, after detection and processing by a lock-in amplifier, yielded a signal proportional to the average diode laser power transmitted through the gas cell. A fast component in the signal, coincident with the $CO_2$ laser pulse, appeared when the diode was tuned to the double-resonance (DR) condition; the fast component was recovered with a boxcar integrator. The boxcar output thus represented the transient change in the probe beam absorption caused by the presence of the pump beam.

Figure 7 shows a schematic diagram of the four DR processes observed, and Figure 8 shows the actual spectral data. Figures 7a and 8a illustrate induced transient absorption due to a laser enhanced occupation of the lower level (level 2). Figures 7b and 8b illustrate induced transmission due to a common-ground-state-process (CGSP) in which the pump depletes the lower level. Figures 7c and 8c illustrate induced transmission due to a depletion of the upper level and strong absorption in the field induced Rabi sidebands. Finally, Figures 7d and 8d illustrate strong induced transmission or bleaching caused by the simultaneous depopulation of the lower level and filling of the upper level. Several different 1-2 transitions are pumped due to power broadening, thus producing the complicated lineshape shown.

Additional recent examples of the use of tunable diode lasers in related areas include: diode laser induced saturated absorption and Lamb dip spectroscopy of $NH_3$ (10) diode laser induced photo dissociation of dimers in molecular beams (11); diode laser induced reaction between $BCL_3$ and a cryogenic $CH_4$ matrix (12); state selective excitation of molecular beams, and Doppler-free spectroscopy of CO and $NO_3$ (12).

## Literature Cited

1. Nill, K. W., Laser Focus (1977) 13, 32

2. Reid, J., Garside, B. K., Shewchun, J., El-Sherbiny, M., and Ballik, E. A., Appl. Optics (1978) 17, 1806

3. Hinkley, E. D., Optical and Quantum Electronics (1976) 8, 155

4. Eng, R. S., Nill, K. W. and Wahlen, M., Appl. Optics (1977) 16, 3072

5. Wahlen, M., Eng, R. S. and Nill, K. W., Appl Optics (1977) 16, 2350

6. McClatchey, R. A., Benedict, W. S., Clough, S. A., Burch, D. E., Calfee, R. F., Fox, K., Rothman, L. S. and Garing, J. C., U.S. Air Force Report, AFCRL-TR-73-0096 (1973)

7. Eng., R. S., Nill, K. W. and Butler, J. F., Final Report, U.S. Environmental Protection Agency, Contract No. 68-02-2482 (1978)

8. Gmitro, J. I. and Vermeulen, Am. Inst. Chem. Eng. Journal (1964) 10, 740

9. Moulton, P. F., Larsen, D. M., Walpole, J. N., Mooradian, A., Optics Lett. (1977) 1, 51

10. Jennings, D. E., Appl. Phys. Lett. (1978) 33, 493

11. Gough, T. E. and Leroy, R., Tenth International Conference on Quantum Electronics, (May 29-June 1, 1978) Atlanta, Georgia

12. Catalano, E. and Barletta, R. E., American Chemical Soc. Meeting, (March 12-17, 1978) Anaheim, California

13. Gough, T. E., Miller, R. E., Scoles, G. Appl. Phys. Lett. (1977) 30, 338

RECEIVED August 23, 1978.

# 3

# Two-Photon Excited Molecular Fluorescence

M. J. WIRTH[1] and F. E. LYTLE

Department of Chemistry, Purdue University, West Lafayette, IN 47907

A two-fold approach is taken in the investigation of the analytical aspects of two-photon spectroscopy. A novel laser source
is introduced and characterized as an expedient means of achieving
two-photon absorption; and two-photon excited fluorescence spectroscopy is demonstrated as a promising method for chemical analysis, with a diversity of applications.

The high peak power and continuous nature of the synchronously pumped cw dye laser allows the generation of a sensitive and
precise two-photon excitation response, and the wide tunability
range allows acquisition of two-photon excitation spectra. It has
been determined that the cavity dumped version of the laser yields
the best performance for two-photon spectroscopy and offers the
most versatile output method.

The difference in selection rules for one- and two-photon
spectroscopy gives rise to a complementary set of excitation spectra. Additionally, polarization information is retained in the
two-photon excitation of randomly oriented molecules, therefore
the excitation response can be selective with respect to the symmetry of the excited state. These features suggest the applicability of two-photon spectroscopy as a unique tool for qualitative
analysis.

Since the wavelength of the incident radiation is twice that
which corresponds to the transition, the two-photon excitation
method can be used to probe species in optically dense media. It
is demonstrated that fluorophors can be quantified in matrices
having large and varying absorbances, with detection limits superior to those of one-photon spectroscopy. Also, the error due to
reabsorption of emission can be minimized by utilizing the spatial
selectivity of the excitation process.

General Considerations. The term nonlinear optics refers to
those phenomena involving light where the induced polarization, P,
of an atomic or molecular electron cloud is not at the same

[1] Current address: Department of Chemistry, University of Wisconsin, Madison.
WI 53706

0-8412-0459-4/78/47-085-024$06.50/0

frequency as that of the driving electric field strength, E.  For
a centrosymmetric molecule, P is related to E by the expression

$$P = \varepsilon_o \{ \chi_1 E + \chi_3 E^3 + \cdots \}$$  Eq. 1

where $\varepsilon_o$ is the permittivity of free space and the $\chi_i$ are the susceptibility tensors of order i and rank (i+1) (1).
  Linear optics occurs when the susceptibilities are space and
time independent, and when $\chi_1 \gg \chi_3 \cdots$.  For this situation Eq. 1
can be rewritten as

$$P_1(\omega) = \varepsilon_0 \chi_1(\omega) E(\omega)$$  Eq. 2

where $\omega$ is the frequency of the driving radiation.  To describe
the behavior of Eq. 2 at all frequencies, the susceptibility must
be considered a complex quantity, i.e.,

$$\chi_1 = \chi_1' + i\chi_1''.$$  Eq. 3

At frequencies far removed from a transition resonance, the real
part of Eq. 3 predominates.  The resultant relationship between P
and E contains a phase lag which is experimentally observed as the
refractive index, where $n^2 = 1 + \chi_1'$.  At frequencies near resonance the imaginary part predominates.  The electric field is then
absorbed to an extent determined by the extinction coefficient, k
where $2nk = \chi_1''$.  The behavior of the system towards any given $\omega$
will depend upon the relative magnitudes of $\chi_1'(\omega)$ and $\chi_1''(\omega)$.

  <u>Non-linear Optics</u>.  The third order polarization of Eq. 1 can
be expanded into the form

$$P_3(\omega_i) = \varepsilon_0 \chi_3(\omega_i, \omega_j, \omega_k, \omega_1) E(\omega_j) E(\omega_k) E(\omega_1)$$  Eq. 4

where four waves are being mixed by $\chi_3$.  Several common combinations of frequencies are shown in Table I.  Like the first order
polarization, the third order case exhibits important subcombina-
tions that are identified by various resonance enhancements.
Since these correspond to atomic or molecular transitions, the
nonlinear effect can be used to obtain structural information.
  The possibility of observing optical frequency nonlinear phenomena has long been established.  An upper bound for the required
field strength can be estimated by the field, $E_0$, binding an electron to the nuclei and the approximate rule that $\chi_1/\chi_3 \sim E_0$ (2).
A typical value for $E_0$ would be $3 \times 10^8$ Vcm$^{-1}$ which corresponds to
an intensity of $\sim 10^{15}$ Wcm$^{-2}$.  The experimental dilemma was alleviated when in late 1960, T. Maiman published the design of the
first laser (3).   After this date nonlinear processes were dis-
covered and/or verified in rapid succession - second harmonic
generation (4) and two-photon absorption (5) in 1961; stimulated
Raman scattering (6), sum and difference frequency generation (7),

Table I. Examples of Four Wave Mixing

| Resultant Frequency | Mixed[a] Frequencies | Resonance[b] Frequency | Phenomenon |
|---|---|---|---|
| $3\omega_1$ | $\omega_1, \omega_1, \omega_1$ | --- | Frequency tripling. |
| $\omega_1$ | $\omega_1^*, \omega_1, \omega_1$ | --- | Self-focusing. |
|  |  | $\omega_1 = \omega_e$ | Self-induced transparence. |
| $\omega_2$ | $\omega_1^*, \omega_1, \omega_2$ | --- | Intensity dependent refractive index. |
|  |  | $\omega_1 + \omega_2 = \omega_e$ | Two-photon absorption. |
|  |  | $\omega_1 - \omega_2 = \omega_v$ | Stimulated Raman emission. |
|  |  | $\omega_2 - \omega_1 = \omega_v$ | Inverse Raman absorption. |
| $2\omega_1 - \omega_2$ | $\omega_1, \omega_1, \omega_2^*$ | --- | Four wave mixing. |
|  |  | $\omega_1 - \omega_2 = \omega_v$ | Coherent anti-Stokes Raman emission. |

(a) The superscript star notation denotes that the complex conjugate of the electric field strength is utilized in the polarization equation.

(b) $\omega_e$ = an electronic transition; $\omega_v$ = a vibrational transition.

optical rectification (8), and frequency tripling (9) in 1962;
self-focusing in 1964 (10); and coherent antiStokes Raman (CARS)
generation in 1965 (11). Thus, much of the early work was involved with the understanding and prediction of these formerly unob-
served effects.

Two-Photon Absorption. The third order susceptibility giving
rise to two-photon absorption can be written as $\chi_3(\omega_2, \omega_1, -\omega_1, \omega_2)$.
For this case the field strength product is written as
$E(\omega_1)E*(\omega_1)E(\omega_2)$ or $\bar{I}_1 E(\omega_2)$, where $\bar{I}_1$, is the cycle averaged intensity of $\omega_1$. The third order susceptibility can then be
written as a correction term, $\delta\chi$, to the first order, where

$$\delta\chi_1(\omega_2) = \chi_3(\omega_2, \omega_1, -\omega_1, \omega_2) \ \bar{I}_1 . \qquad \text{Eq. 5}$$

The polarization at $\omega_2$ then becomes

$$P(\omega_2) = \varepsilon_0 \{\chi_1(\omega_2)E(\omega_2) + \delta\chi_1(\omega_2)E(\omega_2)\} \qquad \text{Eq. 6}$$

As long as $\chi_1''$ and $\delta\chi_1''$ are negligible, $\omega_2$ will not be absorbed.
This gives rise to an intensity dependent refractive index as the
$\delta\chi'$ term approaches the magnitude of $\chi_1'$. Whenever $\chi_1''$ is large
and positive, direct absorption of $\omega_2$ occurs. Whenever, $\delta\chi''$ is
large and positive, an intensity dependent absorption of $\omega_2$
occurs. Finally whenever $\delta\chi_1''$ is large and negative, an intensity
dependent stimulated emission of $\omega_2$ occurs.
      In the two-photon absorption process, an excited state is
created with an energy twice that of the incident photons. The
absorption law that the process obeys is similar to that for one-
photon except that the absorption is intensity dependent, as predicted in the previous section. For small values, the fraction
of light absorbed (12) can be determined by

$$\Delta P/P = [\delta P/A] \ \ell C \qquad \text{Eq. 7}$$

where P is the incident power, $\Delta P$ is the change in power due to
absorption, $\delta$ is the two-photon absorptivity, C is the concentration, $\ell$ is the path length, and A is the transverse area of
the incident beam. From equation 7 it is seen that the two-
photon absorbance is proportional to concentration and path
length as in Beer's law, and in addition it is proportional to
the light intensity, P/A. Thus, the absorption can be enhanced
by increasing the power or by focusing the beam more tightly.
The laser parameter dependence makes measurements of absolute
absorptions difficult.
      A typical value for $\delta$ is $10^{-50}$ $cm^4$ s $photon^{-1}$ $molecule^{-1}$,
which becomes $10^{-11}$ L cm $mole^{-1}$ $Watt^{-1}$ for molar concentration
and 333 nm radiation. The laser system used in this study could
generate a 1 kW pulse and focus it to a 10 μm spot. Thus, the
two-photon cross-section, $\delta P/A$, is typically $10^{-2}$ L $mol^{-1}$ $cm^{-1}$,

i.e., six orders of magnitude smaller than the corresponding one-photon cross-section.

The small magnitude of the cross-section is the basis of an experimental challenge in two-photon spectroscopy. Two-photon absorbance can be detected either by measuring the attenuation of the beam power, which is a relatively insensitive means, or by monitoring thermal, acoustical, ionization, or luminescence effects in the sample. In the reported work the response is monitored exclusively by fluorescence because of its sensitivity. From equation 7 it can be seen that the fluorescence intensity is proportional to $\Delta P$, and therefore to $P^2$.

## The Synchronously Pumped CW Dye Laser As A Source for Two-Photon Spectroscopy

The small magnitude of the absorption cross-section and the non-linear nature of the process, have required that pulsed laser sources be employed in two-photon spectroscopy in order to generate a measurable number of excited states. The usual difficulty with this method is that the excitation pulses vary unpredictably in amplitude, necessitating some means of correcting the measured response for laser pulse characteristics. Pulse height variations present a particularly severe problem in two-photon spectroscopy because the excitation depends upon the square of the incident power. This problem might be minimized by the use of continuous, mode-locked lasers because pulse fluctuations with these devices are small.

The synchronously pumped dye laser (SPDL) is a continuous, mode-locked laser with demonstrated ability to excite two-photon transitions (13). Pulse generation is achieved by matching the cavity length of the dye laser to that of the continuously mode-locked argon ion laser (14, 15, 16). Since mode-locking produces a train of pulses highly reproducible in amplitude and temporal profile, the peak power of each pulse is proportional to the average power of the train. Measurement of the average power of a continuous laser is straight forward and can be used to correct the measured two-photon excitation response for the incident peak power.

The Laser. The optical and electronic layout of the system is shown in Figure 1. A detailed description of the laser has been given previously by Harris et al. (14,17). A Coherent Radiation CR-6 argon-ion laser is mode-locked by a Coherent Radiation Model 464 acousto-optic modulator driven at 44 MHz, producing a continuous train of 0.4 ns wide pulses spaced 11 ns apart. This train is used to pump a Coherent Radiation Model 490 jet stream dye laser, the cavity length of which is adjusted to equal the pulse spacing. A Spectra-Physics Model 365 acousto-optic deflector is incorporated into the dye laser in order to dump pulses at a controlled rate. The synchronization between the mode-locked optical pulse circulating in the cavity and the deflector is

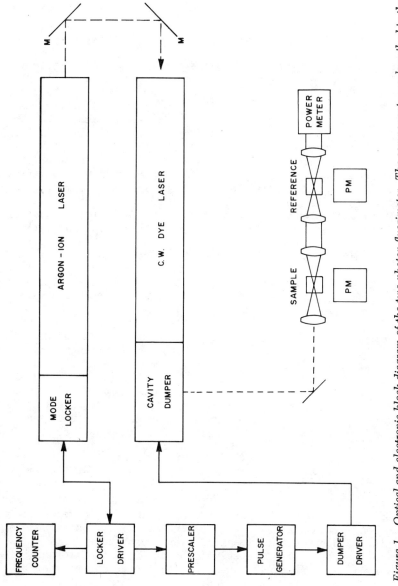

*Figure 1.   Optical and electronic block diagram of the two-photon fluorimeter. The components are described in the text.*

provided by a high speed prescaler obtained from Electronic Digital Systems, Lafayette, Indiana. This unit provides a variable
output rate ($\sim$ 10 MHz to $\sim$ 5 KHz) by activating a Hewlett-Packard
Model 8013B pulse generator, which subsequently gates the 365 rf
power. The dye laser was cavity dumped at repetition rates near
2 MHz to optimize the fluorescence intensity. The wavelength was
monitored with a prism spectroscope having a precision of $\sim$0.2 nm.

Spectral Coverage. Three different dyes were used to obtain
the fluorescence data, sodium fluorescein, rhodamine 6G, and rhodamine B. For the rhodamine dyes, all four mirrors in the dye
laser cavity were coated for rhodamine 6G. For sodium fluorescein
the pair of mirrors in the dye laser head were coumarin 6 mirrors
and the dumper mirrors were coated for the argon-ion laser. The
tuning curves for the dyes are given in Figure 2. From the figure
it can be seen that the overall range of accessible wavelengths
extends from 530 to 670 nm. Taking into account that the final
states are one-half the wavelength of the incident beam, the
effective tunability range extends from 265 to 325 nm. A wide
variety of molecules have transitions in this spectral region,
thus it is a useful working range for exploring the analytical
possibilities of two-photon excited fluorescence spectroscopy.

In addition to the above dyes other groups have constructed
sources based on a Krypton-ion laser and the dyes coumarin-102,-30
and -7 (18), and oxazine-1, DOTC and HITC (19). This gives a potential tuning range of 470-920 nm to access two-photon states
between the wavelength limits of 235-460 nm.

Temporal Properties. The simplest experimental approach to
obtaining two-photon spectra is to adjust the wavelength by
rotation of the Lyot filter and to measure the resulting fluorescence intensity and laser power. After subtraction of a blank
reading, the fluorescence intensity is normalized for the square
of the incident power. Corrections of this type require that the
shape of the picosecond pulses remain constant throughout the
range of wavelengths. If the synchronously pumped laser is truly
mode-locked, then the pulse shape will always remain constant.
Mode-locked pulses are transform limited, meaning that the pulse
width is the inverse of the spectral bandwidth of the lasing transition. Since the bandwidth is constant, the pulse width of a well
mode-locked laser should remain fixed throughout the tuning range.
In practice, however, the modulation in gain that causes mode locking is not perfect in that it is dependent upon the magnitude of
the gain. Since the gain itself is wavelength dependent, it is
expected that the pulse shapes will be altered at different points
in the excitation spectra. Such changes in the output must be
taken into account to obtain accurate two-photon excitation spectra.

There are two possible means of characterizing the two-photon
response of the synchronously pumped laser: measuring the pulse
width as a function of wavelength in order to calculate the actual

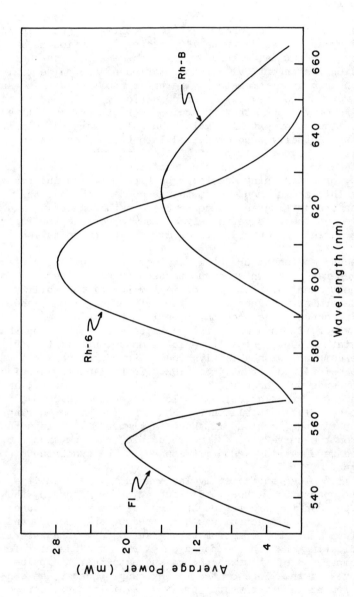

*Figure 2.   Tuning curves for the synchronously pumped dye laser. Fl, fluorescein; Rh-6, rhodamine 6G; and Rh-B, rhodamine B.*

peak power; and generating the excitation spectrum of a known compound to obtain correction factors applicable to all successive spectra. Both methods were applied in the work to determine their relative merits.

The pulse width of the synchronously pumped dye laser has been reported as to be 10 ps or less (15,20,21,22). Thus it cannot be measured by any detector, with the possible exception of a streak camera. The usual method employed to measure such short pulse durations is an optical autocorrelation of the pulse train using a Michelson interferometer. The pulse profiles were measured in this work, under several laser conditions. The results of the interferometry showed that the pulses were transform limited only at very low gain. At high gains the pulses were not simply broadened, but actually were organized into two pulses. As a result an interferogram will be of limited utility in correcting excitation spectra because the pulse profiles are too complex to be reliable for determining the laser peak power. The information gained from this measurement supports the contention that the pulse shapes are not guaranteed to be uniform throughout the tuning range and there is definitely a need to correct for laser pulse shape variations in order to obtain the true excitation spectra.

The second approach for obtaining corrected excitation spectra is to generate a known spectrum to be used as a reference for all subsequent spectra. This method is limited by the ability to precisely determine the spectrum of the reference compound and can therefore introduce large uncertainties into the measurement. At present, however, it is a more practical means of correction than the pulse width measurement. It would be most convenient to use a reference compound with a fairly broad, structureless spectrum in order to maintain constant precision. In preliminary studies, several compounds were observed to have featureless spectra, and one compound in particular, bis-methylstyrylbenzene (bisMSB), appeared to be relatively flat throughout the rhodamine 6G range. The spectrum for the compound is shown in Figure 3a. Points that deviated from the curve were not reproducible from one spectrum to the next and were attributed to mismatches in the synchronous cavity length.

Rhodamine 6G has sufficiently large gain to allow cavity-dumped laser operation without mode-locking, thus affording the capability to scan the excitation spectrum with a well defined peak power. A bisMSB spectrum was corrected by this method and is shown in Figure 3b. The spectrum was measured to be flat to within 15%, indicating that the compound can serve as a useful reference. A comparison of the two spectra suggests that the pulse shape improves at the wings of the tuning range because the synchronously pumped laser generated spectrum exhibits over-corrections in this region.

Qualitative Analysis Via Two-Photon Spectroscopy

The two-photon absorption process was first predicted in 1931 by Geoppart-Mayer (23) from recognizing that the Dirac theory for Raman scattering could be modified to describe the simultaneous absorption of two photons. Since the early 1960's, group theory and quantum mechanics have been exclusively used as tools to relate the measured absorptivity to the transition tensor in order to extract the characteristic molecular information. For electric dipole transitions in molecules possessing a center of symmetry, it has been shown that the parity of the excited state resulting from two-photon absorption is opposite to that from one-photon absorption (5). A two-photon spectrum would therefore reveal transitions due to gerade (even) states that are conventionally considered forbidden in electronic spectroscopy. This is analogous to the complementary relationship of infrared and Raman spectra.

Another unique feature of two-photon spectra is the presence of absorption peaks due to two electron transitions (24). In one-photon spectroscopy, the states connected by a transition may differ by only one orbital. In two-photon spectroscopy, since the intermediate state differs from the initial state by one orbital, then the final state may differ by two orbitals. The final state can therefore result from two promotions of one electron or one promotion of two electrons. The latter is strictly forbidden in one-photon spectroscopy.

A related area with analytical applicability is multiple photon ionization. Such methods typically employ a two-photon induced ionization, where selectivity is brought about by the presence of a resonant intermediate state to enhance the cross-section, and good detectability is achieved from the availability of sensitive detection methods for ions (25). A similar method is involved in the pursuit of isotope separation via multi-photon ionization. Efforts are concentrated in the infrared region where typically 30 or more photons are necessary for ionization. Studies are presently centered about the physics of the excitation process in order to understand the factors that determine the selectivity (26).

Two-Photon Transition Moment. For centrosymmetric molecules the one-photon transition only has significant oscillator strength when the parity of the electronic wave function changes upon absorption. This is because the electric dipole operator is an odd function, thus, in order for the transition moment to be nonzero, the states connected by the transition must have opposite parity (27). In most cases the ground state is the totally symmetric state and the energy levels detectable by one-photon spectroscopy correspond to the odd, or ungerade, states.

The two-photon absorption process can be thought of as two simultaneous one-photon absorptions, with the first photon

achieving an intermediate state and the second photon taking the
molecule to the final state as shown in Figure 4. From this picture it can be ascertained that the two-photon excited state will
be opposite in parity to the one-photon excited state. The transition moment is nonzero if the intermediate level has ungerade
character and the final state is gerade. The two-photon spectrum
will therefore be characteristic of the locations of the conventionally forbidden gerade states (5).

The intermediate state, $|i>$ can be considered an off-resonance
level of all $|u_k>$. This is possible since each $|u_k>$ could be de-
scribed by a Lorentzian curve and thus extend to all frequencies.
The transient nature of $|i>$ can be explained via the Heisenberg
Uncertainty Principle, i.e., if $E(u_1) - E(i) = 10,000$ cm$^{-1}$, $\Delta t$ is
computed to be $\sim$ 1 fsec. This short lifetime requires that the
photons interact simultaneously to produce the state $|g_1>$.

The two photon transition moment between $|g_0>$ and $|g_1>$ can
be written as

$$M(g_0,g_1) = \sum_k \left[ \frac{[e_1 \cdot M(g_0,u_k)][e_2 \cdot M(u_k,g_1)]}{E(u_k) - \hbar\omega_1} + \frac{[e_2 \cdot M(g_0,u_k)][e_1 \cdot M(u_k,g_1)]}{E(u_k) - \hbar\omega_2} \right] \qquad \text{Eq. 8}$$

where $M(g_0,u_k)$ and $M(u_k,g_1)$ are the one-photon transition moments
connecting the states $|g_0>$, $|g_1>$ and $|u_k>$, $e_1$ and $e_2$ are the
polarization vectors of the two photons. A two-photon spectrum
would consist of all j moments to even parity states.

Several characteristics of two-photon absorption can be in-
ferred from Equation 8. First, as the energy of either photon
approaches that of one of the $|u_k>$ states, the magnitude of the
transition moment increases. Since the oscillator strength depends
upon the square of the transition moment, this can provide a rather
dramatic enhancement in the absorption cross-section. Again an
analogy can be made with the Raman spectroscopy. Second, the
summation is performed over all k ungerade states since $|i>$ is
considered to be an off-resonance superpositioning of each of them.
However, those states closest to $|i>$ will dominate the transition
moment expression because of the resonance effect mentioned above.
Finally, the orientation of the two photon polarization vectors
are independent of each other. Both of these factors play a role
in the magnitude of the transition moment.

Symmetry Considerations. Experimentally, spectra can be generated by the absorption of two photons of the same frequency, or
one each of two different frequencies. With one frequency the
optical polarization can be linear or circular, while the additional possibilities of perpendicular linear and contrarotating

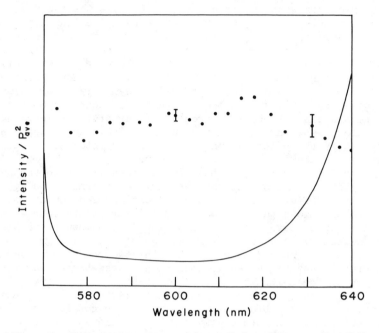

*Figure 3. Excitation spectrum of bis-methylstyrylbenzene (bisMSB). (——) Dye laser synchronously pumped (peak power > - kW) and (· · ·) cavity dumped (peak power > 5 W).*

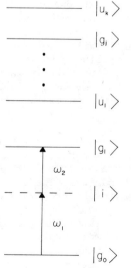

*Figure 4.   Schematic of the two-photon absorption process. Gerade and ungerade states are denoted |g> and |u>, respectively. |i> represents the intermediate level while $\omega_1$ and $\omega_2$ are the frequencies of the two photons.*

circular exists with two frequencies.  Because the two photons are
absorbed simultaneously, their relative polarizations map directly
into the symmetry of the electric susceptibility, and it is therefore possible to perform polarization measurements in fluid solution.  The mathematical derivation by McClain (28) proves rigor-
ously that the polarization terms do not vanish when the molecules
are randomly oriented, and therefore the symmetry information is
retained.  By contrast, in one-photon spectroscopy, symmetry
assignments can only be made from single crystal studies.  Again,
the analogy between infrared and Raman can be made.  In Raman
spectroscopy the polarization information is retained because the
excitation and emission are simultaneous.

In order to relate the measured cross-sections to the symmetry of the transition, it is necessary to determine the spectrum
under three different polarization conditions and compare the results to the known patterns of the molecular point group.  In
practice tables have been worked out (29) to allow one to do this.
It is necessary to have prior knowledge of the point group of the
molecule but it should be noted that the two-photon experiment can
be useful in uncovering environmental effects which lower the
symmetry of the molecule.

Two-photon spectroscopy is particularly useful in identifying
the symmetries of vibrational modes which are coupled to electronic transitions.  The state symmetry is calculated by the direct
product of the electronic term with the vibrational term (27) and
compared with the experimentally determined state symmetry.  The
ability to make symmetry assignments for electronic and vibronic
transitions is a primary advantage of two-photon spectroscopy.

The most simple two-photon experiments are performed using
only one laser for the excitation process.  In this case the only
possible polarizations are parallel linear and corotating circular.
Since three independent polarization measurements are required to
uniquely specify the symmetry of the final state, the one laser
method is inadequate for this purpose.  With two lasers, the additional possibilities of perpendicular linear and contra-rotating
circular permit complete polarization studies.  It is therefore
necessary to utilize two separately tunable lasers in order to
determine molecular symmetry from two-photon excitation measurements.

The Naphthalene Spectrum.  The two-photon excitation spectrum
of naphthalene serves to demonstrate the concepts discussed above.
As an example, the partial energy level diagram of Figure 5 can be
used to predict differences based on parity.  The one-photon spectrum should have two bands corresponding to the $A_{1g} \rightarrow B_{3u}$ transitions, while the two-photon spectrum should have one band corresponding to the $A_{1g} \rightarrow B_{1g}$ transition.  Mikami and Ito (30) have
studied this system and found such a simple analysis to be partially correct.  That is, the $A_{1g} \rightarrow B_{1g}$ transition appears very
weakly, if at all, in the one-photon spectrum; while the $A_{1g} \rightarrow B_{2u}$

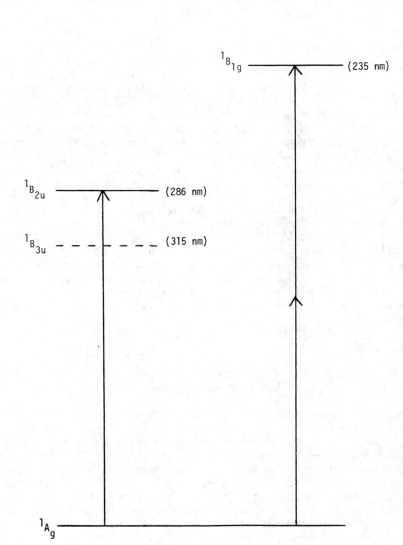

*Figure 5.  Electronic energy level diagram for naphthalene*

transition appears very weakly in the two-photon spectrum. This
a priori generates large qualitative differences in the shape of
the two spectra in these wavelength regions.

On the other hand, the $A_{1g} \rightarrow B_{3u}$ transition represents a fail-
ure of such a simple analysis. With one-photon excitation this
transition is symmetry forbidden due to other selection rules. As
a result the absorption to the $B_{3u}$ state appears as weak structure
on the far stronger $B_{2u}$ background. (See Figure 6.) With two-
photon excitation the transition is weak and appears only because
of coupling to $b_{3u}$ vibrations. (See Figure 7.) Note the large
qualitative differences between the spectra even when the bands
are derived from the same electronic transition. There are two
reasons for this dramatic change. First, the two-photon spectrum
does not have a strong transition of comparable energy, while the
one-photon spectrum does. This fact is responsible for the quite
different baselines. Second, with one-photon excitation the vibronic progression corresponds to even parity vibrations, and with
two-photon excitation they correspond to $b_{3u}$ vibrations.

The naphthalene example illustrates that the features of one-
and two-photon excitation spectra differ because of the change in
selection rules and unpredictable features arising from the possibility of unique configuration interactions. This supports the
drive to utilize two-photon excitation spectra as a tool in chemical analysis because additional information can be obtained from
the spectra and added degrees of selectivity are granted.

## Quantitative Analysis In Complex Samples Via Two-Photon Spectroscopy

The application of fluorimetry as an analytical technique is
limited in many cases by the spectroscopic properties of the
sample environment. When a significant fraction of the incident
radiation is absorbed by the matrix, the measured fluorescence
intensity ceases to be a simple function of the fluorophor concentration. This problem has been addressed by Holland, et al.(31),
who have corrected the emission with a simultaneously measured
value of solution absorbance. Such a scheme was shown to be valid
for optical densities $\leq 2$. Often, however, the analyte is found
in a more highly absorbing medium where conventional techniques
are very unreliable and such correction procedures can be difficult. The two-photon method is quantitative in absorbing media
because there is negligible attenuation of the beam in this process. First of all, the incident beam is twice the wavelength of
the transition, thus the radiation is not absorbed by the one-
photon process. Second, the two-photon process itself is only
weakly absorbing.

### Fluorimetric Analysis in Complex Samples. The rate of fluor-
escence emission is, by definition, equal to the rate of light
absorption times the fluorescence quantum yield.

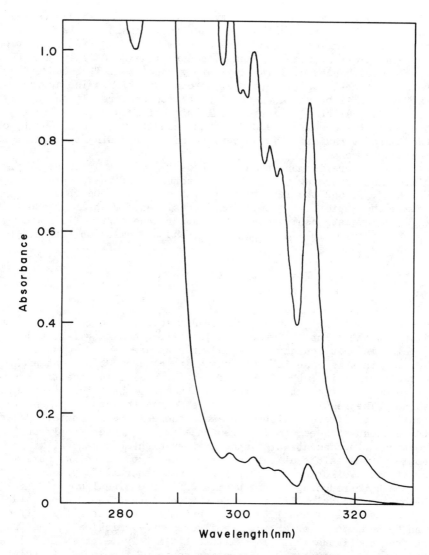

*Figure 6.    One-photon excitation spectrum of naphthalene*

$$F = I_A \emptyset$$

or

$$F = I_o(1-T)\emptyset \qquad\qquad\qquad \text{Eq. } 9$$

where F is the emission intensity, $I_A$ is the absorbed excitation
intensity, $I_o$ is the incident excitation intensity, T is the
sample transmission and $\emptyset$ is the quantum yield.  A linear relation
between emission intensity and concentration  holds only when the
sample absorbance, A, is approximately equal to 1-T, because A,
rather than 1-T, is proportional to concentration.  The approximation A $\simeq$ 1-T breaks down at high absorbances, resulting in roll-
off of the calibration curve.  This situation is referred to as
the inner filter effect.  Under these conditions, the intensity of
the incident radiation is attenuated before reaching the center of
the sample cell.

When there is more than one absorbing species present, $I_o$ is
diminished according to the total absorbance of the sample.
Using Eq. 9, and the fact that the ratios of the absorbances
equals the ratio of the emission intensities for absorbing samples
(32), the relationship between the absorbance of the fluorophore,
$A_F$, the total sample absorbance, $A_T$, and the emission intensity
can be derived as

$$F = I_o \frac{A_F}{A_T}(1-T)\emptyset \qquad\qquad\qquad \text{Eq. } 10$$

where T is now the total sample transmission.  According to Eq. 10,
if the total solution absorbance is small, then $A_T \simeq$ 1-T, and the
species in solution have independent responses.  The emission intensity in this case is proportional to concentration.  At high
optical densities, the amount of radiation exciting the fluorophor
is reduced by the ratio of its absorbance to the total solution
value.  The resulting inner filter effect alters the incident intensity at different distances along the cell path length.  Under
these circumstances, the fluorescence is no  longer simply proportional to concentration and, at very high absorbances, will
not even be visible at the center of the sample.  Unlike pure
substances, diluting the solution is not generally a practical
approach to reducing the problem.  Often the signal would fall
below the detection limit or the nature of the fluorophor could
change because of a shifted equilibrium.  The inner filter effect
can be reduced by observing the fluorescence emission in the front
surface configuration.  This method ultimately fails at high concentrations because the penetration depth of the incident radiation
is dependent upon the sample absorbance.

Absorption Interferences at Excitation Wavelengths.  The
effect of absorbing interferences was studied by using a model
system consisting of p-terphenyl as the fluorophor and bipyridine

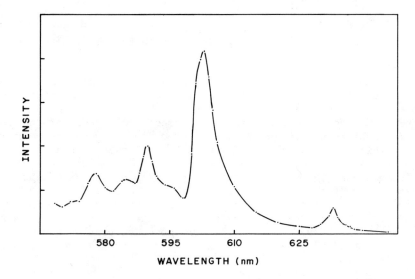

*Figure 7.   Two-photon excitation spectrum of naphthalene*

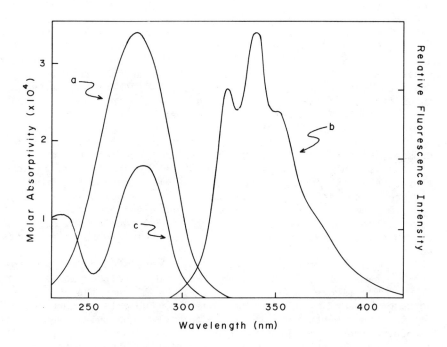

*Figure 8.   Spectral data for* p-terphenyl *and bipyridine.* (a) *Excitation and* (b) *emission spectrum of* p-terphenyl; (c) *absorption spectrum of bipyridine.*

as the interfering chromophore, in the solvent cyclohexane. The
spectral data for this system are shown in Figure 8. The absorption band of bipyridine overlaps that of p-terphenyl almost uni-
formily, while the emission is in a transparent spectral region. A
fixed amount of p-terphenyl was excited in the presence of a varying concentration of bipyridine while the fluorescence of p-terphenyl was monitored. The results, which are plotted in Figure 9,
show that the one-photon excited fluorescence varies with the
sample absorbance ratio, as predicted. The fluorophor concentration information is lost upon one-photon excitation when the concentration of the chromophore is unknown. In two-photon excited
fluorescence, the inner filter effect is nonexistent because the
wavelength of the incident radiation is far removed from the solution absorbance and a negligible amount of power is extracted by
the nonlinear process. Therefore, the intensity of the beam is not
affected by the variation in bipyridine concentration and, even at
high solution absorbance, the fluorophor concentration information
is retained.

Absorption Interferences at Emission Wavelengths. A common
problem encountered in the fluorescence analysis of complex samples
is the reabsorption of emission. This occurs when the emission
band of the analyte is overlapped by the absorbance band of another
species in solution. In right angle detection the emission must
pass through a cell path length of 0.5 cm before reaching the detector, thus the absorbance of the solution cannot exceed 0.025
units at the emission wavelength in order to keep the quantitation
error below 5%. For a chromophore with a molar absorptivity of
$10^4$, its concentration must be below 2.5 μM to keep the emission
intensity representative of the fluorophor concentration. As in
the previously discussed interference case, dilution of the sample
would not necessarily be a practical approach.

The reabsorption problem is circumvented with two-photon spectroscopy because it is possible to utilize the fact that the excitation efficiency is inversely proportional to the transverse area
of the beam. By focusing the incident beam close to the front
surface of the cell, the path length of the emission is decreased
thus tolerating a higher chromophore concentration. The path
length observed in this work was estimated to be 100 μm, allowing
the solution absorbance at the emission wavelength to be as high
as 3.

The model system used in this study consisted of the fluorophors bis-methylstyrylbenzene (bisMSB) and 2,5-diphenyloxazole
(PPO). The fluorescence spectra of Figure 10 show that the absorbance band of bisMSB strongly overlaps the emission band of PPO.
For the experiment, the concentration of PPO was held constant, the
concentration of bisMSB was varied, and the fluorescence intensity
of PPO was monitored following one- and two-photon excitation. The
experimental results are presented in Figure 11. In the one-photon
analysis, front surface detection was implemented in order to effect

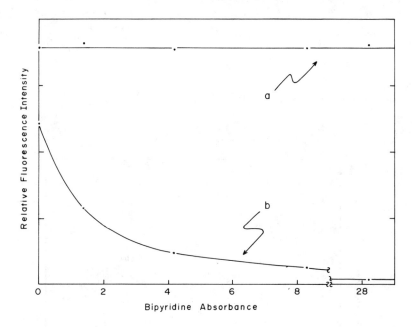

*Figure 9.   Fluorimetry data for the p-terphenyl determination. (a) Two-photon and (b) one-photon excitation.*

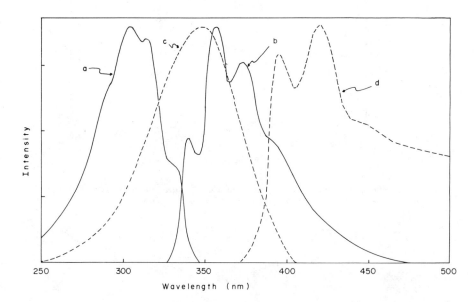

*Figure 10.   Spectral data for 2,5-diphenyloxazole (PPO) and bis-methylstyrylbenzene (bisMSB). (a) Excitation and (b) emission spectra of PPO; (c) excitation and (d) emission spectra of bisMSB.*

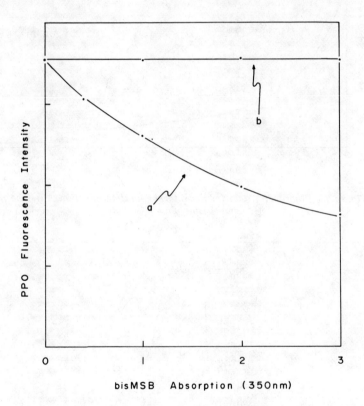

*Figure 11. Fluorimetry data for the mixture analysis. (a) One-photon and (b) two-photon excitation.*

a short path length, however, this emission was still diminished at high sample absorbances due to the reabsorption process. The distance through which the fluorescence traveled was sufficiently large to result in quantitation errors. In the two-photon case, the intensity remains constant, independent of the interference concentration up to solution absorbances of 3.

It should be noted that the effects of emission reabsorption can be alleviated to some extent in one-photon spectroscopy by constructing a spectrometer with very precise focal parameters. It is possible to collect fluorescence intensity from only the first 100 μm of the sample, by using high quality optics. There are two limitations to this approach. First, 100 μm is about the smallest practical distance that can be achieved, whereas the two-photon method can get down to < 10 μm. Second, the usual front surface interferences are still able to hamper the analysis: a) the background scatter is large,  b) the inner surface of the cell is subject to adsorption contamination, and c) the cell it-self may fluoresce. These problems are avoided with two-photon excitation because the incident light is not focused through the sample cell in the spatial region where the fluorescence is observed.

Fluorimetric Analyses in Absorbing Solvents.  An important special case of an interfering chromophore is the optically dense solvent. With one-photon excitation, it is imperative that the solvent be transparent where the species of interest absorb. When this restriction precedes chemical consideration of the solvent choice, the analysis is a priori less than the optimum. As a worst case, the fluorophor is often in, and cannot be removed from, an optically dense matrix. With two-photon excitation, the incident radiation is twice the wavelength of the solvent absorbance, thus it easily penetrates into the matrix to excite the species of interest.

The spectral data for a model system, PPO in acetone, are given in Figure 12. Visual inspection of the solutions indicates that virtually none of the exciting radiation reaches the center of the sample cell. As a result, a front surface configuration is mandatory for one-photon excitation. Even with such an arrangement, sensitivity is decreased by the numerical value of the solvent, according to Eq. 10. Since two-photon excitation is not attenuated by the solvent, a right angle configuration may be used.

Figure 13 shows the fluorescence calibration curves obtained for the model systems discussed above. With the laser source used in this study, the detection limit (S/N = 1) for two-photon excitation of PPO in acetone is approximately 0.5 μM. This result is primarily determined by the peak power of the source, which itself can certainly be improved by at least an order of magnitude. The one-photon detection limit is approximately the same as that for the two-photon case. Although the one-photon value can conceivably be lowered, it is ultimately limited by the amount of scattered

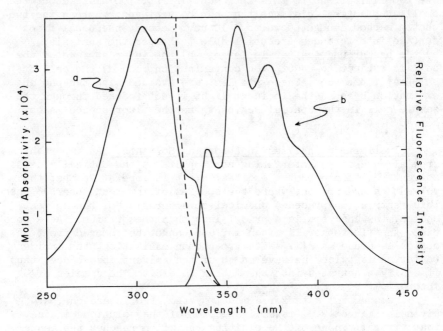

*Figure 12.  Spectral data for PPO in acetone. (a) Excitation and (b) emission spectra of PPO.  The dashed curve represents the acetone cut off.*

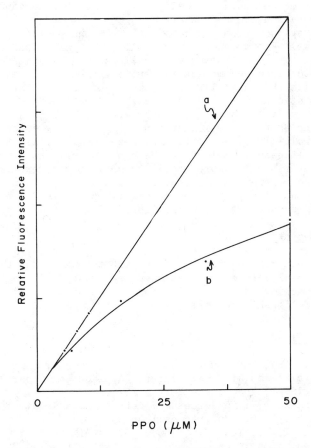

*Figure 13. Fluorimetry data for the PPO in acetone determination. (a) Two-photon and (b) one-photon excitation.*

excitation entering the emission monochromator.  This is an
inherent problem in that the excitation and emission frequencies
are usually close to each other.  Naturally, the front surface
arrangement maximizes the difficulty.  There are no a priori reasons to assume that an increase in source power will improve the
detection limit, because the background noise is increased pro-
portionally.  Again, two-photon excitation minimizes this problem
since the frequencies are usually far from each other and a right
angle observation can be used.

It is evident from Figure 13 that the one-photon curves exhibit the well-known inner filter roll-off at high concentrations.
The linearity in any fluorescence calibration fails as soon as the
emitter absorbance becomes sufficiently large as to break down the
approximation that $A \simeq (1-T)$.  In optically dense solvents this roll-
off occurs at concentrations several hundred times higher than in
transparent solvents due to the shorter effective path length.  It
should be noted that the linear range isn't really extended by the
increased roll-off concentration because the lower limit of detection is simultaneously raised by the same factor.  For two-photon
excitation the total absorption is so small that there is no inner
filter effect operating and, therefore, no curvature in the calibration graph.  Thus, for fluorophors in optically dense matrices,
this method produces the largest linear range.

## Acknowledgements

This research was supported in part through funds provided
by The National Science Foundation under Grant CHE77-24312.  M.J.W.
gratefully acknowledges the American Association of University
Women for fellowship support.

## Literature Cited

1.  For a brief, but comprehensible discussion of tensors, see
    F. Zernike and J. E. Midwinter, "Applied Nonlinear Optics",
    Wiley-Interscience, New York,  1973.
2.  Bloembergen, N. in "Quantum Electronics: A Treatise", H. Rabin
    and C. L. Tang, Eds., Academic Press, New York   1975.
3.  Maiman, T. H., Nature, (1960), 187, 493.
4.  Franken, P. A. et al., Phys. Rev. Lett., (1961), 7, 118.
5.  Kaiser, W. and Garrett, C. G., Phys. Rev. Lett., (1961), 9,
    455.
6.  Eckhardt, G., et al., Phys. Rev. Lett., (1962), 7, 229.
7.  Bass, M., et al., Phys. Rev. Lett., (1962), 8, 18.
8.  Bass, M., et al., Phys. Rev. Lett., (1962), 9, 446.
9.  Terhune, R. W., Maker, P. D., and Savage, C. M. Phys. Rev.
    Lett., (1962), 8, 404.
10. Chaio, R. Y., Garmire, E., and Townes, C. H., Phys. Rev.
    Lett., (1964), 12, 279.
11. Maker, P. D. and Terhune, R. W., Phys. Rev., (1965), 137, 801.

12. McClain, W. M., <u>Acc</u>. <u>Chem</u>. <u>Res</u>., (1974), <u>7</u>, 129.
13. Wirth, M. J. and Lytle, F. E., <u>Anal</u>. <u>Chem</u>., (1977), <u>49</u>, 2054.
14. Harris, J. M., Chrisman, R. W., and Lytle, F. E., <u>Appl</u>. <u>Phys</u>. <u>Lett</u>., (1975), <u>26</u>, 16.
15. Chan, C. K. and Sari, S. O., <u>Appl</u>. <u>Phys</u>. <u>Lett</u>., (1974), <u>25</u>, 403.
16. Mahr, H. and Hirsch, M. D., <u>Opt</u>. <u>Commun</u>., (1975), <u>13</u>, 96.
17. Harris, J. M., Gray, L. M., Pelletier, M. J., and Lytle, F. E., <u>Mol</u>. <u>Photochem</u>., (1977), <u>8</u>, 161.
18. Steinmetz, L. L., Richardson, J. H., Wallin, B. W., and Bookless, W. A., presented at the Topical Meeting for Picosecond Phenomena, Hilton Head, South Carolina, May 1978.
19. Kuhl, J., Lambrich, R., and von der Linde, D., <u>Appl</u>. <u>Phys</u>. <u>Lett</u>., (1977), <u>31</u>, 657.
20. Jain, R. K. and Heritage, J. P., <u>Appl</u>. <u>Phys</u>. <u>Lett</u>., (1978), <u>32</u>, 41.
21. Ausschnitt, C. P. and Jain, R. K., <u>Appl</u>. <u>Phys</u>. <u>Lett</u>., (1978), <u>32</u>, 727.
22. Frigo, M. J., Daley, T., and Mahr, H., <u>IEEE</u> <u>J</u>. <u>Quant</u>. <u>Electron</u>., (1977), <u>13</u>, 101.
23. Geoppart-Mayer, M., <u>Ann</u>. <u>Phys</u>. (Leipzig), (1931), <u>9</u>, 273.
24. McClain, W. M. and Harris, R. A., in "Excited States", Vol. 3, (1977), E. C. Lim, Ed., Academic Press, New York 1977.
25. Gelbwachs, J. A., Klein, C. F., and Wessel, J. E., <u>Appl</u>. <u>Phys</u>. <u>Lett</u>., (1977), <u>9</u>, 489.
26. Letokhov, V. S., <u>Ann</u>. <u>Rev</u>. <u>Phys</u>. <u>Chem</u>., (1977), <u>28</u>, 133.
27. Cotton, F. A., "Chemical Applications of Group Theory", Wiley-Interscience, New York 1971.
28. Monson, P. R. and McClain, W. M., <u>J</u>. <u>Chem</u>. <u>Phys</u>., (1970), <u>53</u>, 29.
29. McClain, W. M., <u>J</u>. <u>Chem</u>. <u>Phys</u>., (1971), <u>55</u>, 2789.
30. Mikami, N. and Ito, M., <u>Chem</u>. <u>Phys</u>. <u>Lett</u>., (1975), <u>31</u>, 472.
31. Holland, J. F., Teets, R. E., Kelley, P. M., and Timnick, A., <u>Anal</u>. <u>Chem</u>., (1977), <u>49</u>, 706.
32. Michaelson, R. C. and Loucks, L. F., <u>J</u>. <u>Chem</u>. <u>Ed</u>., (1975), <u>52</u>, 652.

RECEIVED August 25, 1978.

# 4

# Laser-Excited Luminescence Spectrometry

J. D. WINEFORDNER

Department of Chemistry, University of Florida, Gainesville, FL 32611

Laser excited atomic and molecular spectroscopy has resulted recently in the detection of ultra low concentrations of species. For example, atomic absorption flame spectrometry (AAS)[1,2] is limited to $\approx 10^8$ atoms/cm$^3$. Mass spectrometry is generally a little less sensitive than AAS. Conventional atomic fluorescence flame spectrometry (FAFS)[2,3] is capable of $\approx 10^4$ atoms/cm$^3$. Doppler-free, two photon atomic fluorescence spectrometry (DAFS)[4] is capable of detecting $\approx 10^5$ species/cm$^3$ but the absorption cross-sections must be large, natural and collisional line widths must be small, and radiation lifetimes must be short. Resonantly enhanced two-photon absorption spectrometry (TPAAS)[5] allows detection of $\approx 10^2$ atoms/cm$^3$, but the absorber must have an intermediate state of the appropriate energy to allow utilization of two counter-propagating or co-propagating laser beams. Single-photon laser excited fluorescence spectrometry (SAFS)[6] has also been used to detect $\approx 10^2$ Na atoms/cm$^3$. SAFS however, requires frequency-doubled dye lasers for many transitions and in some cases difficult frequency-mixing systems to obtain good detection limits. Laser-excited non-resonance AFS (LNRAFS)[7] has been used to detect $10^4$ atoms/cm$^3$, although detection limits of $\approx 10$ atoms/cm$^3$ have been predicted. In the LNRAFS case, the atom must have 3 levels with appropriate optical and mixing properties. Finally, photoionization detection of a laser-excited gaseous system (PLE)[12,13] of Cs has been found to yield a detection limit of the order of 1 atom/cm$^3$. The PLE system is extraordinarily sensitive but is plagued with problems difficult to circumvent in analytical spectrometry, such as the sampling method, including the means of producing atoms (or molecules), and the laser source which must cover a wide-wavelength range. Photon catalysis[14] which involves the use of active nitrogen produced by passing N$_2$ through a microwave discharge, has been used to detect $\approx 10^4$ atoms/cm$^3$ of Bi in an Ar atmosphere. Photon catalysis and mass spectrometry do not involve the use of laser excitation but do

0-8412-0459-4/78/47-085-050$07.25/0

result in good detection limits, i.e., order of or below $10^8$ atoms/cm$^3$.

It is apparent that active work is currently on-going in the area of ultra-trace detection of atoms and molecules. The detection limits indicated above are truly exciting when one considers that a species with a molecular weight of 100 amu represents $1.67 \times 10^{-22}$ g/cm$^3$ assuming a detection limit of 1 atom/cm$^3$ or $1.67 \times 10^{-14}$ g/cm$^3$ assuming a detection limit of $10^8$ atoms/cm$^3$. If the atoms are produced in a typical analytical flame (the detection limit of 1 cm$^{-3}$ is valid only for a quartz vessel), then the conversion factor of sample concentration (in µg/ml) aspirated into a chamber type laminar flame system to gas concentration (atoms/cm$^3$) assuming a sample introduction (transport) rate of 3 cm$^3$/min, an unburnt gas flow rate (room temperature) of 20 ℓ/min, a flame temperature of 2500°K, and a 10% nebulization efficiency is $\approx 10^{-9}$, i.e., to convert atoms/cm$^3$ to µg/ml and $10^8$ atoms/cm$^3$ corresponds to $\approx 0.1$ µg/ml.

Fundamental Considerations

Pseudo-Continuum Laser Excited Atomic Fluorescence Spectrometry, AFS. Boutilier, et al.[13] and others[8,14,15,16,17] have considered the atomic fluorescence radiance expressions for the case of "broad-band" (pseudo-continuum, i.e., $\delta\nu_S > \delta\nu_A$, where $\delta\nu_S$ = spectral half-width of source of excitation and $\delta\nu_A$ = absorption line half-width) excitation of atoms present in a medium at low optical densities. The general expression for $B_F$, the fluorescence radiance is given by:

$$B_F = \left(\frac{\ell}{4\pi}\right) Y_{pF} E_{\nu_A}\left(\frac{h\nu_A}{c}\right) B_A \, n_\ell [1 - \frac{g_\ell}{g_m} \frac{n_m}{n_\ell}], \; W \, m^{-2} sr^{-1} \tag{1}$$

or

$$B_F = \left(\frac{\ell}{4\pi}\right) A_F \, h\nu_A \, n_j, \; W \, m^{-2} sr^{-1} \tag{2}$$

where:

$\ell$ = fluorescence path length in direction of observation, m,

$Y_{pF}$ = fluorescence power efficiency, dimensionless,

$E_{\nu_A}$ = absorbed spectral irradiance from source of excitation, W m$^{-2}$,

$h\nu_A$ = absorbed photon energy, J,

$B_A$ = Einstein induced absorption coefficient, s$^{-1}$(Jm$^{-3}$Hz$^{-1}$)$^{-1}$,

$n_\ell$ = density of analyte species in lower level of absorption transition, $m^{-3}$,

$n_m$ = density of analyte species in upper level of absorption transition, $m^{-3}$,

$g_\ell$, $g_m$ = statistical weights of levels $\ell$ and $m$, respectively, dimensionless,

$A_F$ = Einstein coefficient of spontaneous emission for fluorescence transition, $s^{-1}$,

$n_j$ = density of analyte species in upper level of fluorescence transition, $m^{-3}$.

For a three-level atom of the Na-type, $B_F$ is generally given by

$$B_{F_{\substack{u \to \ell \\ \ell \to u'}}} = \left(\frac{\ell}{4\pi}\right) A_{u\ell} h \nu_{u\ell} n_T \left[ \frac{1}{1 + \left(\frac{A_{u\ell} + k_{uu'} + k_{u\ell}}{k_{u'u}}\right)\left(1 + \frac{g_\ell}{g_{u'}}[1 + \frac{E^*_{\nu_{\ell u'}}}{E_{\nu_{\ell u'}}}]\right)} \right] \tag{3}$$

where all terms are as defined above except that the k's are pseudo-first order radiationless deactivation rate constants $(s^{-1})$, $E^*_{\nu_{\ell u}}$ is a modified saturation spectral irradiance and is given by

$$E^*_{\nu_{\ell u'}} = \frac{c\, A_{u'}}{Y_{u'\ell} B_{u'\ell}}, \quad W\, m^{-2} \tag{4}$$

where $Y_{u'\ell}$ is the fluorescence quantum efficiency and u, is the upper level involved in the excitation process, and $\ell$ is the lower level involved in the absorption process (note for some transitions u = u'), and $n_T$ is the total density of analyte atoms in all electronic states. The saturation spectral irradiance, $E^S_{\nu_{\ell u'}}$, is given by

$$E^S_{\nu_{\ell u'}} = \left(\frac{c}{B_{u'\ell}}\right) \left[ \frac{k_{u'\ell} + k_{u'u} + A_{u'\ell} - k_{u'u}[\frac{k_{uu'}}{k_{u\ell} + k_{uu'} + A_{u\ell}}]}{1 + \frac{g_\ell}{g_{u'}} + \frac{k_{u'u}}{k_{u\ell} + k_{uu'} + A_{u\ell}}} \right] \tag{5}$$

For a three-level atom of the Tℓ-type, $B_F$ is generally given by

$$B_{F_{\substack{u \to \ell \\ \ell \to u}}} = \left(\frac{\ell}{4\pi}\right) A_{u\ell'} h\nu_{u\ell'} n_T \left[\frac{1}{1+\dfrac{g_\ell}{g_u}[1+\dfrac{E^*_{\nu_{\ell u}}}{E_{\nu_{\ell u}}}][1+\dfrac{g_{u'}}{g_\ell}e^{-E_{\ell\ell'}/kT}]+\dfrac{A_{u\ell'}+k_{u\ell'}}{k_{\ell'\ell}}}\right] \tag{6}$$

where all terms are as defined above except for

$$E^*_{\nu_{\ell u}} = \frac{c\, A_{u\ell}}{Y_{u\ell} B_{u\ell}}, \; W\, m^{-2}, \tag{7}$$

and the subscripts u, ℓ', ℓ are the upper level, the intermediate (metastable) level, and the lower level (for some transitions ℓ = ℓ'), respectively. Finally, the saturation spectral irradiance, $E^s_{\nu_{\ell u}}$ is given by

$$E^s_{\nu_{\ell u}} = \left(\frac{c}{B_{\ell u}}\right)\left[\frac{A_u+A_{u\ell'}+k_{u\ell}+k_{u\ell'}}{\dfrac{g_\ell}{g_u}+\dfrac{k_{\ell\ell'}+A_{u\ell'}+k_{u\ell'}}{k_{\ell\ell'}+k_{\ell'\ell}}}\right] \tag{8}$$

It should be noted that either the Na-type case or the Tℓ-type case reverts to the 2-level case if in the former u'→u and in the later ℓ'→ℓ, i.e.,

$$B_{F_{\substack{u \to \ell \\ \ell \to u}}} = \left(\frac{\ell}{4\pi}\right) A_{u\ell} h\nu_{u\ell} n_T \left[\frac{1}{1+\dfrac{g_\ell}{g_u}\left(1+\dfrac{E^*_{\nu_{\ell u}}}{E_{\nu_{\ell u'}}}\right)}\right] \tag{9}$$

From the above expressions, particularly in the limiting cases of high source spectral irradiance ($E_\nu >> E^*_\nu$) and in the case of low source spectral irradiance ($E_\nu << E^*_\nu$), several interesting conclusions result.

(1) For low optical densities, $B_F$ is linearly related to $n_T$, the total atom density;

(2) For low source spectral irradiance, $B_F$ is linearly related to source spectral irradiance and to the quantum efficiency of the fluorescence transition;

(3) For high source spectral irradiance, $B_F$ is independent of source spectral irradiance; for the 2 level atom case, a simplistic relation between $B_F$ and $n_T$ results, but for a

3-level atom, non-radiational rate constants must be
known, as well as the flame temperature, T, for the case
of excitation of an excited lower level, in order to evaluate absolute values of $n_T$ from absolute $B_F$ measurements; for the case of saturation fluorescence measurements, $B_F$ must be measured under steady state conditions,
i.e., the radiative lifetime of the excited state must be
much less than the temporal pulse width of the exciting
source. In the case of a Na-type atom, the measurement
of $B_{F_{3\to1 \atop 1\to3}}$ and the ratio $n_3/n_2$, i.e., $B_{F_{2\to1 \atop 1\to3}}/B_{F_{3\to1 \atop 1\to3}}$ enables

absolute $n_T$ values to be measured without the need for
radiationless rate constants. For atoms of a Tℓ-type
atom, it is not possible to determine absolute $n_T$-values
unless several radiationless rate constants are known or
unless

$$\left(\frac{g_1+g_3}{g_3}\right) > \left(\frac{A_{32}+k_{32}}{k_{21}} + \frac{g_2}{g_3} e^{-E_{12}/kT}\right)$$

which is simply the 2-level approximation for a 3-level
atom.

(4) The saturation spectral irradiance, $E_\nu^S$, i.e., the source
spectral irradiance where $B_F$ becomes 50% the maximum possible value, depends upon the frequency, $\nu$, of the transition ($A_{u\ell}/B_{u\ell} = 8\pi h\nu^3/c^3$) and upon the radiational and
radiationless rate constants (refer to equations 5 and
8). Therefore, theoretical estimation of $E_\nu^S$ values from
fundamental aspects is difficult even though experimental
measurement is quite easy. For a 2-level atom, measurement of $E_\nu^S$ values allows estimation of quantum efficiencies, Y. However, for 3-level atoms, estimation of
quantum efficiencies requires not only measurement of $E_\nu^S$
but also explicit knowledge of certain radiational and
radiationless rate constants.

Narrow Line Laser Excitation Molecular Luminescence Spectrometry, MLS. Boutilier and Winefordner[18] have considered the
molecular luminescence radiance expressions for the case of
"narrow-line" excitation of molecules ($\delta\nu_S < \delta\nu_A$) in a medium at low
optical densities. The general expressions (Eqns. 1 and 2) for
$B_L$, the molecular luminescence radiance are identical to those for
atomic fluorescence (see Eqns. 1 and 2). However, with molecules,
several additional factors must be considered in evaluating the
Einstein expressions and the densities of the various states involved in the molecule (it is possible to simplify the molecular
energy state diagram to a 3-level, Na-type system, where 1 is the
lower, 3 is the upper singlet, and 2 is the corresponding excited

triplet). These additional factors include the vibrational overlap integral between the vibrational levels involved in the two
electronic states involved in the absorption and luminescence processes and luminescence spectral profile and average luminescence
frequency as compared to the excitation frequency.

For a 2-level molecule, the general expression for $B_L$ is
given by

$$B_L = \left(\frac{\ell}{4\pi}\right) \sum_{i=0}^{i=\infty} A_{20,1i} h\nu_{20,1i} n_T \left[ \frac{1}{1+ \dfrac{g_1}{g_2}\left(1+\dfrac{E^*_{\nu_{12}}/\xi_{2j,10}}{E_{\nu_{12}}/\delta\nu_A}\right)} \right] \tag{10}$$

where the summation is over all ith vibrational levels in the
lower electronic state involved in the luminescence processes,
$h\nu_{20,1i}$ are the corresponding photon energies, $n_T$ is the total
electronic state population of the molecules, the g's are statistical weights of electronic states 1 and 2, $E_{\nu_{12}}$ is the spectral
irradiance of the exciting source, $E^*_{\nu_{12}}$ is the modified saturation spectral irradiance ($cA_{21}/\gamma_{21}B_{21}$); $\delta\nu_A$ is the half-width of
the molecular (electronic) absorption band and $\xi_{2j,10}$ is the vibrational overlap-luminescence profile term for the absorption
transition from the 0'th vibrational level of the ground electronic state and is defined by

$$\xi_{2j,10} = \nu_{2j,10}^3 <\nu_L^{-3}>_{AV} V_{2j,10} \tag{11}$$

where

$$<\nu_L^{-3}>_{AV} = \frac{\displaystyle\sum_{i=0}^{i=\infty} V_{20,1i} \nu_{20,1i}^3}{\displaystyle\sum_{i=0}^{i=\infty} V_{20,1i}} \tag{12}$$

and

$$V_{2j,10} = |<\theta_{2j}(Q)|Q_{10}(Q)>|^2 \tag{13a}$$

$$V_{20,1i} = |<\theta_{20}(Q)|Q_{1i}(Q)>|^2 \tag{13b}$$

where $|<Q(Q)|Q(Q)>|$ is the vibrational overlap integral (Franck-
Condon factor) between vibrational levels in the two electronic
states involved in the absorption and luminescence processes (Q
is the vibrational coordinate); the Born-Oppenheimer approximator
is assumed to apply here (the overlap term is dimensionless).

For a three level molecule, Boutilier, et al.[18] showed that the fluorescence radiance $3 \rightarrow 1$ for $1 \rightarrow 3$ excitation or the forbidden process of $2 \rightarrow 1$ for $1 \rightarrow 2$ excitation is given by

$$B_L = \left(\frac{\ell}{4\pi}\right) \sum_{i=0}^{i=\infty} A_{u0,1i} h\nu_{u0,1i} n_T \cdot$$

$$\cdot \left[ \frac{1}{1 + \dfrac{g_1}{g_u}\left(1 + \dfrac{E^*_{\nu_{1u}}/\xi_{uj,10}}{E_{\nu_{10,uj}}/\delta\nu_A}\right) + \dfrac{k_{uu'}}{\sum\limits_{i=0}^{i=\infty} A_{u'0,1i}+k_{u'1}+k_{u'u}}} \right] \quad (14)$$

where all symbols have been previously defined except u represents the radiationally excited upper state and u' represents the other upper level (in case $1 \rightarrow 3$ excitation, u = 3 and u' = 2).

For a three level molecule, Boutilier, et al.[18] showed that the luminescence radiance for $1 \rightarrow 3$ excitation and $2 \rightarrow 1$ emission or for $1 \rightarrow 2$ excitation and $3 \rightarrow 1$ emission is given by

$$B_L = \left(\frac{\ell}{4\pi}\right) \sum_{i=0}^{i=\infty} A_{u'0,1i} h\nu_{u'0,1i} n_T \cdot$$

$$\cdot \left[ \frac{1}{1 + \left[1 + \dfrac{g_1}{g_u}\left(1 + \dfrac{E^*_{\nu_{1u}}/\xi_{uj,10}}{E_{\nu_{10,uj}}/\delta\nu_A}\right)\right]\left(\dfrac{\sum\limits_{i=0}^{i=\infty} A_{u'0,1i}+k_{u'1}+k_{u'u}}{k_{uu'}}\right)} \right] \quad (15)$$

where all terms have been defined above (note that u is the radiationally excited upper state and u' is the other upper state; for $1 \rightarrow 3$ excitation and $2 \rightarrow 1$ luminescence, u = 3 and u' = 2.

Finally, for the case of delayed fluorescence ($1 \rightarrow 3$ excitation, $3 \dashrightarrow 2$ intersystem crossing, $2 \dashrightarrow 3$ intersystem crossing, $3 \rightarrow 1$ emission)

$$B_{DF} = \left(\frac{\ell}{4\pi}\right) \sum_{i=0}^{i=\infty} A_{30,1i} h\nu_{30,1i} n_T \cdot$$

$$\cdot \left[ \frac{1}{\left[1 + \dfrac{g_3}{g_1} + \dfrac{g_3}{g_1}\left(\dfrac{k_{32}}{\sum\limits_{i=0}^{i=\infty} A_{20,1i}+k_{21}+k_{23}}\right)\right] + \dfrac{E^*_{\nu_{13}}/\xi_{3j,10}}{E_{\nu_{10,3j}}/\delta\nu_A}} \right] \cdot$$

· (eqn. cont.)

(Eqn. continued from previous page)

$$\cdot \left[ \frac{k_{23}k_{32}}{\left( \sum_{i=0}^{i=\infty} A_{30,1i} + k_{31} + k_{32} \right) \left( \sum_{i=0}^{i=\infty} A_{20,1i} + k_{21} + k_{23} \right)} \right] \quad (16)$$

The saturation spectral irradiance $E^S_{\nu_{10,2j}}$ for a 2-level molecule is given by

$$E^S_{\nu_{10,2j}} = \left( \frac{g_1}{g_1 + g_2} \right) \left( \frac{E^*_{\nu_{12}} \delta\nu A}{\xi_{2j,10}} \right) \quad (17)$$

and for a three level molecule with 1→3 excitation

$$E^S_{\nu_{10,3j}} = \frac{\left( \frac{g_1}{g_3} \right) \left( \frac{E^*_{\nu_{13}} \delta\nu A}{\xi_{3j,10}} \right)}{1 + \frac{g_1}{g_3} + \frac{k_{32}}{\sum_{i=0}^{i=\infty} A_{20,1i} + k_{21} + k_{23}}} \quad (18)$$

and for a three level molecule with 1→2 excitation

$$E^S_{\nu_{10,2j}} = \frac{\left( \frac{g_1}{g_3} \right) \left( \frac{E^*_{\nu_{12}} \delta\nu A}{\xi_{2j,10}} \right)}{1 + \frac{g_1}{g_2} + \frac{k_{23}}{\sum_{i=0}^{i=\infty} A_{30,1i} + k_{31} + k_{32}}} \quad (19)$$

The major conclusions resulting from the molecular luminescence radiance expressions are listed below.
(1) The radiance expressions for molecular luminescence are similar to those for atomic fluorescence and reduce to the atomic case if $\xi = 1$.
(2) For low source (spectral) irradiances, the fluorescence radiance depends directly upon the source irradiance, the fluorescence quantum efficiency, the emission transition probability, and the total density of analyte.
(3) For high source (spectral) irradiances, the fluorescence radiance depends directly upon the emission transition probability, and the total analyte density but is independent of the source irradiance and the fluorescence

quantum efficiency.

(4) For the 2-level case under saturation conditions, absolute $n_T$ values can be measured by measuring $B_L$ under steady state conditions and by knowing $A_{20,1i}$, $g_1$, $g_2$, and $\ell$.

(5) The saturation irradiance $E^S$ for a 3-level molecule at room temperature is $10^5$ to $10^7$ × less than for a 2-level atom or molecule at any temperature or for a 3-level atom or molecule at high temperature, as in flames. Because molecules have broad bandwidths compared to atoms, saturation can be achieved either by a high source spectral irradiance over a narrow spectral region or a lower source spectral irradiance over a much wider bandwidth, $\delta\nu_A$, i.e., $E_\nu$ of the source must exceed $E^S/\delta\nu_S$ for narrow line excitation.

(6) Assuming saturation is reached, direct excitation of the triplet state is essentially as efficient as conventional first singlet excitation followed by radiationless crossover to the corresponding triplet state. Thus Ar ion-dye lasers can be used to excite triplets assuming they can be focussed down to $\sim 10$ μm to achieve $\sim$MW cm$^{-2}$ (assuming $Y_p \lesssim 0.1$).

Narrow-Line Laser Excited Luminescence Spectrometry.  In this case, the specific nature of the broadening processes, namely homogeneous vs heterogeneous broadened absorption lines, and the specific source characteristics, namely, single narrow line vs source with multiple discrete spectral components such as modes, must be considered.  Killinger, Wang, and Hanabusa,[19] and E. H. Piepmeier[21,22,23] have considered these cases in considerable detail and have given fluorescence radiance expressions.  No attempt will be made here to duplicate these expressions because:  (1) the reader can go to the cited literature if it is desired; (2) the expressions are considerably more complex; and (3) the major analytical use of lasers has been with the ones given above and not with the narrow line systems.  Nevertheless, several interesting conclusions of these studies are:  (i) with homogeneous broadened absorption (Lorentzian broadening) transitions induced by a single frequency transition, the fluorescence radiance expression is similar to the ones given in the section concerning atoms and identical to the ones given in the section concerning molecules except that for atoms the absorption line shape factor (Hz$^{-1}$) must be considered explicitly; (ii) with inhomogeneous (heterogeneous) broadened absorption transition induced by a single frequency transition, the fluorescence radiance expression differs considerably from those in both of the previous sections because of the need to consider both the absorption line shape factor (Hz$^{-1}$) and the fractional number of absorbers with the proper frequencies (velocities) to interact with the excitation line must be considered; (iii) with homogeneous and/or inhomogeneous broadening induced by a continuum

source with constant spectral distribution, the identical fluorescence radiance expressions as in the section for atoms result; and
(iv) with inhomogeneous broadened absorption transitions induced
by radiation with discrete narrow line spectral components, as
laser modes, the expressions can vary from those in the section
for atoms and in the section for molecules to those in item (ii)
above with the necessary change to include the effect of the
source flux in each spectral component within the absorption line
width.

It should be stressed that in the case of narrow line excitation and homogeneous broadening, in the case of continuum excitation and homogeneous and/or inhomogeneous broadening, and in the
case of multiple narrow line excitation and homogeneous broadening,
the fluorescence radiance expressions are identical to or similar
to those in the sections for atoms and for molecules. However,
for the cases of inhomogeneous broadening with single narrow line
or multiple narrow line excitation, the fluorescence radiances are
proportional to the square root (rather than the first power) of
the source irradiance, the integrated absorption coefficient, and
the Einstein spontaneous emission transition probability assuming
high source intensity.

Multiple Photon Laser Excited Luminescence Spectrometry.[23-26]
No attempt will be made here to give explicit expressions for multiple photon excitation luminescence spectrometry. The luminescence radiances for atoms or molecules, however, are proportional
to the following parameters:

$$B_F \propto n_\ell \; \ell\sigma(v) \; E(v_1) \; E(v_2) \; . \; . \; . \; E(v_v)$$

where $n_\ell$ is the density of analyte species in the lower level involved in the absorption process, $\ell$ is the fluorescence path
length, $\sigma(v)$ is the absorption cross section for the multiple (v)
photon process, and $E(v_1)$, $E(v_2 0$, . . . $E(v_v)$ are the source excitation irradiances of multiple frequencies, $v_1, v_2, . . . v_v$. It
should be stressed that for the case of strong resonance interaction, the luminescence signals will approach those of the one-
photon absorption process. However, an additional and very important advantage occurs with multiple photon excitation (2 and 3-
photons are the most common) namely a very significant improvement
in selectivity over the one-photon process, particularly for molecules where selectivity with one photon excitation is poor. Various excitation modes are possible via multiple photon excitation, namely: (i) the first photon excites a resonant level, the
second excites an intermediate energy level, and the third, if
used, excites a higher level or even ionizes the species; (ii)
the first photon excites a resonant level which relaxes to some
metastable level as a triplet and the second and third photons
excite higher intermediate levels and/or cause ionization; (iii)
the first photon excites a metastable level and the second and

third photons excite higher intermediate levels and/or cause ionization.

## Experimentation

The pulsed laser excited atomic fluorescence flame spectrometric system used by Weeks, Haraguchi, and Winefordner[29] is shown in Figure 1. This system is similar to the one used by other workers. Except for the replacement of the flame cell by a conventional quartz cell, the experimental system for pulsed laser excited molecular luminescence of condensed phase species is similar to the one for atomic fluorescence flame spectrometry in Figure 1, and so a block diagram setup will not be given here.

## Analytical Results

Atomic Fluorescence Flame Spectrometry. Pulsed tunable dye lasers have been used increasingly as excitation sources for atomic fluorescence flame spectrometry.[27-41] The most recent and comprehensive study of such a system has been conducted by Weeks, Haraguchi, and Winefordner.[27] These workers utilized a pulsed $N_2$-laser-dye laser source, flame atomizer, and gated detection and obtained detection limits superior to or similar to the best results previously obtained by all analytical methods (refer to Tables 1 and 2). Other advantages discussed by these workers were: (i) the large linear dynamic ranges (refer to Figures 2-5 for typical results) for most elements studied covered 5- to 7-orders of magnitude in concentration of analyte which compared favorably with the ranges listed by workers using ICP's for atomic emission spectrometry and considerably greater than the ranges listed for atomic absorption flame or furnace spectrometry; (ii) spectral interferences were considerably less than those obtained in atomic absorption flame- or furnace-spectrometry, atomic emission flame- or ICP-spectrometry, and atomic fluorescence excited with a continuum source spectrometry (refer to Figure 6 and Table 3 for a typical example of the ease of circumventing the rare case of a spectral interference in atomic fluorescence flame spectrometry with a pulsed laser source. The effective resolution in laser excited AFS is determined by the laser line width rather than the spectrometer bandpass (see Figure 7). The only potentially-serious interference in pulsed laser AFS with gated detection would arise from molecular fluorescence of species formed in the flames by concomitants and flame gases and by Rayleigh and Mie scatter. The former has been shown by Weeks, et al.[27] to be minimal in most cases as long as $PH_3$ has been removed from the acetylene fuel ($PH_3$ results in formation of POH which fluoresces intensely in the flame.) The latter has been shown by Weeks, et al.[40] to be avoidable in most cases; Mie scatter can be avoided by use of efficient chamber type nebulizers, nebulization of solutions containing less than 1% solids and use of acetylene flames and Rayleigh and Mie

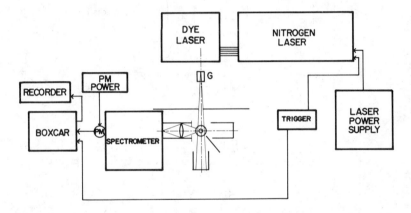

Figure 1. *Diagram of laser-excited atomic fluorescence flame spectrometry system*

TABLE I. DETECTION LIMITS BY LASER-EXCITED ATOMIC FLUORESCENCE FLAME SPECTROMETRY

| Element | Ex/Fl[a] (nm) | Type of AF[b] | Weeks et al.[27] | | | Previous Works[c] | | | |
|---|---|---|---|---|---|---|---|---|---|
| | | | LOD (ng/ml) | UL (mg/ml) | log(LDR) (dimens) | LOD (ng/ml) | UL (mg/ml) | log(LDR) (dimens) | Ref'n. |
| Ag | 328.1 | RF† | 4 | 0.06 | 4.2 | — | — | — | — |
| Al | 396.1 | E-RF△ | 2 | 0.6 | 5.4 | 300 | 0.1 | 4 | 28 |
| | 394.4/396.1 | S-DLF△ | 0.6 | 0.3 | 5.7 | 5 | 0.2 | 4.6 | 28 |
| Ba | 553.7 | RF† | 100 | 10 | 5 | 8 | >1 | >5 | 38 |
| | 553.7 | RF△ | 8 | >1 | >5 | 40 | — | — | 40 |
| Bi | 306.8 | RF† | 3 | 0.5 | 5.2 | — | — | — | — |
| Ca | 422.7 | RF† | 0.08 | 0.006 | 4.9 | 5 | 0.05 | 4 | 28 |
| Cd | 228.8 | RF† | 8 | 0.03 | 3.5 | — | — | — | — |
| Co[d] | 357.5/347.4 | AS-DLF† | 1000 | >2 | >3.3 | 200 | 0.2 | 3 | 28 |
| | 230.9 | RF† | 1000 | >2 | >3.3 | — | — | — | — |
| Cr | 359.3 | RF† | 1 | 0.3 | 5.5 | 20 | 0.02 | 3 | 28 |
| Cu | 324.7 | RF† | 1 | 0.1 | 5 | — | — | — | — |
| Fe | 296.7/373.5 | S-DLF† | 30 | >1 | >4.5 | 100 | 0.5 | 3.7 | 28 |
| Ga | 403.3 | RF† | 7 | 0.3 | 4.6 | 20 | 0.02 | 3 | 28 |
| | 403.3/417.2 | S-DLF† | 0.9 | 0.2 | 5.4 | 10 | 0.5 | 3.7 | 28 |
| In | 410.4 | RF† | 0.8 | 0.4 | 5.7 | 2 | 0.5 | 4.4 | 28 |
| | 410.4/451.1 | S-DLF† | 0.2 | 0.3 | 6.2 | — | — | — | — |
| Li | 670.8 | RF† | 0.5 | >0.001 | >4.3 | 0.3 | — | — | 36 |
| Mg | 285.2 | RF† | 0.2 | 0.02 | 5 | — | — | — | — |
| Mn | 403.1 | RF† | 1 | 0.08 | 4.9 | 10 | 0.02 | 3.3 | 28 |
| | 279.5 | RF† | 0.4 | 0.1 | 5.4 | — | — | — | — |
| Mo | 379.8 | RF△ | 12 | >1 | >4.9 | 1000 | 0.1 | 2 | 28 |
| | 390.3 | RF△ | 12 | >1 | >4.9 | 300 | 0.1 | 2.5 | 28 |
| Na | 589.0 | RF† | <.1 | 0.05 | >5.7 | 0.1 | — | — | 40 |
| | 589.6/589.0 | TA-SLF† | 1 | 0.06 | 4.8 | — | — | — | — |

| Element | Ex/Fl | Type | | | | | | | |
|---|---|---|---|---|---|---|---|---|---|
| Ni | 232.0 | RF† | 12 | 0.1 | 3.9 | — | — | — | — |
| Pb | 361.0/352.4 | E-AS-DLF† | 2 | 1 | 5.7 | 50 | 0.2 | 3.6 | 28 |
| | 405.8 | E-RF† | 180 | >1 | >3.7 | 6 | — | — | 37 |
| | 405.8/283.3 | AS-DLF† | 30 | >1 | >4.5 | — | — | — | — |
| | 283.3 | RF† | 20 | 1 | 4.7 | — | — | — | — |
| | 283.3/405.8 | S-DLF† | 13 | >1 | >4.9 | 30 | — | — | 36 |
| Sr | 460.7 | RF† | 0.3 | 0.03 | 5 | 10 | 0.02 | 3.3 | 28 |
| Ti | 399.9 | RF△ | 5 | 1 | 5.3 | 100 | 0.2 | 3.3 | 28 |
| | 365.4 | RF△ | 2 | 0.4 | 5.2 | — | — | — | — |
| Tl | 377.6 | RF† | 4 | 0.3 | 4.9 | 1000 | 0.05 | 1.7 | 28 |
| | 377.6/535.0 | S-DLF† | 7 | 0.6 | 4.9 | 200 | 0.1 | 3.7 | 28 |
| V | 411.2 | E-RF△ | 50 | >1 | >4.3 | — | — | — | — |
| | 370.4/411.2 | E-S-SLF△ | 30 | >1 | >4.5 | 500 | — | — | 32 |

†A/A or air/acetylene.

△N/A or nitrous oxide/acetylene flame.

a Ex/Fl = excitation wavelength/fluorescence wavelength (if different than excitation wavelength). The energy levels involved in the transition and their gf and gA values can be found in C. H. Corliss and W. R. Bozman, "Experimental Transition Probabilities for Spectral Line of Seventy Elements," NBS Monograph 53, 1962.

b RF = resonance fluorescence; E-RF = excited resonance fluorescence; S-DLF = Stokes direct line fluorescence; AS-DLF = anti-Stokes direct line fluorescence; TA-SLF = thermally assisted stepwise line fluorescence; E-AS-DLF = excited anti-Stokes direct line fluorescence; and E-S-SLF = excited Stokes stepwise line fluorescence.

c LOD = Limit of Detection, UL = Upper Limit of linearity, and LDR = linear dynamic range=UL/LOD.

d Experimental difficulty was encountered in obtaining good laser output at the Co lines attempted.

TABLE II. COMPARISON OF DETECTION LIMITS IN FLAME AND FURNACE SPECTROMETRY AND INDUCTIVELY COUPLED PLASMA (ICP)

Detection limit, ng/ml

| Element | $AF^a$ (laser) | $AF^b$ (conventional source) | $AE^b$ | $AA^b$ | ICP pneumatic nebulization$^c$ | ICP ultrasonic nebulization$^d$ |
|---|---|---|---|---|---|---|
| Ag | 4 | $0.1\beta^e(0.4)$ | 2 | 1(0.01) | 4† | ---$^f$ |
| Al | 0.6β | 100 | 3 | 30*(0.1) | 2 | 0.5** |
| Ba | 8 | --- | 1 | 20(0.6) | 0.1+β | 0.01 |
| Bi | 3β | 5β(10) | 20,000 | 50(0.4) | 50† | --- |
| Ca | 0.08β | 20(0.1) | 0.1β | 1*(0.04) | 0.07+β | 0.0001 |
| Cd | 8 | 0.001β(0.01) | 800 | 1(0.008) | 1.0 | 0.07* |
| Co$^g$ | 1000 | 5β(1) | 30 | 2β(0.2) | 2β | 0.1* |
| Cr | 1β | 5 | 2β | 2β(0.2) | 0.9β | 0.08* |
| Cu | 1 | 0.5(1) | 0.1β | 1*(0.06) | 0.2β | 0.04* |
| Fe | 30 | 8(10) | 5 | 4(1) | 0.2β | 0.09 |
| Ga | 0.9β | 10(50) | 10* | 50(0.1) | 14† | 0.6 |
| In | 0.2β | 100 | 0.4β | 30(0.04) | 30† | --- |
| Li | 0.5 | --- | 0.02β | 1(0.3) | --- | --- |
| Mg | 0.2β | 0.1β(1) | 5 | 0.1β(0.004) | 0.7† | 0.003 |
| Mn | 0.4β | 1(5) | 1 | 0.8(0.02) | 0.1β | 0.01* |
| Mo | 12β | 500 | 100 | 30(0.3) | 4β | 0.2 |
| Na | <0.1 | --- | 0.1β* | 0.8 | 0.2+β | 0.02 |
| Ni | 2β | 3β(5) | 20 | 5β(0.9) | 4β | 0.2 |
| Pb | 13β | 10β(3) | 100 | 10β(0.2) | 10β | 1* |
| Sr | 0.3 | 30 | 0.2 | 5(0.1) | 0.02+β | 0.003 |
| Ti | 2β | 4000 | 30 | 90*(4) | 3+β | 0.03 |
| Tl | 4β | 8β(20) | 20 | 20(1) | 200† | 0.03 |
| V | 30 | 70 | 7 | 20(0.3) | 1β | 0.06 |

Footnotes to Table II:

[a] Limits of detection represent concentrations required to produce a line signal three times as great as the standard deviation of the background noise. All other values listed in the table represent concentrations required to produce a line signal twice as great as the standard deviation of the background noise, except where noted. Values taken from S. J. Weeks, H. Haraguchi, and J. D. Winefordner, Anal. Chem., in press.

[b] Values taken from J. D. Winefordner, J. J. Fitzgerald, and N. Omenetto, Appl. Spectrosc., 29, 369 (1975) except for those designated *, which were taken from V. A. Fassel and R. N. Kniseley, Anal. Chem., 46, 1110A (1974). Values in parantheses are for furnace AF and AA.

[c] All values taken from K. W. Olson, W. J. Haas, Jr., and V. A. Fassel, Anal. Chem., 49, 632 (1977) except those with †, which are from V. A. Fassel and R. N. Kniseley, Anal. Chem., 46, 1110A (1974).

[d] All values taken from P. W. J. M. Boumans and F. J. deBoer, Spectrochim. Acta, 30B, 309 (1975) except those designated *, which were taken from K. W. Olson, W. J. Haas, Jr., and V. A. Fassel, Anal. Chem., 49, 632 (1977) and those designated **, which were taken from M. H. Abdallah, R. Diemiaszonek, J. Jarosz, J. M. Mermet, J. Robin, and C. Trassy, Anal. Chim. Acta, 84, 271 (1976). Limit of detection designated ** represent concentrations required to produce a line signal six times as great as the standard deviation of the background noise.

[e] β designates best value with pneumatic nebulization. All values within a factor of 3 are considered to be equal.

[f] --- indicates no value reported.

[g] Experimental difficulties were encountered in obtaining good laser output at the Co lines.

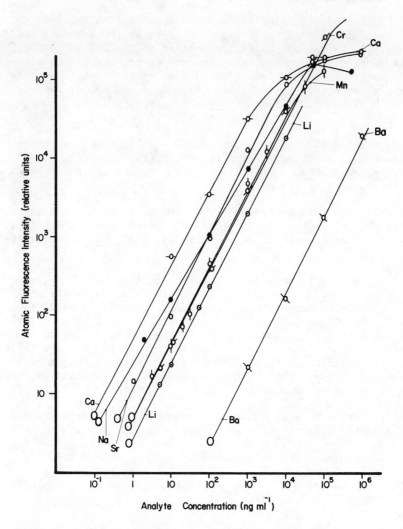

*Figure 2.    Analytical calibration curves for elements having only strong reso-
nance transitions above 355 nm in air–acetylene flame.*

|  |  | $\lambda_{ex} = \lambda_{fl}(nm)$ |
|---|---|---|
| ⊶ | – *resonance fluorescence of Ba* | *554* |
| –⊙– | – *resonance fluorescence of Ca* | *422* |
| ⊶ | – *resonance fluorescence of Cr* | *359* |
| ⊙ | – *resonance fluorescence of Li* | *670* |
| ⊙ | – *resonance fluorescence of Mn* | *403* |
| ● | – *resonance fluorescence of Na* | *589* |
| ○ | – *resonance fluorescence of Sr* | *460* |
| (○ | – *indicates the limit of detection)* | |

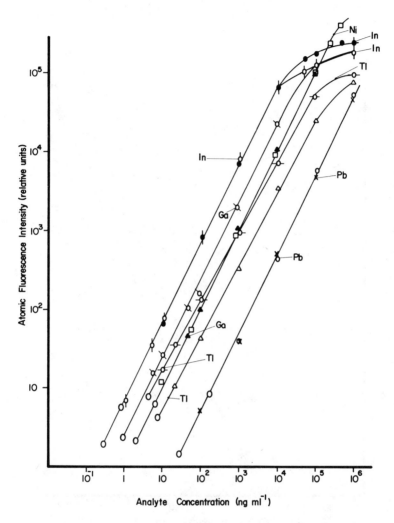

**Figure 3.**   *Analytical calibration curves for elements having both strong resonance and nonresonance transitions excited above 355 nm in an air–acetylene flame.*

|  |  | $\lambda_{ex}(nm)$ | $\lambda_{fl}(nm)$ |
|---|---|---|---|
| ▲ | — resonance fluorescence of Ga | 403 | 403 |
| ○ | — nonresonance fluorescence of Ga | 403 | 417 |
| ● | — resonance fluorescence of In | 410 | 410 |
| ○ | — nonresonance fluorescence of In | 410 | 450 |
| □ | — nonresonance fluorescence of Ni | 361 | 352 |
| ○ | — resonance fluorescence of Pb | 405 | 405 |
| × | — nonresonance fluorescence of Pb | 405 | 283 |
| –○– | — resonance fluorescence of Tl | 377 | 377 |
| △ | — nonresonance fluorescence of Tl | 377 | 535 |

(⊙ — *indicates the limit of detection*)

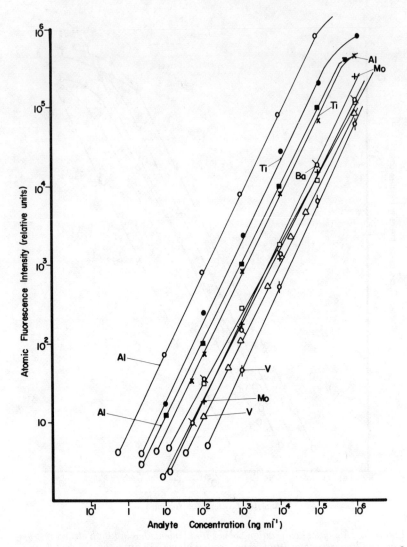

*Figure 4.    Analytical calibration curves for elements having transitions excited above 355 nm in a nitrous oxide–acetylene flame.*

|  |  | $\lambda_{ex}(nm)$ | $\lambda_{fl}(nm)$ |
|---|---|---|---|
| ■ | – resonance fluorescence of Al | 396 | 396 |
| ○ | – nonresonance fluorescence of Al | 394 | 396 |
| ⚲ | – resonance fluorescence of Ba | 553 | 553 |
| + | – resonance fluorescence of Mo | 380 | 380 |
| □ | – resonance fluorescence of Mo | 390 | 390 |
| ● | – resonance fluorescence of Ti | 365 | 365 |
| × | – resonance fluorescence of Ti | 400 | 400 |
| ▽ | – nonresonance fluorescence of V | 370 | 411 |
| ⚴ | – resonance fluorescence of V | 411 | 411 |
| (⚴ | – indicates the limit of detection) | | |

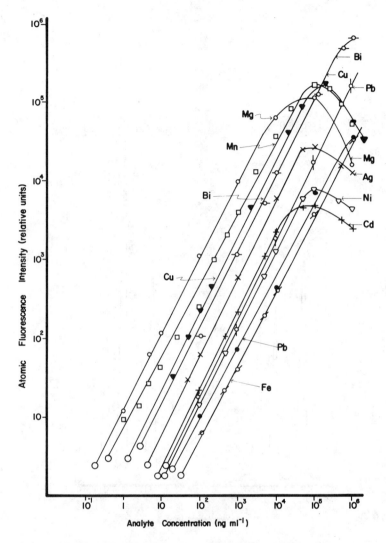

**Figure 5.** *Analytical calibration curves for elements having transitions excited below 355 nm in an air–acetylene flame.*

| | $\lambda_{ex}(nm)$ | $\lambda_{fl}(nm)$ |
|---|---|---|
| ✕ — resonance fluorescence of Ag | 328 | 328 |
| –◯-- — resonance fluorescence of Bi | 306 | 306 |
| + — resonance fluorescence of Cd | 228 | 228 |
| ▼ — resonance fluorescence of Cu | 325 | 325 |
| ◯⁻ — nonresonance fluorescence of Fe | 296 | 373 |
| ◯ — resonance fluorescence of Mg | 285 | 285 |
| ☐ — resonance fluorescence of Mn | 280 | 280 |
| ▽ — resonance fluorescence of Ni | 232 | 232 |
| ● — resonance fluorescence of Pb | 283 | 283 |
| ◔ — nonresonance fluorescence of Pb | 283 | 405 |
| (◯ — indicates the limit of detection) | | |

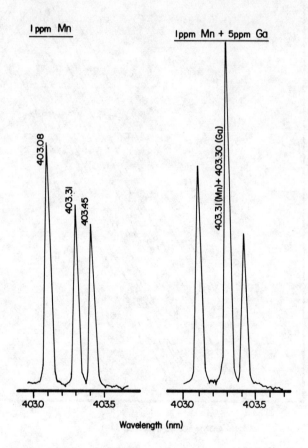

*Figure 6. Fluorescence excitation spectrum for (A) a 1 ppm Mn solution and (B) a 1 ppm Mn + 5 ppm Ga solution*

TABLE III.    INVESTIGATION OF SPECTRAL INTERFERENCES BETWEEN
MANGANESE AND GALLIUM

(i)    Excited at 403.08 nm/Observed at 403.08 nm
[Observe manganese atomic fluorescence]

| Composition | Relative atomic fluorescence intensity |
|---|---|
| Mn 1 ppm | 69 |
| Mn 1 ppm + Ga 5 ppm | 70 |
| Mn 1 ppm + Ga 100 ppm | 68 |
| Mn 0.5 ppm + Ga 100 ppm | 34 |
| Mn 0.1 ppm + Ga 100 ppm | 7 |

(ii)    Excited at 403.30 nm/Observed at 403.30 nm
[Observe gallium atomic fluorescence]

| Composition | Relative atomic fluorescence intensity |
|---|---|
| Ga 5 ppm | 67 |
| Ga 5 ppm + Mn 1 ppm | 108 |

(iii)    Excited at 403.30 nm/Observed at 417.01 nm
[Observe gallium atomic fluorescence]

| Composition | Relative atomic fluorescence intensity |
|---|---|
| Ga 5 ppm | 151 |
| Ga 5 ppm + Mn 1 ppm | 151 |

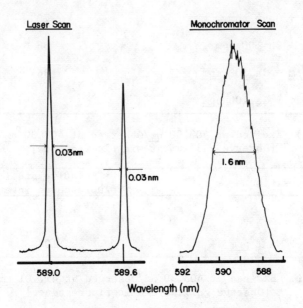

*Figure 7.    Fluorescence excitation and fluorescence emission profiles of sodium D lines (at 589.0 and 589.6 nm) in the air–acetylene flame (slit width was 800 μm in both cases)*

scatter can be avoided by use of non-resonance fluorescence (however, even for resonance fluorescence, elastic scatter does not
result in signals more than several times the dark current level).
Detection limits in laser-excited AFS could most likely be improved by up to several orders of magnitude by:[27] (i) optimization
of their optical system; (ii) by optimization of the laser beam
diameter; (iii) by use of a better quality laser beam shape over
the entire spectral range; (iv) by use of higher output peak powers, especially in the frequency-doubled region; (v) by use of ultrasonic nebulization; (vi) by reduction of flame instability via
an improved flow system and mixing chamber design; (vii) by use of
an improved burner shape; (viii) by optimization of the electronic
measurement system; and (ix) by reduction of radio frequency interference noise due to the $N_2$-laser.

Atomic FLuorescence Furnace Spectrometry. Relatively few
laser excited atomic fluorescence spectrometric studies have been
conducted where the atoms have been produced in a furnace designed
to atomize real samples.[43,44] S. Neumann and Kriese[43] using a frequency-doubled flashlamp pumped dye laser to excite lead atoms
produced with a graphite rod atomizer were able to detect 0.2 pg
BP (direct line fluorescence, 283.3 nm excitation and 405.8 nn
fluorescence) and to achieve a linear dynamic range of $>10^5\times$.
Bolshov, et al.[44] with a frequency-doubled dye laser pumped by a
YAG:Nd$^{3+}$ laser and a graphite tube atomizer have detected 25 pg/ml
relative and 0.75 pg absolute Fe (direct line fluorescence with
excitation at 296.7 nm and fluorescence of 373.5 nm) and 2.5 pg/ml
relative and 0.075 pg absolute Pb (direct line fluorescence, with
excitation at 283.3 nm and fluorescence at 405.8 nm); the linear
dynamic ranges were $>10^5\times$ and $>10^7\times$, respectively, for Fe and Pb.
Detection limit data via laser excited atomic furnace fluorescence
spectrometry are not given in tabular form due to their scarcity.
Several groups of workers have utilized laser excitation of
Na-atoms produced in quartz cells maintained at elevated temperatures (quartz tube within a furnace). These studies have included
the classic work in 1975 of Fairbanks, Hänsch, and Schawlow[45] who
detected $10^2$ atoms of Na/cm$^3$ (upper limit was $\sim10^{11}$ atoms/cm$^3$) and
who predicted that under optimal conditions 0.1 Cs atom/cm$^3$ should
be detectable; these same workers also predicted that many other
atoms and molecules should be detectable to $10^2$-$10^4$ atoms/cm$^3$ depending upon the oscillator strength of the absorption transition.
Kuhl and Marowsky[42] several years earlier in 1971 had detected Na
in a resonance cell at concentrations of 3 pg/cm$^3$. Mayo, et al.[46]
in 1976 detected Na atoms in an open contaminated quartz tube
heated to 1000°C and obtained a detection limit of $5\times10^5$ atoms/
cm$^3$. Gelbwachs, Klein, and Wessel[39] in 1977 obtained a detection
limit of 10 Na atoms/cm$^3$ for a flashlamp pumped dye laser excitation of the atomic fluorescence of Na produced in an enclosed
environment. Finally, Brod and Yeing[47] determined a detection
limit of 7 fg/cm$^3$ for Na produced in a quartz container and exci-

TABLE IV.  DETECTION LIMITS BY LASER EXCITED FLUORIMETRY

| Molecule | Laser Peak Power (kW) | Excitation Wavelength (nm) | Emission Wavelength (nm) | Detection Limit (µg/ml) | Ref'n. |
|---|---|---|---|---|---|
| Quinine Sulfate | 2.5 | 365 | 454 | $1 \times 10^{-5}$ | 49 |
| Fluorescein | 3.3 | 480 | 514 | $1 \times 10^{-4}$ | 49 |
| Acridine | 1.4 | 360 | 415 | $1 \times 10^{-3}$ | 49 |
| Quinine Sulfate | 150 | 337 | 456 | $1 \times 10^{-5}$ | 50 |
| Fluorescein | 150 | 337 | 514 | $1 \times 10^{-4}$ | 50 |
| Acridine | 150 | 337 | 415 | $3 \times 10^{-5}$ | 50 |
| Anthracene | 150 | 337 | 397 | $1 \times 10^{-5}$ | 50 |
| Chrysene | 150 | 337 | 388 | $3 \times 10^{-5}$ | 50 |
| Fluoranthene | 150 | 337 | 460 | $1 \times 10^{-5}$ | 50 |
| Phenanthrene | 150 | 337 | 400 | $3 \times 10^{-5}$ | 50 |
| Pyrene | 150 | 337 | 390 | $2 \times 10^{-5}$ | 50 |
| Chlorophyll (a or b) | 75 mW (cw) | 442 | 660 | $1 \times 10^{-6}$ | 57 |
| Riboflavin | 1-15 | 375 | 540 | $4.7 \times 10^{-7}$ | 55 |

| | | | | | |
|---|---|---|---|---|---|
| Aflatoxin ($B_1$, $B_2$, $G_1$, $G_2$) | 8 mW (cw) | 325 | Visible | $1.8 \times 10^{-6}$ | 53 |
| Benzene | 2-5 | 260 | 302, 273 | $1.9 \times 10^{-2}$ | 55 |
| Naphthalene | 2-5 | 273 | 340, 360 | $1.3 \times 10^{-6}$ | 55 |
| Anthracene | 2-5 | 254 | 404 | $4.4 \times 10^{-6}$ | 55 |
| Fluoranthene | 2-5 | 287 | 450 | $1 \times 10^{-6}$ | 55 |
| Pyrene | 2-5 | 273 | 395 | $5 \times 10^{-7}$ | 55 |
| Rhodamine 6G | 100 | 337 | Visible | $3.9 \times 10^{-7}$ | 52 |
| Aflatoxin ($B_1$, $G_1$ 1:1 Mixture) | 100 | 337 | Visible | $2.5 \times 10^{-6}$ | 52 |
| 2,5 Diphenyl oxazole* | 1.5-5 | 600 | 350-450 | $1.1 \times 10^{-1}$ | 56 |
| p-Terphenyl* | 1.5-5 | 545 | 300-400 | $4.6 \times 10^{-2}$ | 56 |

*Two photon excited molecular fluorescence—the remainder are all single photon excited molecular fluorescence.

ted with a flashlamp pumped dye laser.

Despite the rather exotic and exciting detection limits obtained for Na (and predicted for other atoms and molecules) in quartz containers, the analytical spectroscopist must temper the excellent results with the difficulties encountered in converting real samples to a form to allow use of a quartz sample cell with the concomitant ideal environment, e.g., an inert gas. Therefore, the world record detection limits in quartz cells are only transferable with sampling difficulties to the world of the analyte.

Molecular Luminescence Spectrometry. Smith, et al.[49] were the first to demonstrate the potential of pulsed tunable dye laser molecular fluorimetry of condensed phase molecules. Van Geel and Winefordner[50] further evaluated pulsed tunable dye lasers for analytical condensed phase molecular fluorimetry. Berman and Zare[51] obtained an absolute detection limit of 0.2 ng for aflatoxins ($B_1$, $B_2$, $G_1$, and $G_2$) by thin layer chromatographic separation followed by time resolved laser excited fluorimetry. Bradley and Zare[54] used pulsed laser ($N_2$-laser) excited fluorimetry of molecules in the condensed phase for sub-part-per-trillion detection limits. Diebold and Zare[53] have used modulated laser excitation (He-Cd laser) of a suspended drop ($\sim$4 $\mu\ell$) of solvent eluting from a column and obtained an absolute detection limit of 7 fg for aflatoxin.

Richardson, et al.,[54] and Richardson and Ando[55] have utilized a system similar to the one of Smith et al.[49] except for a more elaborate excitation optics and sample cell and a more powerful $N_2$-laser pump to detect riboflavin at the sub-part-per-trillion level. Finally, Wirth and Lytle[56] have utilized two photon excitation-molecular fluorimetry to detect selectively, low concentrations of several molecules (a cavity-dumped, synchronously-pumped cw dye laser was used).

In Table 4, the state of the art detection limits for several organic molecules excited by laser sources are given.

The analytical advantages of using pulsed laser sources for molecular fluorimetry of condensed phase species are less obvious than for atomic fluorescence spectrometry. For example, the difficulties with removal of ultra-trace luminescent impurities from solvents and reagents can lead to detection limits determined by luminescent background flicker noise and so conventional and laser sources should give similar detection limits. However, multiphoton excited (with and without resonance enhancement) fluorescence should allow an extension of the upper concentration limit prior to deviation from non-linearity and freedom from many, if not most, scatter and potential spectral interferences as compared to conventional (single-photon) laser excited fluorimetry. In addition, optically-dense solutions (optical density due to some interferent) which may be impossible to do via conventional laser excited molecular fluorimetry may be readily possible by multiphoton laser excited molecular fluorimetry. Finally, multiphoton laser excited fluorimetry can be readily used in the right-angle configuration which is less prone to wall adsorption effects and also should be free from the inner (pre) filter effect (however, it is just as susceptible to the post filter effect just as in single photon excitation). Multiphoton-excited resonance enhanced molecular luminescence of low pressure gas phase[58] and even condensed phase[59] species has tremendous analytical potential despite its lack of use in published analytical studies; the great analytical potential should encompass <u>great sensitivity</u> and <u>low detection limits</u> due to resonance enhancement, <u>great selectivity</u>, especially at low pressures, but, to some extent, also for condensed phase species due to selective excitation of vibrational levels; and freedom from most spectral interferences and calibration curvature problems of conventional single photon luminescence.

<u>Literature Cited</u>

1.  L'vov, B. V., "Atomic Absorption Spectroscopy," Translated from Russian, Israel Program for Scientific Translation, Jerusalem, 1969.
2.  Winefordner, J. D., Svoboda, V., and Cline, L. J., <u>CRC</u> <u>Crit.</u> <u>Rev.</u> <u>Anal.</u> <u>Chem.</u> (1970), <u>1</u>, 233.
3.  Sychra, V., Svoboda, V., and Rubeska, I., "Atomic Fluorescence Spectrometry," Translated by M. Cresser, Van Nostrand-Reinhold Co., London, 1975.
4.  Gelbwachs, J. A., <u>Appl.</u> <u>Optics</u> (1976), <u>15</u>, 2654.
5.  Bjorkholm, J. E., and Liao, P. F., <u>Optics</u> <u>Commun.</u> (1976), <u>18</u>, 4.
6.  Fairbank, W. M., Hänsch, T. W., and Schawlow, A. L., <u>J.</u> <u>Opt.</u> <u>Soc.</u> <u>Amer.</u> (1975), <u>65</u>, 199.
7.  Omenetto, N., and Winefordner, J. D., <u>Appl.</u> <u>Spectrosc.</u> <u>Rev.</u> (1973), <u>7</u>, 147.
8.  Omenetto, N., Omenetto, P., Hart, L. P., Winefordner, J. D., and Alkemade, C. Th. J., <u>Spectrochim.</u> <u>Acta</u> (1973), <u>28B</u>, 289.
9.  Gelbwachs, J. A., Klein, C. F., and Wessel, J. E., <u>Appl.</u> <u>Phys.</u> <u>Lett.</u> (1977), <u>30</u>, 489.
10. Hurst, G. S., Nayfeh, M. H., and Young, J. P., <u>Phys.</u> <u>Rev.</u> (1977), <u>15A</u>, 2283.
11. Nayfeh, M. H., <u>Phys.</u> <u>Rev.</u> (1977), <u>16A</u>, 927.
12. Capelle, G. A., and Sutton, D. G., <u>Appl.</u> <u>Phys.</u> <u>Lett.</u> (1977), <u>30</u>, 407.
13. Boutilier, G. D., Blackburn, M. B., Mermet, J. M., Weeks, S. J., Haraguchi, H., and Winefordner, J. D., <u>Appl.</u> <u>Optics</u>, in press.
14. Measures, R. M., <u>J.</u> <u>Appl.</u> <u>Phys.</u> (1968), <u>39</u>, 5232.
15. O'livares, D. R., Ph.D. Thesis, Indiana University, Bloomington, IN, 1976.
16. Daily, J.W., <u>Appl.</u> <u>Optics</u> (1976), <u>15</u>, 955.
17. Omenetto, N., and Winefordner, J. D., Chapter on Atomic Fluorescence Spectroscopy with Laser Excitation in "Analyti-

cal Laser Spectrometry," N. Omenetto, ed., John Wiley, New York, in press.

18. Boutilier, G. D., Winefordner, J. D., and Omenetto, N., Appl. Optics, in press.

19. Killinger, P. K., Wang, C. C., and Hanabusa, M., Phys. Rev. (1976), 13A, 13.

20. Pantell, P. H., and Puthoff, H. E., "Fundamentals of Quantum Electronics," John Wiley, New York, 1969.

21. Piepmeier, E. H., Spectrochim. Acta (1972) 27B, 431.

22. Ibid. (1972), 445.

23. Piepmeier, E. H., Chapter on Atomic Absorption Spectroscopy with Laser Primary Sources, in "Analytical Laser Spectrometry," N. Omenetto, ed., John Wiley, in press.

24. Gelbwachs, J. A., Jones, P. F., and Wessel, J. E., Appl. Phys. Lett. (1975), 27, 40.

25. Gelbwachs, J. A., and Wessel, J. E., Appl. Phys. Lett. (1975), 27, 551.

26. McClain, W. M., Acc. Chem. Res. (1974), 7, 129.

27. Weeks, S. J., Haraguchi, H., and Winefordner, J. D., Anal. Chem., in press.

28. Fraser, L. M., and Winefordner, J. D., Anal. Chem. (1971), 43, 1693.

29. Denton, M. B., and Malmstadt, H. V., Appl. Phys. Lett. (1971), 18, 485.

30. Fraser, L. M., and Winefordner, J. D., Anal. Chem. (1972), 44, 1444.

31. Omenetto, N., Hatch, N. N., Fraser, L. M., and Winefordner, J. D., Anal. Chem. (1973), 45, 195.

32. Omenetto, N., Hatch, N. N., Fraser, L. M., and Winefordner, J. D., Spectrochim. Acta (1973), 28B, 65.

33. Omenetto, N., Hart, L. P., Benetti, P., and Winefordner, J. D., Spectrochim. Acta (1973), 28B, 301.

34. Omenetto, N., Benetti, P., Hart, L. P., Winefordner, J. D., and Alkemade, C. Th. J., Spectrochim. Acta (1973), 28B, 289.

35. Kuhl, J., Neumann, S., and Kriese, M., Z. Naturforsch (1973), 28a, 273.

36. Kuhl, J., and Spitschan, H., Opt. Commun. (1973), 7, 256.

37. de Olivares, D. R., Ph.D. Thesis, Indiana University, 1976.

38. Green, R. B., Travis, J. C., and Keller, R. A., Anal. Chem. (1976), 48, 1954.

39. Gelbwachs, J. A., Klein, C. F., and Wessel, J. E., Appl. Phys. Lett. (1977), 30, 489.

40. Smith, B. W., Blackburn, M. B., and Winefordner, J. D., Can. J. Spectrosc. (1977), 22, 57.

41. Daily, J. W., and Chan, C., University of California, Berkeley, CA, unpublished work.

42. Kuhl, J., and Marowsky, G., Opt. Commun. (1971), 4, 125.

43. Neumann, S., and Kriese, M., Spectrochim. Acta (1974), 29B, 127.

44. Bolshov, M. A., Zybin, A. V., Zybina, L. A., Koloshnikov, V.

G., and Majorov, I. A., Spectrochim. Acta (1976), 31B, 493.

45. Fairbanks, Jr., W. M., Hänsch, T. W., and Schawlow, A. L., J. Opt. Soc. Am. (1975), 65, 199.

46. Mayo, S., Keller, R. A., Travis, J. C., and Green, R. B., J. Appl. Phys. (1976), 47, 4012.

47. Brod, H. L., and Yeung, E. S., Anal. Chem. (1976), 48, 344.

48. Sharp, B. L., and Goldwasser, A., Spectrochim. Acta (1976), 31B, 431.

49. Smith, B. W., Plankey, F. W., Omenetto, N., Hart, L. P., and Winefordner, J. D., Spectrochim. Acta (1974), 30A, 1459.

50. Van Geel, T. F., and Winefordner, J. D., Anal. Chem. (1976), 48, 335.

51. Berman, M. R., and Zare, R. N., Anal. Chem. (1975), 47, 1200.

52. Bradley, A. B., and Zare, R. N., J. Amer. Chem. Soc. (1976), 98, 620.

53. Dieböld, G. J., and Zare, R. N., Science (1977), 196, 1439.

54. Richardson, J. H., Wallin, B. W., Johnson, D. C., and Hrubesh, L. W., Anal. Chim. Acta (1976), 86, 263.

55. Richardson, J. H., and Ando, M. E., Anal. Chem. (1977), 49, 955.

56. Wirth, M. J., and Lytle, F. E., Anal. Chem. (1977), 49, 2054.

57. LeBlanc, R. M., Galinier, G., Tessier, A., and Lemieux, L., Can. J. Chem. (1974), 52, 3723.

58. Bjorkholm, J. E., and Liao, P. F., Phys. Rev. Lett. (1974), 33, 128.

59. Adams, G. E., Fielden, E. M., and Michael, B. D., "Fast Processes in Radiation Chemistry and Biology," John Wiley, New York, 1975.

RECEIVED August 7, 1978.

# 5

# Laser Fluorimetry: Detection of Aflatoxin B₁ in Contaminated Corn

G. J. DIEBOLD' and R. N. ZARE

Department of Chemistry, Stanford University, Stanford, CA 94305

Aflatoxins, metabolites from Aspergillus fungi, are among the most potent naturally occurring carcinogens known.(1)   The presence of these toxins in varying amounts in a wide variety of grain and food products in virtually every country of the world has given rise to concern over the potential public health hazard caused by aflatoxins in the human food supply.(2) The carcinogenic activity of these compounds at the low ppb level, documented in feeding experiments with laboratory animals, (1) ipso facto demands analytical detection methods for aflatoxins at this level or better.  From the feeding experiments, the most pronounced effects of aflatoxin, both accute and chronic, are known to occur in the liver.  In trout fry, aflatoxin has been shown to induce hepatoma in statistically significant percentages at a level of only 100 ppt (1)--a disquieting fact given that conventional analytical techniques are generally capable of detecting aflatoxin at ten to a hundred times this concentration.

By far, the most widely used method for aflatoxin detection relies upon separation of the aflatoxins on a TLC plate followed by visual observation of their natural fluorescence when excited by a UV lamp.  Depending upon the skill of the individual experimenter, this method has a detection limit from 1 to 10 ppb in corn.  Attempts to improve upon this procedure by forming an extract from a larger grain sample, or equivalently by spotting a larger amount of grain extract on the TLC plate are of little value since overloading of the TLC plate results, i.e. band spreading of various components in the extract occurs in the region of aflatoxin fluorescence, precluding more sensitive detection.

Taking advantage of the partial cleanup of the extract afforded by an overloaded TLC plate, we report here a two-step chromatography procedure, preparative TLC followed by reverse phase HPLC, for quantitation of aflatoxin B₁ in corn.  Detection

'Current address: Department of Chemistry, Brown University, Providence, RI 02912

0-8412-0459-4/78/47-085-080$05.00/0

of aflatoxin $B_{2A}$ (formed from aflatoxin $B_1$) is carried out with
a high sensitivity laser fluorimeter that can detect as little
as 750 fg of aflatoxin. The procedure outlined is capable of
linearly quantitating aflatoxin $B_1$ from 0.1 to 10 ppb in white
and yellow corn.

## Apparatus

The laser fluorimeter (3) is based on phase sensitive
detection of fluorescence excited by an amplitude modulated,
8 mW, He-Cd ion laser. The normal drift in output power of the
laser is virtually eliminated by a feedback loop consisting of
an acousto-optic light modulator, difference amplifier, and
photodiode employed in the Liconix Model 405 UV laser. As shown
in Fig. 1, an oscillator drives the difference amplifier at
50 kHz, which by virtue of the feedback loop, produces a 100%
amplitude modulated beam directly in phase with the oscillator.
After passing through a UV pass filter (Corning 7-60) to remove
background radiation from the plasma tube, the beam is focused
by a quartz lens into a flowing liquid droplet of eluent from
the HPLC column. By positioning the collimator so that the
surface of the droplet where the laser enters is excluded from
view, scattering of the laser radiation into the detection
optics is minimized. Fluorescence excited in the droplet passes
through an interference filter, a quartz lens, and a visible
pass filter located in a separate polished brass chamber. The
first filter after the collimator is a front surface, long wavelength pass interference filter on a spectrosil quartz substrate.
The 1.25 in. focal length quartz lens focuses light from the
droplet onto the photocathode of a low noise photomultiplier
(Centronix 4249BA). The photomultiplier signal is fed into a
lock-in amplifier and detected in phase with the oscillator
signal. The output of the lock-in amplifier, which is proportional to the fluorescence intensity from the droplet, is
displayed on a stripchart recorder.

The fluorescence cell is a liquid droplet of eluent in the
shape of Plateau's unduloid (4) which is supported by surface
tension in a gap between the 1/16 in. O.D. tubing from the
chromatography column and a solid stainless steel rod of the
same diameter. The droplet forms a detection cell with a volume
of only 4 μl and yet does not suffer from problems of cell wall
fluorescence. Bubbles are prevented from entering the droplet
by notching the tubing near the end, and plugging the tip so
that the eluent is forced to flow down the sides of the tubing
allowing bubbles to rise to the surface. After passing down the
outside of the stainless steel rod, the eluent is removed by an
aspirator. Some scattering of the beam by the droplet cannot be
avoided. To minimize the resulting fluorescence from the light
shield, a coating of fine carbon (Fisher Norit A in chloroform)
was applied to the interior surfaces of the light shield.

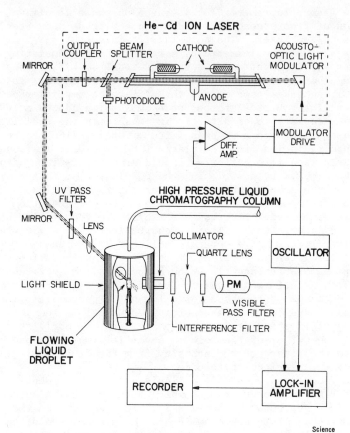

*Figure 1. Diagram of the feedback stabilized laser, flowing droplet fluorescence cell, and detection electronics (3)*

The sensitivity of this device for aflatoxin detection is demonstrated in the chromatograms shown in Fig. 2. Here, the aflatoxins $B_1$ and $G_1$ have been derivatized to the more fluorescent aflatoxins $B_{2A}$ and $G_{2A}$.

As a result of the partitioning processes in the HPLC column, the aflatoxins elute from the column considerably more dilute than the solution injected onto the column; thus, the detector must respond to a correspondingly less fluorescent solution. The peak eluting from the column has a Gaussian profile given by $f(x) = (2\pi)^{-\frac{1}{2}} \sigma^{-1} \exp(-x^2/2\sigma^2)$ where $3.56\ \sigma$ is the full width at half maximum intensity of the peak. A typical peak has a full width at half maximum of 0.4 min which corresponds to $\sigma = 0.17$ ml at a flow rate of 1.5 ml/min. Since $f(x)$ is normalized to unity, the concentration of aflatoxin at the detection limit (Fig.2) becomes $c(x) = 750\ f(x)$ in fg/ml. At the maximum in the peak, $c(0) = 1800$ fg/ml corresponding to $6 \times 10^{-12} M$. Since the detection volume is only 4 μl, the amount of aflatoxin in the droplet is only 7 fg corresponding to $1 \times 10^7$ molecules.

## Aflatoxin B₁ Detection in Contaminated Corn

Extraction of aflatoxin from corn is carried out using the method of Seitz and Mohr.(5) The final extract represents 10 g of grain and is dissolved in 0.5 ml of a benzene-acetonitrile solution. The first cleanup step consists of spotting 50 μl of this extract onto a Brinkman SIL-G-25-HR TLC plate which is developed in an 88:12 v/v chlororform-acetone solution. Now, even at 1 ppb, the 50 μl of extract corresponds to only 1 ng of aflatoxin--an amount difficult to identify on a TLC plate. To provide certain identification of the position of the aflatoxins in the unknown samples, 10 ng standards of aflatoxin $B_1$ are spotted adjacent to the unknowns. Following development of the plate, the portion of the silica gel containing the unknown sample can be easily found by noting the position of the 10 ng standards under a UV lamp. The silica gel containing the aflatoxin is then removed from the TLC plate, agitated several minutes in a vial with 2 ml of chloroform and the supernatant collected. The sample is evaporated to dryness under a stream of nitrogen on a steam bath and the aflatoxin $B_1$ converted to aflatoxin $B_{2A}$, (1) known to have a high fluorescent quantum efficiency in hydrogen bonded solvents.(6) Although trifluoroacetic acid has been used, (7) we prefer to use 100 μl of $1\underline{N}$ H Cl (8) which is allowed to react for 10 min. The acid is then evaporated under nitrogen and the extract dissolved in 100 μl of the HPLC elution solvent.

The HPLC column used in these experiments is a Waters Inc. C18 μBondapak, reverse phase column operated at 1.5 ml/min with a 75:25 water-ethanol solution. Solvents are of extremely high purity. Ethanol is prepared (9) by distilling 95% "gold shield"

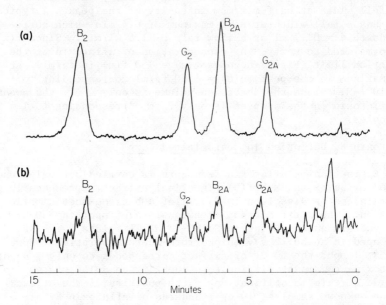

*Figure 2.* (a) *Chromatogram of aflatoxins $B_1$, $G_1$, $B_2$, and $G_2$ eluting from a C18 μBondapak HPLC column at a flow rate of 1.5 mL/min; 30 pg each. The aflatoxins $B_1$ and $G_1$ have been converted to aflatoxins $B_{2A}$ and $G_{2A}$, respectively, with HCl.* (b) *The fluorimeter response at the detection limit of 750 fg. A three-second time constant was used in (b); at higher levels a one-second or shorter time constant on the lock-in amplifier can be used* (3).

ethanol to which 1 g KOH pellets per liter has been added.
After discarding the first few ml of distillate, approximately
2/3 of the original volume is collected. Water is filtered,
deionized, passed over activated charcoal, and distilled. After
mixing, solvents are degassed in an ultrasonic cleaner for 1/2
hour. Great care must be taken to insure that all surfaces
coming into contact with the solvents are free of contamination.
Thorough cleaning with a 10% HF solution is recommended. The
purity of the solvents can be given a final test by visually
observing fluorescence excited by the laser. In a completely
darkened room, fluorescence over a few cm path length should
be faintly visible, or not visible at all. The column also must
be free of contamination. Passing high purity ethanol through
the column, as recommended by the manufacturer, is effective in
removing various fluorescent contaminants from the column.

  After a stable baseline is obtained on the recorder, 10 µl
of the extract are injected onto the column. The fluorimeter
sensitivity, and column retention time for aflatoxin $B_{2A}$ are
determined by preparation of known quantities of aflatoxin $B_1$
which are spotted on TLC plates, derivatized, etc. in the same
manner as the unknown sample. The aflatoxin content of the
contaminated grain is determined by comparing the peak in the
unknown sample to those from standards. If the above procedure
is followed exactly, 1 ppb of aflatoxin contamination corresponds
to 100 pg of a standard injected directly onto the HPLC column.

## Results

  In a previous paper, (3) the linear response of the detector
was demonstrated over the range from 750 fg to 30 ng for
aflatoxins $B_{2A}$, $G_{2A}$, $B_2$ and $G_2$. The linearity of this method
for aflatoxin quantitation rests on a constant conversion of
aflatoxin $B_1$ to $B_{2A}$, and therefore the conversion efficiency,
although reported to be high, (8) must be scrutinized over the
entire range of interest. Thus, aflatoxin $B_1$ standards ranging
from 10 pg to 5 ng were individually derivatized, redissolved in
elution solvent, and injected onto the HPLC column. The
magnitudes of the fluorescence signals, as shown in Fig. 3,
exhibit the expected linearity over roughly three orders of
magnitude. The straight lines are least squares fits to the data
determined by minimizing the fractional error between the data
points and a line through the origin. (This procedure weights
each point equally, whereas a conventional least squares fit
strongly favors data points with large values.) The root mean
square (rms) error was then calculated for each run giving an
average of 28% for the two runs.

The overall precision of this method is determined by errors in recovery from the TLC plate, derivatization, and quantitation in the fluorimeter. Further errors introduced in the extraction procedure have been previously investigated.(5) Standards of aflatoxin $B_1$ were spotted on TLC plates, recovered, derivatized, and injected onto the HPLC column. The results shown in Fig. 4 surprisingly show a marked departure from linearity above 1 ng indicating an increased recovery from the TLC plates. Since this change in recovery is not particularly pronounced, standards could be used to calibrate the procedure permitting accurate quantitation at any level of aflatoxin contamination from 0.1 to 50 ppb (10 pg to 50 ng). However, since the simpler method of fluorimetric quantitation directly on TLC plates can be used above the 10 ppb level it appears prudent to limit the range of the HPLC-laser fluorimetric method to levels below 10 ppb, thus simplifying the error analysis. With this constraint an rms error of 26% (an average of both runs in Fig. 4) obtains for the range between 0.1 and 10 ppb.

The efficacy of the two-step chromatography procedure for eliminating interfering components in the corn extract is shown in Fig. 5a. The smoothness of the baseline can be compared to the signal in Fig. 5b, representing a contamination of 250 ppt, thus indicating a limit of detection for this method of approximately 100 ppt. Note that since the detection limit is determined by the concentration of contaminants still remaining in the final extract, higher fluorimeter sensitivity (below 10 pg) would not further improve detection limits. Thus a reduction in the above figure for detection of aflatoxin in corn is contingent upon the development of either more specific detectors, or further improvements in cleanup techniques.

Discussion

An inherent advantage of this technique lies in the ability to use the derivatization step as a confirmatory procedure for the presence of aflatoxin $B_1$. Since aflatoxin $B_1$ has a low fluorescent quantum efficiency in solution, comparison of chromatograms where the derivatization step has been deleted provides additional evidence of its presence in the grain sample.

The ultimate sensitivity of the fluorimeter described here is contingent upon a fortuitous coincidence between the laser line at 325 nm and an absorption maximum of the species of interest. However, in practice remarkable sensitivity is attainable even when this condition is not fulfilled. Fluorescein, for instance, has an absorption maximum at 500 nm, a considerable shift from the laser line. While the optical density at 325 nm differs from that at the peak by four, (10) corresponding to a factor of $10^4$ in absorption, the fluorimeter

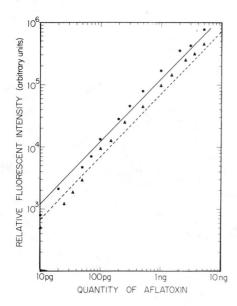

Figure 3. *The fluorimeter signal, proportional to the amount of aflatoxin $B_{2A}$, is plotted as a function of the quantity of aflatoxin $B_1$ derivatized to determine the linearity of the HCl-derivative formation procedure. The displacement of the two lines on the log–log plot corresponds to slightly different fluorimeter gains for the two runs. (– ● –) Run 1. (-- ▲ --) Run 2.*

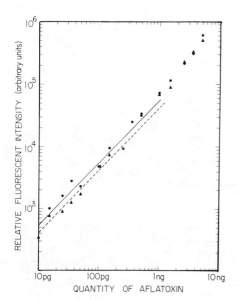

Figure 4. *Aflatoxin $B_1$ standards were spotted on TLC plates, removed, derivatized, and quantitated with the fluorimeter. The fluorimeter response, plotted on the ordinate, shows a slight nonlinearity above 1 ng. (– ● –) Run 1. (-- ▲ --) Run 2.*

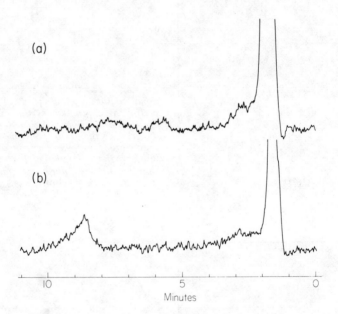

Figure 5. (a) Chromatogram of an aflatoxin-free sample of yellow corn using the cleanup procedure described in the text. The
flatness of the baseline compared with the signal from the 25 pg
aflatoxin $B_{2A}$ ($B_1$) standard in (b) indicates a sensitivity of approximately 100 ppt. The tailing seen in these chromatograms is
attributable to deterioration in the two-year-old column. The
sharper peaks expected from a new column would suggest a
slightly improved sensitivity.

is still capable nevertheless of detecting 4 pg of this dye
injected onto the HPLC column.  In the case of the aflatoxins,
absorption maxima lie at 360 nm, yet the detection limit of this
device is 750 fg of each of the four aflatoxins injected onto
the HPLC column.

We believe that laser fluorimetry is applicable to a number
of trace analysis problems, and has special advantage in those
cases where sensitivity is a limiting factor.

## Acknowledgments

We would like to thank Dr. Larry Seitz for supplying us
with grain extracts.  The assistance of N. Karny, J. Kinney and
S. Lidofsky in various phases of this work is gratefully
acknowledged.  This work was supported by National Cancer
Institute grant 1-R01-CA-18271-01.

## Abstract

A high sensitivity laser fluorimeter designed specifically
for use with high pressure liquid chromatography (HPLC) is
described.  An amplitude modulated He-Cd ion laser at 325 nm
irradiates a flowing droplet of eluent from an HPLC column, and
fluorescence is detected in phase with the modulation by a lock-
in amplifier.  The fluorimeter is capable of detecting 750 fg
of each of the four commonly occurring aflatoxins, and has a
linear range of over three orders of magnitude.  Using a two-
step chromatography procedure, this device is capable of
quantitating aflatoxin $B_1$ to 100 ppt in corn.  Following
extraction of the aflatoxin from corn, the extract is given
a preliminary cleanup on a normal phase thin layer chromatography
(TLC) plate.  The aflatoxin $B_1$ is recovered, and injected onto
a reverse phase HPLC column.  Experiments with aflatoxin $B_1$
standards show a constant ratio for conversion of aflatoxin $B_1$
to aflatoxin $B_{2A}$ over roughly three orders of magnitude.  The
recovery of aflatoxin $B_1$ from the TLC plates, although slightly
nonlinear above 10 ppb permits linear quantitation of aflatoxin
$B_1$ in white and yellow corn in the range from 0.1 to 10 ppb with
an average root mean square (rms) error of 26%.

## Literature Cited

1.  Goldblatt, L. A., "Aflatoxin: Scientific Background, Control, and Implications," Academic Press, New York, 1969.

2.  Shank, R. C., in "Mycotoxins and Other Fungal Related Food Problems," Rodricks, J., Ed. American Chemical Society, Washington, D.C., 1976.

3.  Diebold, G. J., and Zare, R. N., Science (1977) 196, 1439.

4.  Bickerman, J. J., "Physical Surfaces," Academic Press, New York, 1970.

5.  Seitz, L. M. and Mohr, H. E., Cereal Chemistry (1977) 54, 179.

6.  Maggon, K. K., Gopal, S., Viswanathan, L., Venkitasubramanian, T. A., Rathi, S., Ind. J. Biochem. Biophys., (1972) 9, 195.

7.  Thorpe, W., and Stoloff, L., in "89th Annual Meeting of the Association of Official Analytical Chemists," Association of Official Analytical Chemists, Washington, D.C., 1975, abstr. 58.

8.  Pohland, A. E., Cushmac, M. E., Andrellos, P. J., J. Assoc. Off. Anal. Chem. (1968) 51, 907.

9.  Parker, C. A., "Photoluminescence of Solutions," p. 421, Elsevier, Amsterdam, 1968.

10. Hansen, P. A., "Fluorescent Compounds used in Protein Tracing," University of Maryland, MD, 1964.

RECEIVED August 7, 1978.

# Laser-Enhanced Ionization for Trace Metal Analysis in Flames

J. C. TRAVIS and G. C. TURK

Center for Analytical Chemistry, U.S. National Bureau of Standards, Washington, D.C. 20234

R. B. GREEN

Department of Chemistry, West Virginia University, Morgantown, WV 26506

Ionization of atoms in flames is more probable from an excited state than a ground state. A dye laser tuned to a discrete atomic transition will sufficiently bias the excited state population of the atom to produce a change in ionization rate which is easily measured with conventional electronics. The excess ionization in the flame due to laser excitation has been generally characterized as an optogalvanic effect[1] but laser enhanced ionization (LEI) is more descriptive, particularly in terms of the mechanism[2].

Generalized plots of the Saha equation[3] (Figure 1) show that most elements (ionization potential $\geq$ 5eV) are predominantly neutral at typical flame temperatures. The absorption of optical energy, moving an atom closer to its ionization limit, will significantly increase the ion population in the flame. According to Figure 1, an electron volt of excitation energy will provide approximately one order of magnitude increase in ionization at 2500 K. LEI spectrometry is a hybrid technique which depends on both laser excitation and thermal ionization. The process may proceed by photoexcitation and thermal ionization or a combination of thermal excitation, photoexcitation and thermal ionization (Figure 2).

The experimental system used is illustrated in Figure 3. The sample is aspirated into a fuel lean air-acetylene flame of a standard premix burner with a 5 cm single slot burner head. The atomized species are excited with a flashlamp-pumped tunable dye laser with capability for frequency-doubled operation. The data reviewed[2] and presented here were obtained at laser bandwidths of 0.05-0.1 nm, although further narrowing is readily possible. The laser dyes used included Fluoral-7GA, Rhodamine 575, Rhodamine 6G, and Rhodamine 640, with frequency doubling in most cases.

The signal is detected with a pair of 1 mm diameter tungsten welding rods 1 cm apart and $\sim$ 1 cm above the burner head. These dual cathodes run parallel to the burner slot and are maintained at -500V to -1000V with respect to the burner head, which is used

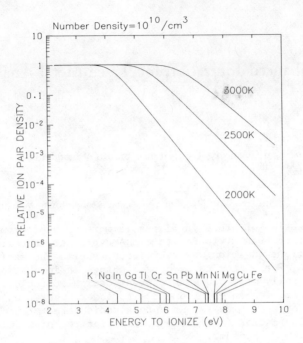

*Figure 1. Relative degree of ionization of a generalized element (3) as a function of its ionization potential for flames of (a) 2000, (b) 2500, and (c) 3000 K*

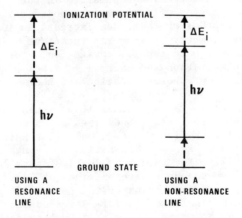

*Figure 2. Typical avenues of laser-enhanced ionization: (a) photo excitation from the ground state followed by collisional ionization; (b) photo excitation from a thermally populated excited state followed by collisional ionization*

as the anode.  The electrodes remain visually outside the flame,
although still in electrical contact with the flame.  This
configuration is slightly less sensitive than when the electrodes
are immersed in the flame, but it avoids fouling and erosion
which lead to long-term signal deterioration.  The burner head is
electrically insulated from the burner body by a strip of electrical tape, so that the current may be monitored on the low voltage
side of the flame.  The signal pulse is separated from the dc
background current with a high-pass filter, amplified, and processed with sample-and-hold circuits and a minicomputer (or a
boxcar signal averager with digital storage).

Figure 4 shows LEI signals from a solution of 25 ng/mL Mg and
7 ng/mL Na.  The LEI intensities for these transitions are not
indicative of the relative concentrations and absorption coefficients alone.  Indeed, the expected absorption ratio for Mg
(285.2 nm) to Na (285.3 nm) is $\simeq$ 1900 for these concentrations.
Oscillator strength, ionization potential, and fractional population all play important roles in determining the signal strength.
The most sensitive line for atomic absorption, atomic fluorescence, and atomic emission, may not necessarily be the best line
for LEI spectrometry.

Table I shows the detection limits for pure, aqueous solutions of several elements.  These detection limits were determined by using the average and standard deviation of the mean of
150 laser pulses ($\sim$ 0.8 $\mu$s pulsewidth) at a pulse repetition rate
of 5 pulses per second.  For comparison, Table I also contains
detection limits reported for other flame spectrometric techniques.  With one exception, LEI detection limits are comparable to
or better than those reported for other flame spectrometric
methods.

A closer inspection of the LEI detection limits is instruc-
tive.  Table II shows pertinent parameters for the transitions
used.  One factor which is particularly important is the energy
difference between the laser populated excited state and the
ionization potential.  This energy difference is referred to as
$\Delta E_i$.  Sodium is a striking example of the combined effect of
transition probability and proximity to the ionization limit.
The detection limits are comparable for both the strong line at
589.0 nm (which is commonly used for spectroscopic analysis) and
the weak line at 285.3 nm, although the laser output is 100 times
more powerful at the strong line.  The effect of $\Delta E_i$ on sensitivity is also illustrated by the low detection limits obtained
using excited-excited transitions of Cr, Cu, Mn, Pb, Sn, and Tl.
In these cases, the loss of sensitivity resulting from the small
fractional population of the lower level is significantly counter-
balanced by the decrease in $\Delta E_i$.  LEI analysis of copper at
324.8 nm is relatively insensitive, since its $\Delta E_i$ is larger than
any of the other transitions attempted.  Indium enjoys the dual
advantages of a small $\Delta E_i$ and a relatively large absorption
coefficient, $B_{\ell u}$.

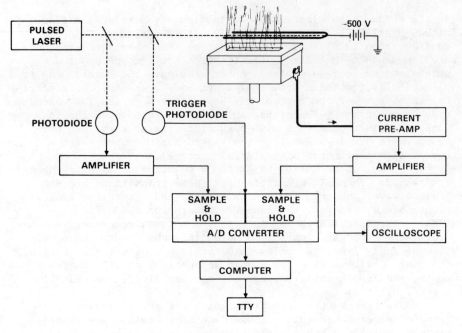

*Figure 3.    Block diagram of the instrument*

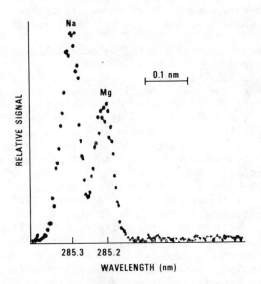

*Figure 4.    LEI spectrum of a solution of 25 ng/ mL Mg and 7 ng/mL Na in a $C_2H_2$/air flame*

TABLE I

Comparative Detection Limits by LEI and Other Flame Techniques

| Element | LEI[a] | FAA[c] | FAE[c] | FAF[c] | Laser FAF[d] |
|---------|--------|--------|--------|--------|--------------|
| Cr | 2 | 2 | 2 | 5 | 1 |
| Cu | 100[b] | 4 | 10 | 0.5 | 1 |
| Fe | 2 | 4 | 5 | 8 | 30 |
| Ga | 0.07 | 50 | 60 | 10 | 0.9 |
| In | 0.008 | 30 | 0.4 | 100 | 0.2 |
| K | 1 | 3 | .05 | -- | -- |
| Mg | 0.1[b] | 3 | 70 | 0.1 | 0.2 |
| Mn | 0.3[b] | 0.8 | 1 | 1 | 0.4 |
| Na | 0.05[b] | 0.8 | 0.5 | -- | 0.1 |
| Ni | 8 | 5 | 20 | 3 | 2 |
| Pb | 0.6[b] | 10 | 100 | 10 | 13 |
| Sn | 6 | 50 | 100 | 50 | |
| Tl | 0.09 | 20 | 20 | 8 | 4 |

[a]This work, except as noted. All limits are in ng/mL.

[b]Reported originally in reference 2.

[c]Taken from J. D. Winefordner, J. J. Fitzgerald, and N. Omenetto, Appl. Spectrosc. 29, 369 (1975). FAA = Flame Atomic Absorption. FAE = Flame Atomic Emission. FAF = Flame Atomic Fluorescence.

[d]S. J. Weeks, H. Haraguchi, and J. D. Winefordner, Anal. Chem. 50, 360 (1978).

TABLE II

Factors Determining the LEI Figure of Merit

| Element | Wavelength (nm) | $\beta$[a] | $B_{12} \times 10^{-17}$ $s^{-1}$ (W $cm^{-2}$ $Hz^{-1})^{-1}$ | $E_\ell$ ($cm^{-1}$) | $g_\ell/g_0$ | $\Delta E_i$ ($cm^{-1}$) | Figure[b] of Merit | Limit of Detection (ng/mL) |
|---|---|---|---|---|---|---|---|---|
| Cr | 298.6 | .065 | 2.53 | 8308 | 1.3 | 12788 | $2.6 \times 10^2$ | 2.0 |
|    | 301.8 | .065 | 4.35 | 8095 | 1 | 13345 | $3.6 \times 10^2$ | 2.0 |
| Cu | 282.4 | 1.0 | .298 | 11203 | 3 | 15719 | 17 | 100 |
|    | 324.8 | 1.0 | 1.77 | 0 | 1 | 31533 | 6.9 | 100 |
| Fe | 298.4 | .4 | .223 | 0 | 1 | 30193 | .78 | 4 |
|    | 302.1 | .4 | .426 | 0 | 1 | 30604 | 1.2 | 2 |
| Ga | 287.4 | .2 | 1.76 | 0 | 1 | 13606 | $4.2 \times 10^4$ | 0.07 |
|    | 294.4 | .2 | 1.76 | 826 | 2 | 13601 | $2.6 \times 10^5$ | 0.1 |
| In | 303.9 | .6 | 2.51 | 0 | 1 | 13778 | $1.6 \times 10^5$ | 0.008 |
| K | 294.3 | .2 | $7.5 \times 10^{-5}$ | 0 | 1 | 1037 | $2.5 \times 10^3$ | 1 |
| Mg | 285.2 | .6 | 5.5 | 0 | 1 | 26620 | $2.2 \times 10^2$ | 0.1 |
| Mn | 279.5 | .6 | .76 | 0 | 1 | 24200 | 30 | 0.3 |
| Na | 280.0 | .6 | 1.11 | 17052 | 1.7 | 7212 | $1.8 \times 10^2$ | 5 |
|    | 285.3 | .9 | $7.0 \times 10^{-3}$ | 0 | 1 | 6407 | $4.7 \times 10^4$ | 0.05 |
|    | 589.0 | .9 | 4.63 | 0 | 1 | 24476 | $9.6 \times 10^4$ | 0.1 |
| Ni | 300.2 | 1.0 | .65 | 205 | .8 | 28078 | 17 | 8 |
| Pb | 280.2 | .7 | 4.76 | 10650 | 5 | 13491 | $9.5 \times 10^2$ | 0.6 |
|    | 283.3 | .7 | 1.03 | 0 | 1 | 24533 | $1.6 \times 10^2$ | 3 |
| Sn | 284.0 | .04 | 2.42 | 3428 | 5 | 20603 | 29 | 6 |
|    | 286.3 | .04 | 3.13 | 0 | 1 | 24318 | 32 | 10 |
| Tl | 291.8 | .5 | 2.35 | 7793 | 2 | 7218 | $6.2 \times 10^4$ | 0.09 |

[a] Taken from Reference 5.

[b] Computed from Equation 1, using the factors given and an assumed spectral irradiance of $3 \times 10^{-9}$ W $cm^{-2}$ $Hz^{-1}$ for all uv transitions and $3 \times 10^{-7}$ W $cm^{-2}$ $Hz^{-1}$ for Na (589.0).

A zero-order figure of merit is useful for predicting the relative sensitivity of atomic transitions:

$$\text{Figure of Merit} = \beta I_\nu \, B_{\ell u} \, \exp\left[\frac{-\Delta E_i}{kT}\right] \exp\left[\frac{-E_\ell}{kT}\right] \frac{g_\ell}{g_o} \qquad (1)$$

Here $\beta$ is the atomization efficiency of the element in the flame; $I_\nu$ the laser spectral irradiance; $B_{\ell u}$ the Einstein coefficient for the probability of absorption from state $\ell$ to u; $E_\ell$ the energy of the lower state of the transition; $g_\ell$ and $g_o$ are lower state and ground state statistical weights; T the flame temperature; and k the Boltzmann constant. The first exponential term expresses the relative probability that a collision in the flame will provide the thermal energy required ($\Delta E_i$) to complete the ionization process. The second exponential term, multiplied by the statistical weight ratio, is simply the Boltzmann population of the lower level of the transition, relative to the ground state.

The uv LEI detection limits are plotted on a log-log scale against the corresponding figures of merit (shown in Table II) in Figure 5. The trend of the data towards a slope of -1 results from the nominal reciprocal relationship between detection limit and sensitivity (for constant limiting noise) and supports the validity of the figure of merit. Current investigations using three and four level model calculations[4] call for several refinements to the figure of merit, especially for excited state transitions. The simple expression is nonetheless more valid than cross sections alone for predicting the sensitivity of a transition.

Given the favorable detection limits of Table I, and the spectral selectivity available with tunable lasers, it is worthwhile to study observed and predicted matrix interferences for real sample analysis by LEI. Such interferences may generally be classified as chemical, spectral, or electrical. Chemical interferences will generally be the same as experienced by other flame spectroscopic methods[6], and will not be further discussed here.

Spectral interferences, on the other hand, have some unique features for LEI. Although atomic spectral overlaps which have been documented for other flame spectrometric methods[7] are still present, the relative degree of interference may differ drastically from optical spectrometry due to the LEI figure of merit of the interfering transition. Thus, some of the documented interferences may be inconsequential, because of a low figure of merit for the interfering line, and conversely, some undocumented coincidences of weak spectral lines may become important due to a high figure of merit. An example of this latter case is the "weak" 285.3 nm Na transition which yields a strong LEI signal and interfers significantly with the 285.2 nm Mg transition, (Figure 4).

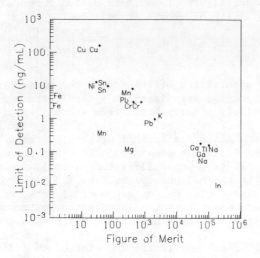

*Figure 5. LEI detection limits as a function of predicted figure of merit*

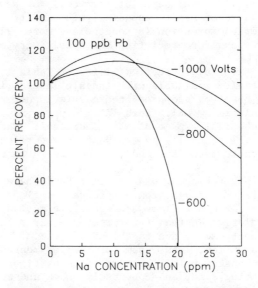

*Figure 6. Percent recovery of 100 ppb lead LEI signal as a function of sodium concentration for applied potentials of −600, −800, and −1000 V*

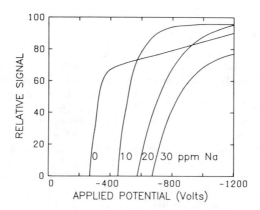

*Figure 7.   Percent recovery of 100-ppb lead LEI
signal as a function of applied potential for sodium concentrations of 0, 10, 20, and 30 ppm*

TABLE III

Relative Interference of Different Matrices
on 100 ppb Lead Signal

| Matrix | I.P. | Percent Signal Recovery | | |
|--------|------|---------|---------|----------|
| (10 ppm) | (eV) | −500V | −750V | −1000V |
| K | 4.3 | 0 | 0 | 180 |
| Na | 5.1 | 45 | 90 | 110 |
| Li | 5.4 | 100 | 110 | 110 |
| Ca | 6.1 | 82 | 100 | 100 |
| Cu | 7.7 | 100 | 100 | 100 |

Analyte:  100 ppb Pb

$\lambda$ = 280.2 nm

Molecular spectral interferences seem to be less of a
problem with LEI than conventional flame spectrometry, since most
of the traditional interfering molecules have high ($\gtrsim$ 10 eV)
ionization potentials. Relatively few molecular species have
been observed in flames to date using LEI[8].

Electrical interferences are unique to LEI (in lieu of such
optical background interferences as flame background, ambient
light, and scattered source light, to which LEI is impervious).
Two types of electrical interference may be identified: 1) the
effect of ambient electron density in the flame on ionization/
recombination rates; and, 2) the effect of the ambient electron
and ion density on the signal collection process.

As an example, Figure 6 illustrates the effect of sodium on
the signal from 100 ppb lead for several values of applied
potential. At each potential, the addition of sodium is first
seen to enhance the signal, then reduce, and finally -- at lower
potentials -- completely extinguish the signal. Figure 7 was
obtained from the same data as Figure 6, and is useful for
explaining the signal behavior. The threshold voltage -- below
which no signal is observed for a given matrix -- is related to
the sheath, or space-charge, of positive ions which surrounds the
two cathode wires. For a given flame temperature and ambient ion
density, a corresponding electrical shielding is provided by this
sheath, reducing the magnitude of the electrical potential at the
measurement site. The shielding effect, and hence the threshold,
increases with increasing matrix ion concentration.

Above threshold, electrons generated by enhanced ionization
are driven by the electric field toward the burner head with a
velocity proportional to the actual electric field. Electrons
which reach the burner head before recombining with a positive
ion provide the LEI signal.

Table III compares the relative degree of interference for
matrices of various ionization potentials. Only the most easily
ionized elements are seen to provide a problem. The electrical
interferences are subject to modification by instrumentation
design and parameter optimization, and an active program to
minimize interferences is underway.

Laser enhanced ionization may be seen to be a sensitive and
selective method. Although presently subject to unique matrix
interferences, these are subject to further instrument development or sample pre-treatment. The method is "blind" to such
common optical interference sources as flame background emission,
ambient light, and scattered excitation light. Because of the
insensitivity to scattered laser light, the ability of lasers to
saturate optical transitions may be utilized to the fullest
advantage. Finally, the vastly modified criteria for spectral
sensitivity gives the method multi-element potential, and the
capability of avoiding traditional spectral interferences.

Implementation of LEI spectrometry requires minimal modification of a laser induced fluorescence (LIF) spectrometer. Though

less thoroughly developed than LIF at this time,[9] LEI represents
a complementary measurement which may be made simultaneously, if
desired.  Comparative LEI and LIF measurements will obviously be
required for a wide variety of samples and flames to accurately
establish the dominant roles of the complementary methods of
laser excited flame spectrometry.

## Literature Cited

1.  Green, R. B., R. A. Keller, P. K. Schenck, J. C. Travis,
    and G. G. Luther, J. Am. Chem. Soc. 98, 8517 (1976).
2.  Turk, G. C., J. C. Travis, J. R. DeVoe, and T. C. O'Haver,
    Anal. Chem. 50, 817 (1978).
3.  In order to render the plots element-independent, the ratio
    of ion-to-atom partition functions has been set equal to
    unity.  The error in degree of ionization should be less than
    one order of magnitude for any given element.  The natural
    electron background population of the flame is assumed to be
    negligible.  See P. J. W. Boumans, Theory of Spectrochemical
    Excitation, Hilger and Watts, London (1966), p 161, for a
    more complete discussion.
4.  Travis, J. C., P. K. Schenck, and G. C. Turk, in preparation.
5.  Willis, J. B., in CRC Handbook of Spectroscopy, Volume I,
    J. W. Robinson, ed., CRC Press, Cleveland (1974) p 799.
    Values from Table 12, p 814, with corrections from Table 13
    for Na and K.
6.  For a brief discussion, and pertinent Tables, see M. L. Parsons,
    B. W. Smith, and G. E. Bentley, Handbook of Flame Spectroscopy,
    Plenum Press, NY (1975), p 61.
7.  See, for instance, R. J. Lovett, D. L. Welch, and M. L. Parsons,
    Appl. Spectrosc. 29, 470 (1975).
8.  Schenck, Peter K., W. Gary Mallard, John C. Travis, and
    Kermit C. Smyth, submitted for publication.
9.  Weeks, S. J., H. Haraguchi, and J. D. Winefordner, Anal. Chem.
    50, 360 (1978).

RECEIVED August 7, 1978.

# 7

# The Study of Biological Surfaces by Laser Electrophoretic Light Scattering

B. R. WARE

Department of Chemistry, Harvard University, 12 Oxford Street, Cambridge, MA 02138

One of the newest applications of lasers is the measurement of very small velocities through the Doppler effect on laser light which has been scattered or reflected from moving objects. This technique, called laser Doppler velocimetry, has been applied to a number of interesting biological problems, and a general review of the progress in this area has recently been published (1). This lecture will focus on the application of laser Doppler velocimetry to the detection of electrophoresis, a technique which I shall call electrophoretic light scattering (ELS). The theory and the first successful experiments of this type were reported by myself and Bill Flygare in 1971 (2). Since then the technique has been developed and applied by several groups to a wide variety of problems. For reviews see references (1,3,4,5). I shall state briefly the principles of electro-phoretic light scattering, describe the methodology of the experiments as we do them, and then summarize the results of a few of the projects which are being pursued in my laboratories at Harvard.

A block diagram of an electrophoretic light scattering apparatus is shown in Figure 1. Laser light illuminates the particles or molecules to be studied, and light which has been scattered from these particles at a selected angle θ is collected and directed to a photomultiplier tube. When an electric field is applied to the suspension, the particles migrate toward the electrode of opposite polarity. Light scattered from them is therefore slightly shifted in frequency by the Doppler effect. In order to measure this shift, it is necessary to combine with the scattered light a beam of unshifted light which is obtained by splitting a second beam from the incident laser light and bypassing the chamber. These two beams, the scattered light and the so-called local oscillator beam, are mixed at the photo-cathode to produce a low-frequency beat which is exactly the Doppler shift frequency. The low-frequency oscillations of the photocurrent are then amplified and processed by a real-time spectrum analyzer, the output of which is the complete spectrum

0-8412-0459-4/78/47-085-102$05.00/0

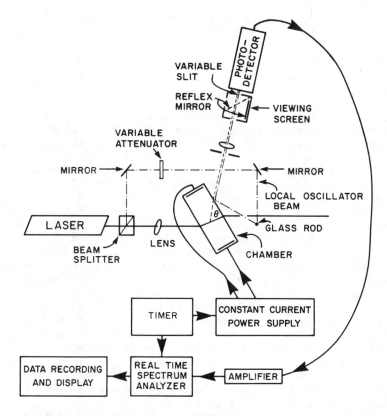

Contemporary Topics in Analytical and Clinical Chemistry

*Figure 1.    Diagram of an electrophoretic light-scattering apparatus.*

The coherent, monochromatic beam from the laser is split into two beams. The forward beam is focused into the electrophoretic light-scattering chamber to illuminate the moving particles. The chamber sits at an angle to the beam in order to obtain a higher scattering angle $\theta$, so the beam is refracted on entrance and exit. A constant electric field is applied to the scattering region by applying pulses of constant current to the electrodes. Duration of and interval between pulses are controlled by a specially constructed timing circuit. Light is scattered from the particles which are drifting in the electric field, and the scattered light is therefore shifted slightly in frequency by the Doppler effect. The scattered light is collected by an optical system and focused onto the surface of a photodetector. The split-off beam is recombined with the scattered light at the window of the chamber in order to form the so-called local oscillator. The alignment of the scattered light and the local oscillator is facilitated by the formation of real images of both, which are viewed on a screen when deflected by a reflex mirror. Once the two have been aligned at the proper point on the screen corresponding to the center of the photocathode, the reflex mirror is moved out of the way, and the two beams pass through a calibrated slit to the photocathode. There they produce a beat or spectrum of beats equal to the Doppler shift magnitudes between the shifted scattered light and the unshifted local oscillator. The photocurrent or voltage is then amplified and analyzed in frequency by a real-time spectrum analyzer, which is triggered by the timing circuit to accept data only when the field is on. The diagram of the scattering chamber is shown greatly enlarged and is highly schematic. For actual designs and descriptions, see Ref. 5.

of all Doppler signals corresponding to the histogram of velocities in the sample.

The equipment required for an electrophoretic light scattering
experiment is relatively simply and inexpensive.  For many
experiments on suspensions of large particles such as blood cells,
a small He-Ne laser costing only a few hundred dollars is sufficient.  The essential optical components can be kept to as little
as one lens and two pinholes, though in practice we use a more
complicated real-image viewing system to facilitate alignment of
the scattered light and the local oscillator (5).  In some cases
the local oscillator may be taken from one or both of the spots
formed by entry and exit of the laser beam through the chamber.
We generally prefer to have a separate optical path for the local
oscillator which bypasses the scattering chamber and then is
recombined with the scattered light, usually after being reflected from the chamber window.  A variable attenuator in the local
oscillator path allows adjustment of the ratio of the local
oscillator intensity to the detected scattered light intensity.
This ratio is usually in the range from 10:1 to 40:1.  An external local oscillator path is essential for scattering angles
above about 20°.  We generally work at angles between 50° and 60°
when analyzing large particles such as blood cells, for which
spectral broadening due to diffusion is negligible.  Much lower
angles must be utilized for the study of solutions of smaller
particles such as proteins, in order to optimize the ratio of the
Doppler shift to the diffusion-controlled half-width (2).  However, for blood cell studies we employ the higher scattering
angles to increase the Doppler shift for a given electrophoretic
velocity.  This adaptation is essential for performing experiments at physiological ionic strength, where the electrophoretic
mobilities are lower and the attainable field strength for a
given tolerable amount of Joule heating is also lower.

The beating detection system required for an electrophoretic
light scattering measurement is simpler and cheaper  than the
high-speed photon counting apparata necessary for many other
laser light scattering applications.  The photodetector can be an
inexpensive photomultiplier tube or an even cheaper photoresistor
or photovoltaic cell.  The signals are generally in the region
between 1 Hz and 200 Hz, so amplification and spectrum analysis
are trivial low-speed problems.  It is essential that the
spectrum analysis, whether done by a spectrum analyzer, an auto-
correlator, or a digital computer or calculator, be done in real
time; i.e., in the minimum time required for measurement with a
given frequency resolution.  For example, to measure a spectrum
with a resolution of 1 Hz requires 1 sec.  We need therefore
apply the electric field for one second only, if the data
processing device can make use of all the information available
during that one second to produce a complete spectrum.  The
ability to use pulsed fields is an intrinsic advantage of electrophoretic light scattering over classical electrophoresis

techniques, since it permits the use of a higher field strength, which in many cases leads to greater electrophoretic resolution. We generally apply constant-current pulses with a duty cycle of about 1:10; the interval between pulses allows the dissipation of Joule heat. The pulses are of alternating polarity so that there is no net transport of mass during the experiment. Timing and triggering are controlled by a specially designed clock circuit. The use of a constant-current power supply is important for maintaining a constant electric field during each pulse, since it automatically corrects for electrode polarization effects and changes in viscosity which accompany Joule heating.

The design of the chamber is a critical feature of the experiment. All chambers have two electrodes for application of the field and an optical path for entry of the laser beam and exit of the scattered light. However, a number of chamber configurations have been employed, and each has its own advantages. Interested persons are referred to one of the reviews of this technique (*1,3,4,5*) for discussion and references. We currently have several different chambers in use for various applications. Common features of these chambers which we have found to be important are low volume, efficient heat dissipation, and substantial separation between the electrode and the scattering region, so that particles, bubbles, and/or local pH gradients formed at the electrodes will not be able to reach the portion of the solution which is being viewed during the measurement.

Although the experiment is not easy, electrophoretic light scattering in its current state of development is capable of measuring complete electrophoretic mobility distributions in a few seconds. Once the apparatus is set up, operation is fully automatic, and adaptation to on-line processing of multiple samples would be a straightforward extension of current capabilities.

In the absence of an electric field, the light scattered from macromolecules in solution is frequency-broadened by the random thermal motions of diffusion. The measured spectrum is a Lorentzian line centered at the incident frequency, or, when beating detection is used, centered at zero. Application of the electric field causes the particles to migrate, and, if they all have the same electrophoretic mobility, the resulting spectrum is a shifted Lorentzian line whose width is still determined by diffusion and the magnitude of whose shift is directly related to the electrophoretic drift velocity, which, when divided by the field strength, gives the electrophoretic mobility. This prediction has been verified experimentally, and an example is shown in Figure 2. The points in the spectrum shown in Figure 2 are data from an electrophoretic light scattering spectrum on a dilute solution of human carbon monoxyhemoglobin (1.6 mg/ml) at pH 9.5. The line is a Lorentzian function fit to the shift of the peak and with a half-width corresponding to the known diffusion coefficient of hemoglobin. We are currently pursuing an

interest in the study of simultaneous diffusion and electrophoresis of concentration fluctuations under conditions for which
fluctuations of different species in solution cannot be considered to be uncoupled. This spectrum is presented only to show
that in the simple case of uncoupled fluctuations, the predictions of the simple theory are observed. We have also used ELS
to study the dissociation of hemoglobin at high pH (8).

If there are more than one type of macroions in solution in
appreciable concentrations, and if the different species have
differing electrophoretic mobilities, then the electrophoretic
light scattering spectrum can be used to detect and quantify
relative amounts of the species. A common example of a useful
analytical electrophoresis determination is the analysis of human
blood plasma. An electrophoretic light scattering spectrum of
human plasma is shown in Figure 3. Such a spectrum bears a
strong resemblance to plasma electrophoresis by classical techniques, except that the lower-mobility peaks, presumably due to
the various globulin fractions, are enhanced with respect to the
large albumin peak because of their higher molecular weight.
This particular measurement is an extremely important clinical
test, and some of our friends in industry tell us that electrophoretic light scattering may be cost-competitive with classical
methods for this application.

When biological particles larger than proteins, particularly
membranous particles, are analyzed, it is observed that there is
substantial electrophoretic heterogeneity. Moreover, these
larger particles have correspondingly low diffusion coefficients,
and the diffusion broadening is therefore often insignificant.
For such particles the electrophoretic light scattering spectrum
is a determination of the electrophoretic mobility distribution
of the sample. As an illustration I present the spectrum in
Figure 4. The sample in this case was a mixture of human and
rabbit red blood cells; human cells have the higher mobility.
The sharp resolution is a vivid demonstration that ELS can be
used to detect several species simultaneously. The electrophoretic mobility of red cells is quite uniform, and in a recent
publication with two other groups we have demonstrated that previous reports that the electrophoretic mobilities of red blood
cells decrease with age were erroneous (9).

We have been using electrophoretic light scattering to study
the surface properties of living cells and organelles, and the
remainder of this lecture will be a brief summary of some of our
work in this area. One of the original areas of interest was the
characterization of cells involved in the immune response, for
which surface characteristics are particularly important. For
example, lymphocytes are the white blood cells involved with
immunological recognition and response. Lymphocytes are usually
divided into two categories: T cells, which are primarily involved with direct cellular immunity, and B cells, which are
responsible for the synthesis of specific antibodies. We have

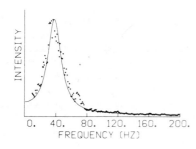

Analytical Biochemistry

*Figure 2.    Electrophoretic light-scattering spectrum (points) of carboxyhemoglobin tetramers, 100 μM in heme.*

*The experimental conditions are* E = 88.8 V/cm, θ = 4.18°, *bath temperature* = 20.0°C, *and a glycine-NaOH-NaCl-EDTA buffer of ionic strength 0.01M and pH 9.5. The solid line is a theoretical curve for these conditions, assuming diffusion is the only source of spectral broadening with a diffusion coefficient* $D_{10}^{20}$ = 6.9 × 10⁻⁷ cm²/sec *and an electrophoretic mobility* $u_{10}^{20}$ = 2.74 × 10⁻⁴ cm²/V-sec (7).

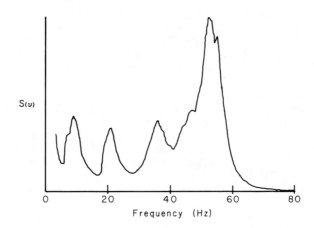

Contemporary Topics in Analytical and Clinical Chemistry

*Figure 3.    Electrophoretic light-scattering spectrum of human blood plasma.*

*Fresh human plasma was dialyzed and then diluted severalfold to final solution conditions of pH 9.1 and ionic strength 0.004. This spectrum was taken with a high field strength (183 V/cm) to maximize the Doppler shift and at a low scattering angle (3.2°) to minimize the diffusion broadening of each peak. The large peak at the highest frequency can be identified as albumin from its relative magnitude and its electrophoretic mobility (3.9 × 10⁻⁴ cm²/V-sec). Positive identification of the peaks at lower mobility cannot be made from the Doppler spectrum alone, but the form of the spectrum is similar to the known electrophoretic pattern of normal human plasma (5).*

been **studying** human lymphocytes and their surface reactions, and we have been comparing them with pathological conditions such as acute lymphocytic leukemia, in which the lymphocytes, or more properly lymphoblasts, produced are malignant, dividing cells which have greatly reduced immunological capacity.

An electrophoretic light scattering spectrum of normal human lymphocytes is shown in Figure 5. The spectrum is labelled in units of electrophoretic mobility, because for these cells diffusion broadening is insignificant, and there is a one-to-one correspondence between frequency and mobility. The solid line is the spectrum from a normal sample of lymphocytes in one-tenth-physiological-salt medium at pH 7.4. Note the bimodal character. To determine whether these two peaks could be attributed to T and B cells we prepared samples from which T or B cells had been selectively removed. The dotted line is the spectrum for this sample from which T cells had been selectively removed by cell rosetting techniques. Note that the higher-mobility peak is selectively diminished. By performing numerous experiments of this type we have established that the higher-mobility peak is due primarily to T cells and the lower-mobility peak is due primarily to B cells (10), which is in agreement with several groups who have obtained this same result and in conflict with some groups who have claimed that the two cell subtypes are electrophoretically indistinguishable. Our method is now by far the fastest means of measuring the T cell/B cell ratio, which is a parameter of both research and clinical interest.

In a further attempt to characterize these lymphocytes we have performed experiments to determine the origin of the cell surface charge and the distinction between cell subtypes on this basis. For example, sialic acid (N-Acetylneuraminic acid) is a ubiquitous source of charge in cell membranes. Sialic acid can be removed by the action of the enzyme neuraminidase, and we have treated lymphocytes with neuraminidase and analyzed separated subfractions. The results are illustrated in Figure 6. Again the solid line represents the whole fraction of the same sample seen in the previous figure except after neuraminidase treatment. The mobilities are lower as expected. The dotted line again represents this same sample from which T cells had been selectively removed. Note that the lower-mobility peak shows the only reduction in intensity. By repeated experiments with both T and B depleted samples we have demonstrated that after neuraminidase treatment the T cells, which were originally of higher mobility, become the lower-mobility fraction, indicating that they have much more available sialic acid on their surfaces. In fact the electrophoretic distinction between the two types of cells is even greater after neuraminidase treatment.

Comparison with diseased states is interesting both for the possible development of the electrophoretic mobility as a clinical indicator and for a characterization of the fundamental differences of the abnormal cells. We have been particularly interested

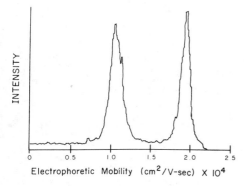

INTENSITY

Electrophoretic Mobility ($cm^2$/V-sec) X $10^4$

*Figure 4. Electrophoretic light scattering spectrum for a mixture of rabbit and human erythrocytes in approximately equal concentrations. Rabbit erythrocytes have the lower mobility.*

The measurement was made in an electrophoresis buffer which had an ionic strength of 0.0097. The electric field was 44 V/cm, the frequency range 200 Hz, and the scattering angle 58°. The chamber temperature was 20°C. The mobility distributions for the two cell types are completely resolved (6).

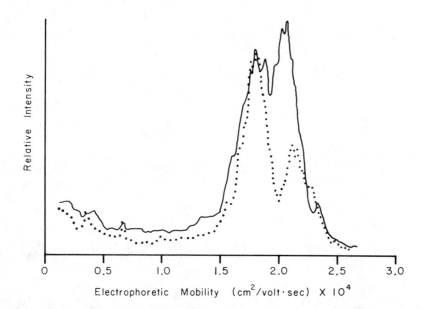

Relative Intensity

Electrophoretic Mobility ($cm^2$/volt·sec) X $10^4$

Journal of Immunology

*Figure 5. A comparison of the electrophoretic mobility distributions (at 0.015M ionic strength) of a fresh human mononuclear, white-blood-cell sample before (solid line) and after (dotted line) $E_{AET}$ rosette depletion (T-cell depletion). The whole sample (solid line) contained 44% cells which form $E_{AET}$ rosettes and 32% cells which form EAC rosettes (primarily B cells). The horizontal axis indicates the magnitude of the electrophoretic mobility since the Doppler technique does not determine the sign of the mobility, which for these cells is negative. The vertical axis is approximately proportional to cell number (10).*

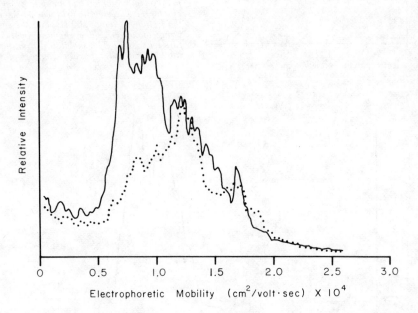

*Figure 6.   A comparison of the electrophoretic mobility distributions (at 0.015M ionic strength) for the same pair of samples shown in Figure 5 after both had been treated with neuraminidase.*

*Again, the solid line represents the whole sample and the dotted line represents the $E_{AET}$-rosette-depleted (T-cell depleted) sample.  T cells are therefore represented primarily in the low-mobility peak between 0.5 and 1.0 mobility units (10).*

in comparisons with leukemic cells (*10,11*). Electrophoretic
comparison of normal lymphocytes and cells obtained in the same
way from patients with acute lymphocytic leukemia is shown in
Figure 7. The solid line is a normal sample with its characteristic bimodal appearance. The dotted line is a sample of
leukemic cells. Note that their mode mobility is lower and that
the distribution is narrower, with no bimodal character, indicative of the lack of differentiation of these cells. The mobility
of leukemic cells is quite variable, ranging from 5% to 25% lower
than normal cells at this salt concentration (0.015 M). Whether
the mobility is a meaningful clinical indicator has not yet been
determined, though a group in France using classical micro-
electrophoresis has recently reported that it may be (*12*).

We have also studied the response of leukemic cells to
neuraminidase. Those experiments are summarized in Figure 8.
The solid line is the normal sample and the dotted line is the
leukemic sample. Note that the leukemic sample has an extremely
narrow mobility distribution and that it falls slightly below the
T cell mobility. This slight difference is reproducible. Recall
that the leukemic cells had a mobility similar to the B cell
mobility before treatment; after neuraminidase treatment they
show a mobility far from B cells and closer to T cells. Clearly
the surface of the leukemic cell is markedly different from
either T or B cells. This fact has also been illustrated by
experiments we have performed on the ionic strength dependence of
the mobilities, which is different for leukemic cells than for T
or B cells. In fact, leukemic cells have a mode mobility which
is about the same as normal samples at physiological ionic
strength.

These experiments on lymphocytes and leukemic lymphoblasts
represent an almost strictly analytical approach to the application of the technique. Are there more fundamental questions
which we can address? I wouldn't ask the question if the answer
were not yes, and in particular I want to describe some experiments we have been performing on the general question of the role
of electrostatic forces in cell-cell interactions. All biological membranes are negative and it is reasonable to expect
electrostatic repulsion between them. However, we know that many
different kinds of cell adhesion and aggregation reactions occur
frequently. This is much easier to accept when we appreciate
that the charges on cells are screened exponentially by the
counterions in solution, with a space constant equal to the
reciprocal of the Debye-Hückel constant, which at physiological
ionic strength is about 8 Å. Still one sees and hears many
arguments in cell adhesion problems on the role of electrostatic
forces, so we have set about the task of measuring cell charge
and correlating with aggregation phenomena.

The first system we studied was the granulocytes, or poly-
morphonuclear white blood cells, which are the phagocytes responsible for eating and digesting foreign material. These cells

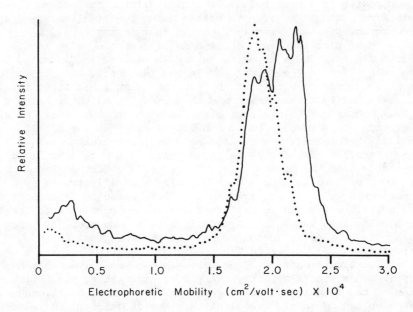

Journal of Immunology

*Figure 7.    A comparison of the electrophoretic mobility distributions for normal (solid line) and leukemic (dotted line) human mononuclear white blood cells at 0.015M ionic strength. The leukemic cells have a distinctly lower mode mobility than the normal cells. In this case, the leukemic cell distribution almost coincides with that portion of the normal distribution that has been identified as B cells (10).*

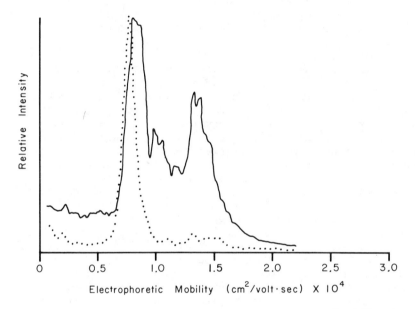

Journal of Immunology

*Figure 8.   A comparison of the electrophoretic mobility distributions of the same pair of samples shown in Figure 7, after neuraminidase treatment.*

*Again, the solid line represents the normal sample and the dotted line represents the leukemic sample. The mobility of the leukemic cells is reduced by a much larger fraction than that of the B cells, so that the leukemic-cell mobility is now slightly lower than the T-cell mobility. Thus the leukemic cells more nearly resemble T cells in their response to neuraminidase treatment (10).*

concentrate in areas of infection in response to soluble protein
factors called lymphokines, which are secreted by lymphocytes in
affected areas.  One possibility advanced was that the lymphokines, called LIF for leukocyte inhibition factor, bind to the
surface of the granulocytes, reduce their charge, and thereby
cause them to adhere to each other and to other surfaces in the
area.  In experiments which are not yet published, we have compared the electrophoretic mobilities of granulocytes before and
after treatment with LIF and before and after treatment with control fractions isolated in the same way as the LIF.  Neither the
LIF nor the controls induced any measurable change in the electrophoretic mobilities of the granulocytes at physiological ionic
strength (6).  Therefore, the charge-reduction mechanism derives
no support from our data.

But what if the surface charge were reduced?  Would this necessarily cause an increase in aggregation?  To address this question, we have initiated a study on mouse fibroblasts (strain
3T3 MIT), which are dividing connective tissue cells.  These
experiments were also done at physiological ionic strength in
phosphate buffered saline to approximate as closely as possible
the relevant physiological parameters.  We considered three different types of modifications of the cell surfaces:  neuraminidase
treatment, viral transformation, and urea treatment.  Electrophoretic mobility histograms were measured by electrophoretic
light scattering, and the degree of change of surface charge was
correlated with the cell aggregation rate for the same cells
measured in a hemacytometer by our collaborators, Morris Karnovsky
and Tom Wright of the Harvard Medical School.  The results have
been described in the thesis of Barton Smith (6) and will be
published in the near future.  To summarize, we found that
neuraminidase treatment of these cells lowers the surface charge
and increases the aggregation rate by more than a factor of two.
Viral transformation with SV-40 and polyoma viruses produces only
a few percent decrease in the average surface charge and yet
increases the aggregation rate by more than a factor of three.
Treatment of the transformed cells with neuraminidase produced a
large reduction in their average electrophoretic mobility but no
perceptible change in their rate of aggregation.  Finally treatment with 0.20 M urea produced no change in the electrophoretic
histogram but increased the rate of aggregation by more than a
factor of three.  We can only conclude that for this system the
cell surface charge does not correlate well with the propensity of
the cells to adhere to each other.  Cell adhesion must be understood on the basis of more detailed molecular recognition and with
an accounting for the balance between the attractive van der Waals
forces and the screened coulombic repulsions.

The final type of study which I would like to describe is an
investigation into the process of vesicular secretion.  The secretion of various hormones and neurotransmitters involves the
release of these molecules from spherical vesicles in which they

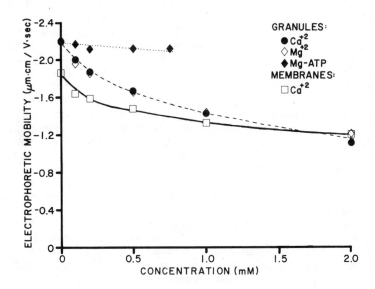

*Figure 9.    Electrophoretic mobilities of chromaffin granules vs. con-centration of Ca⁺², Mg⁺², and Mg-ATP; and electrophoretic mobility of plasma membrane vesicles vs. concentration of Ca⁺².*

*Mobilities are negative, viscosity corrected to pure water at 20°C, and are given in units of $\mu$m-cm/V-sec. The ionic strength of the suspension medium was 15 mM and the pH was 6.9. Note the Ca⁺² and Mg⁺² have identical effects on the mobilities, and hence on the surface charge, of chromaffin granules.*

are stored. The secretory vesicles are thought to release their contents by fusing with the plasma membrane of the cell in which they reside. This fusion is generally triggered by an influx of calcium ion, which is specific for this process. We have been investigating the effects of calcium and magnesium ions on the surface charge and aggregation of secretory vesicles. As an example I show the result of one such study on the chromaffin granules from the adrenal medulla, in this case from a cow. These granules are vesicles which contain adrenalin and noradrenalin. They are easily isolated and purified. We have titrated them with $Ca^{+2}$ and $Mg^{+2}$ and have monitored the effect of these ions on granule surface charge by electrophoretic light scattering. The results of this titration are shown in Figure 9. Broken lines represent the titration of granules and the solid line shows a titration of vesicles formed from the plasma membranes of the chromaffin cell. One of the most interesting results of this study was the finding that $Ca^{+2}$ and $Mg^{+2}$ have the same affinity for the granule surface, which means that the specific role of calcium in inducing exocytosis cannot be determined by its binding constant. We have also performed experiments in which mixtures of the granules and the plasma membrane vesicles are observed first separately and then in the same solution to detect aggregation of the two species. Our experiments show no aggregation below 1 mM $Ca^{+2}$ and considerable aggregation above that concentration. We are currently pursuing experiments of this type to study the neurosecretory process.

I trust that these examples serve adequately to illustrate the various types of applications for which electrophoretic light scattering can be useful. Probably the two most useful techniques in biophysical studies have been spectroscopy and electrophoresis. This new technique, which is a spectroscopically-detected electrophoresis, combines the advantages of speed, accuracy, resolution, and objectivity and will, I believe, be applied to an increasing number of important problems in biology and surface chemistry in the years to come.

LITERATURE CITED

1.  Ware, B. R., "Applications of Laser Velocimetry in Biology and Medicine," in *Chemical and Biochemical Applications of Lasers*, C. B. Moore, ed., Chapter 5, Academic Press, New York, 1977.

2.  Ware, B. R., and Flygare, W. H., "The Simultaneous Measurement of the Electrophoretic Mobility and Diffusion Coefficient in Bovine Serum Albumin Solutions by Light Scattering," *Chem. Phys. Lett.* (1971) *12*, 81.

3.  Ware, B. R., "Electrophoretic Light Scattering," *Adv. Colloid Interface Sci.* (1974) *4*, 1.

4. Flygare, W. H., Ware, B. R., and Hartford, S. L., "Electrophoretic Light Scattering," in *Molecular Electro-Optics*, C. T. O'Konski, ed., Chapter 9, Marcel Dekker, Inc., New York, 1976.

5. Smith, B. A., and Ware, B. R., "Apparatus and Methods for Laser Doppler Electrophoresis," in *Contemporary Topics in Analytical and Clinical Chemistry*, Hercules et al., eds., Plenum Press, New York, in press.

6. Smith, B. A., "The Study of Cell Surface Charge by Electrophoretic Light Scattering," Ph.D. Thesis (1977) Harvard University, Cambridge, Massachusetts.

7. Haas, D. D., and Ware, B. R., "Design and Construction of a New Electrophoretic Light Scattering Chamber and Applications to Solutions of Hemoglobin," *Anal. Biochem.* (1976) *74*, 175.

8. Haas, D. D., and Ware, B. R., "Electrophoretic Mobilities and Diffusion Coefficients of Hemoglobin at High pH," submitted for publication.

9. Luner, S. J., Szklarek, D., Knox, R. J., Seaman, G. V. F., Josefowicz, J. Y., and Ware, B. R., "Red Cell Charge is Not a Function of Cell Age," *Nature (London)*, (1977) *269*, 719.

10. Smith, B. A., Ware, B. R., and Yankee, R. A., "Electrophoretic Mobility Distributions of Normal Human T and B Lymphocytes and of Peripheral Blood Lymphoblasts in Acute Lymphocytic Leukemia: Effects of Neuraminidase and of Solvent Ionic Strength," *J. Immunol.* (1978) *120*(3), 921.

11. Smith, B. A., Ware, B. R., and Weiner, R. S., "Electrophoretic Distributions of Human Peripheral Blood Mononuclear White Cells from Normal Subjects and from Patients with Acute Lymphocytic Leukemia," *Proc. Natl. Acad. Sci. (USA)* (1976) *73*, 2388.

12. Sabolovic, D., Pompidou, A., and Amiel, J. L., "Blood Lymphocytes in Acute Lymphoid Leukaemia in Remission and in Relapse. Predictive Value of Electrophoretic Mobility and Refringence," *Biomed.* (1975) *23*, 283.

13. Siegel, D. P., Ware, B. R., Green, D. J., and Westhead, E. W., "The Effects of $Ca^{+2}$ and $Mg^{+2}$ on the Surface Charge of Chromaffin Granules Measured by Electrophoretic Light Scattering," *Biophys. J.* (1978) *22*, 341.

RECEIVED August 7, 1978.

# 8

# New Laser-Based Methods for the Measurement of Transient Chemical Events

GARY M. HIEFTJE and J. MICHAEL RAMSEY

Department of Chemistry, Indiana University, Bloomington, IN 47401

GILBERT R. HAUGEN

Department of Chemistry, Lawrence Livermore Laboratory, Livermore, CA 94550

One of the trends in modern chemical research is toward the observation and measurement of progressively briefer events. Such observations and measurements might be of transient chemical species, of excited state lifetimes, of energy transfer processes, or of chemical reaction rates themselves. Obviously, the ability to characterize ever briefer chemical phenomena will lead to an improved understanding of many areas of chemistry; consequently, the methodology of high-speed observations has almost become an end in itself.

In keeping with these improvements in methodology, our definitions of "brief" and "transient" have changed over the years. Whereas before 1950 it was common to consider millisecond events brief, measurements on such a time scale became commonplace after that time and we learned to consider microsecond events readily measurable. In the 1960's, nanosecond processes were the subjects of study while the present decade has extended our thinking to the picosecond and sub-picosecond time scale.

This movement toward faster and faster time scales is not without its limit. As far as spectroscopic monitoring is concerned, there is little reason to attempt examination of events faster than one femtosecond ($10^{-15}$ sec), since measurements on such a time scale have a Heisenberg energy uncertainty approximately equal to that of the chemical bond. Significantly, measurements on a femtosecond time scale are already feasible (1) and might be expected to become commonplace in the next decade.

In this chapter, a new approach will be presented for the measurement of transient chemical events. Basically, the new measurement techniques are an outgrowth of information theory, particularly that branch of information theory dealing with linear response theory, correlation analysis and spectral power measurement. Although the methods have potentially broad application to areas as diverse as chemical kinetics and nuclear magnetic resonance spectroscopy, their use in fluorescence lifetime determination will serve here to illustrate their utility.

To begin, it is necessary to lay some basic groundwork so the

0-8412-0459-4/78/47-085-118$05.00/0

nature and scope of the new approach can be appreciated.  The following section establishes this groundwork.

Fluctuation Analysis Spectroscopic Techniques (FAST).

The basis for the new family of techniques for studying transient phenomena can be found in linear response theory.  Accordingly, let us adopt a linear-response-theory view of chemical measurements to understand the techniques.  From such a view, any chemical measurement can be thought of as an attempt to ascertain the response function of a chemical substance, instrument, energy level, or whatever.  Conveniently, the time response function is one of the most frequently and easily determined kinds of response functions, and well-established linear-response-theory approaches for its determination have been established.  Perhaps the most easily understood and conveniently applied such technique involves the determination of an impulse-response function.

Measurement of an impulse-response function is straightforward.  As shown in Figure 1, any system (substance, energy level, etc.) can be considered to have one or more inputs and one or more outputs, each of which can be used to learn something about the system.  For convenience, let us assume that the system to be measured has only one input and one output.  As will be obvious later, this simple two-terminal model can be used to represent many systems of chemical interest.  The impulse response of the system is then just the observed output which results from application of a suitable impulse to the input.  In this treatment, it is assumed that the tested system responds linearly to the applied stimulus.

For example, if the system to be measured were a simple resistor-capacitor (RC) electronic network, its time response would be exponential.  Application of an impulse (or pulse) to the input of the RC network would then produce the expected stretched pulse at the output of the network.  From this simple example, it can be appreciated that the time response function is merely a convolution (2, 3) of the input impulse and the system's impulse response function and, indeed, if we do apply a perfect impulse (delta function), the observed output will be the impulse response function itself.

Significantly, the impulse response function is merely one of a family of response functions, each of which results from application of a different kind of input to the system under investigation.  In general, it can be shown that each particular response function is approximated by the convolution of a specified input with the transfer function of the tested system. More exactly, the transfer function of the system (which is the information actually being sought) is the ratio of the Laplace transform of the observed output to that of the perturbing input.

From a more qualitative standpoint, the impulse response function can be viewed as a time-domain representation of the

frequency response of the system being tested.  Because an ideal
impulse (effectively a delta function) contains all frequencies,
application of the impulse to a tested system involves sending all
frequencies simultaneously into the tested network.  The resulting
output then reflects the frequency response of the network, but
reveals the network's phase response as well.

The importance of the impulse-response function to chemistry
can be readily illustrated.  For instance, temperature-jump and
pressure-jump methods of reaction-rate measurement are essentially
impulse-response approaches.  In addition, the measurement of
luminescence decay times is ordinarily accomplished by application
of an impulse of optical radiation and measurement of the resulting response; obviously, this procedure constitutes another
impulse-response measurement.  From these simple examples, it
should be appreciated  that the input impulse need not be an electrical function but could be any impulse-shaped perturbation which
produces a meaningful response from the system under test.

An alternative approach can be used to obtain impulse-
response functions.  In this second approach, a random or pseudorandom input perturbation is employed and the resulting output
observed.  The output is then either autocorrelated or cross-
correlated with the stochastic perturbing function to yield, respectively, the autocorrelation of the impulse response or the
impulse response function directly (2,3).  Although less intui-
tively obvious than the direct determination of an impulse response function described above, this latter technique has several
advantages.  Most importantly, the perturbing function need not be
a "spike", containing a great deal of power at one moment in time,
but rather can distribute the perturbing energy over a much
greater time, thereby  placing less stress on the system under
test.

Qualitatively, this latter stochastic method can be easily
understood if one remembers that autocorrelation of a waveform or
cross-correlation of two waveforms results in a phase-registration
of all frequency components present in the original waves.  For a
completely stochastic (random) function, autocorrelation yields a
delta function or impulse (2,3).  Consequently, cross-correlation
of a random function with the response it elicits produces the
impulse-response function.

This stochastic-excitation approach has already found application in chemistry.  In NMR spectroscopy, Ernst (4) has found
that application of a stochastic radio-frequency perturbing function to sought-for nuclei, followed by cross-correlation of the
response of the nuclei to the original perturbing function,
results in a waveform identical to that obtainable by conventional
pulse-Fourier-transform NMR techniques.  However, Ernst noted that
the stochastic exciting function could be applied at much higher
average power than could a conventional pulse without producing
saturation of the nuclei under observation.

In the microscopic world, the stochastic-excitation approach to measurement takes on new meaning.  On a microscopic scale, all energies are quantized, and (above absolute zero) all species are in constant, random motion.  Consequently, most microscopic events are continuously and unintentionally perturbed in a stochastic or semi-stochastic way, so that external perturbation is unnecessary. In such cases, temporal or kinetic information can be obtained merely by autocorrelating the stochastically induced fluctuations. For example, Brownian motion leads to constant movement of all species in any fluid medium.  Scattering of laser light from the resulting inhomogeneities in refractive index then enables measurement of the localized fluctuations.  In turn, the measured fluctuations can be autocorrelated to yield such information as diffusion rates and net velocities of species within the medium (5,6,7.  See also the chapter by B. R. Ware in this book).  These measurements are the basis of techniques which are now established and have become known either as laser doppler velocimetry or laser doppler anemometry (6,8).  The elegant experiments by Ware and Flygare (9) illustrate how useful such methods can be to chemistry.

In other microscopic experiments, the fluctuations of one component in a reacting mixture have been measured fluorimetrically. Autocorrelation of the measured fluorescence fluctuations then enables the rates of formation and loss of that component to be measured, even though the reaction mixture was at macroscopic equilibrium.  This latter measurement is the basis of the new and exciting field of fluorescence correlation spectroscopy (10,11,12).

In many cases, it is more convenient to measure the power spectrum of measured fluctuations than to determine the autocorrelation or cross-correlation functions themselves (13,14).  Whichever approach is employed, the results are essentially the same, since the power spectrum and autocorrelation function of a waveform constitute a Fourier pair.  That is, one function can be readily obtained from the other merely by application of a Fourier transformation.  Similarly, the cross-correlation function is merely the Fourier transform of the cross-power spectrum of two waveforms.

The novel approach to fluorescence lifetime measurement which is outlined below is similar in concept to the procedures cited above.  Because it, like the others, involves the analysis of fluctuations induced in a species of chemical interest, and because the fluctuations are measured spectroscopically, we have coined the acronym FAST (Fluctuation Analysis Spectroscopic Techniques) to categorize them.

## F.A.S.T. Luminescence Lifetime Measurement

As implied earlier, luminescence lifetimes are ordinarily determined by methods which, in essence, are impulse-response function determinations.  Accordingly, it would seem to be straightforward to implement such techniques with a correlation approach.  An instrument for such measurements is illustrated in

Figure 2.  As illustrated in Figure 2, the elements of a correlation lifetime fluorimeter would be a randomly modulated excitation source, excitation and luminescence monochromators, a fast detector, and either a correlation computer or spectrum analyzer.  The specifications for each one of these units will be governed by the necessary excitation and luminescence wavelengths and by the time range of the luminescence lifetime.

In the simplest kind of instrument, the excitation source would be a free-running flashlamp, the detector could be a fast photomultiplier tube, and correlation could be carried out using any one of a number of commercial hardware correlators.  Such an approach was tested in our laboratory for slowly decaying luminescence signals and has revealed the practicality of the technique.  In these initial studies, it was found that it is important for the excitation source to flash randomly or for the duration between flashes to be considerably longer than the luminescence process being observed.  If these criteria are not met, overlap of luminescence decay signals with each other makes a lifetime determination rather difficult.

Clearly, this preliminary kind of device cannot be employed for the measurement of short luminescence lifetimes.  Hardware correlators simply are not capable of sufficiently rapid response to enable calculation of correlation functions on a nanosecond time scale.  To achieve nanosecond time resolution with this approach, somewhat different instrumentation is required.

Nanosecond time resolution requires that the excitation source fluctuate or be modulated on a sub-nanosecond time scale and at a fairly large amplitude.  In addition, for maximum signal-to-noise ratio, the fluctuations should occur continuously and should not be separated in time as would the pulses from a flashlamp.  In preliminary investigations, several potential sources were tested for this application and a continuous-wave laser was found to be most suitable.  In addition, because nanosecond-scale correlation was required, we found it more expedient to employ spectrum analysis than software or hardware correlation.  The resulting instrument and its performance have been described in a recent publication (13), and will only be briefly and qualitatively outlined here.

In the new instrument, laser mode noise is used as a pseudorandom fluorescence excitation function.  Mode noise is just the rapid fluctuation in laser output amplitude which results from "beating" (mixing) of the laser oscillation modes with each other. Because laser modes occur at discrete frequencies (wavelengths) (15), they produce variations in the laser's output which are also at discrete frequencies, as revealed by the comb-like fluctuation power spectrum of the laser's output (16,17,18).  These discrete-frequency fluctuations occur in intervals of $c/2\ell$ (c = speed of light; $\ell$ = laser cavity length) up to frequencies as high as 4 GHz for an argon-ion laser, [i.e., up to the Doppler width of the emission profile of the active medium (Ar ions)].  For a typical

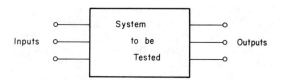

*Figure 1. Conceptual view of a system whose time response is to be measured. The system might be an electronic network, a reacting chemical system, or a fluorescing molecule. The desired corresponding time response might then be, respectively, the RC time constant, the chemical reaction rate, or the fluorescent lifetime.*

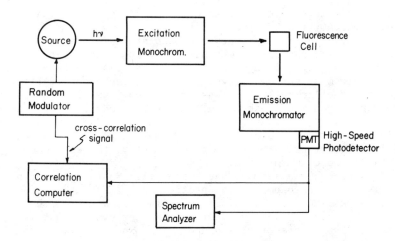

*Figure 2. Diagram of an instrument to measure luminescence lifetime using a randomly varying light source*

rare-gas ion laser, with a 1 meter cavity, $c/2\ell$ = 150 MHz. Essentially, the laser output fluctuates in power at all these discrete frequencies (150 MHz, 300 MHz, 450 MHz, etc.) simultaneously, thus causing fluctuations in excitation of the illuminated sample at the same frequencies.

However, because the excited state of a fluorophore exhibits a finite lifetime, fluctuations in the induced luminescence cannot occur at the highest frequencies present in the varying laser output. Therefore, the power spectrum of luminescence fluctuations is attenuated at higher frequencies. From this attenuation, the luminescence lifetime can be calculated. For example, luminescence from a fluorophore having an upper state lifetime of 1 ns (i.e., a frequency response of 1 GHz) would be able to follow the lower frequency laser fluctuations (i.e., at 150, 300, 450 MHz, etc.) but would not be able to faithfully follow the highest frequency fluctuations (i.e., above 1 GHz). Consequently, these higher frequencies would be attenuated in the power spectrum of luminescence variations.

Mathematically, the luminescence lifetime can be found from the envelope of the discrete-frequency peaks in the luminescence fluctuation power spectrum. After deconvolution, this envelope is Lorentzian, revealing the exponential time-domain profile of luminescence decay. Deconvolution itself is simplified in this approach, and merely involves a division, since data are already in the frequency (Fourier) domain (2,3).

The advantages of this new approach are numerous. For one, the technique is capable of measuring luminescence lifetimes as short as those accessible with a mode-locked laser. In fact, the power spectrum measurement involved in this technique implicitly correlates the laser fluctuations and thereby emulates the laser's performance when mode locked (19). However, mode locking itself is not necessary, so that laser operation is rendered both simpler and more reliable. Also, this method requires no large amplitude output pulse from the photodetector, thereby reducing the likelihood of saturation.

This new method has drawbacks as well. Most important of these is the need to perform a spectrum analysis of the induced fluorescence fluctuations. This analysis must be performed with the aid of a high frequency spectrum analyzer, whose cost is substantial. From a practical standpoint, it would be far more attractive to use less expensive instrumentation. One possibility would be to station fixed-frequency bandpass detectors (such as UHF television tuners) at each of the discrete fluctuation frequencies. Of course, the exact location of each of these frequencies is dependent on the particular laser used, and the bandpass frequencies would have to be adjusted if laser sources were exchanged. Another limitation in the system as now configured is the accessible wavelength and time resolution range. Although a rare gas ion laser emits only at a number of discrete wavelengths, it would be desirable to have available ultraviolet radiation or radiation tunable over a broad wavelength range. In addition, mode noise from such a system extends only to approximately 4 GHz, limiting time resolution to approximately 0.1 ns. Presumably, both these latter objections could be overcome through use of a continuous-wave dye laser. With frequency doubling, such a laser would be usable over most of the wavelength range commonly employed for luminescence excitation. Moreover, the laser should exhibit mode noise to frequencies as high as 100 GHz, making detector speed the limiting device in the measurement of ultra-short lifetimes.

## Literature Cited

1. Ippen, E. P., and Shank, L. V., Opt. Commun. (1976) 18, 27.
2. Bendat, J. S., and Piersol, A. G., "Random Data: Analysis and Measurement Procedures", Wiley-Interscience, New York, NY, 1971.
3. Bracewell, R., "The Fourier Transform and Its Application", McGraw-Hill, New York, NY, 1965.
4. Ernst, R. R., J. Mag. Resonance (1970) 3, 10.
5. Gabler, R., Westhead, E. W., and Ford, N. C., Biophys. J. (1974) 14, 528.
6. She, C. Y., and Wall, L. S., J. Opt. Soc. Amer. (1975) 65, 69.
7. Brown, J. C., and Pusey, P. N., J. Phys. D. (1974) 7, L31.
8. LeBlond, J., and El Badawy, E. S., Appl. Opt. (1975) 14, 902.
9. Ware, B. R., and Flygare, W. H., Chem. Phys. Lett. (1971) 12, 81.
10. Magde, D., Elson, E., Webb, W. W., Phys. Rev. Lett. (1972) 29, 705.
11. Elson, E. L., Magde, D., Biopolymers (1974) 13, 1.
12. Magde, D., Elson, E. L., Webb, W. W., Biopolymers (1974) 13, 29.
13. Hieftje, G. M., Haugen, G. R., and Ramsey, J. M., Appl. Phys. Lett. (1977) 30, 463
14. Chu, B., "Laser Light Scattering", Academic Press, New York, NY, 1974.
15. Lengyel, B. A., "Introduction to Laser Physics", John Wiley and Sons, New York, NY, 1966.
16. Casperson, L. W., Opt. Commun. (1975) 13, 213.
17. Bridges, T. J., and Rigrod, W. W., IEEE J. Quantum Electron. (1965) QE-1, 303.
18. Sedel'nikov, V. A., Sinichkin, Y. P., and Tuchkin, V. V., Opt. Spectrosc. (1971) 31, 408.
19. Weber, H. P., and Danielmeyer, H. G., Phys. Rev. A (1970) 2, 2074.

RECEIVED August 7, 1978.

# 9

# Laser Applications in Photoelectrochemistry

S. P. PERONE', J. H. RICHARDSON, B. S. SHEPARD',
J. ROSENTHAL', J. E. HARRAR, and S. M. GEORGE

General Chemistry Division, Lawrence Livermore, Laboratory,
Livermore, CA 94550

Photoemission Studies. The UV-visible irradiation of an
electrode/solution interface can stimulate any of several interesting electrode processes. If the solution does not absorb
and the electrode is a metallic conductor, photoemission of
electrons may occur, with the formation of solvated electrons
and initiation of reactions with available scavengers. If the
solution absorbs the radiation and photolysis occurs, electroactive photolytic intermediates and products may be detected at
an indicator electrode by their electrolysis currents under potentiostatic conditions. If the electrode is a semiconductor
and absorbs radiation sufficient to promote electrons through
the band gap, oxidation or reduction process may be induced
which would not occur in the absence of radiation. If a dye
absorbed on a semiconductor electrode is excited by the irradiation, the excited state may undergo an oxidative or reductive
electron transfer step which would not occur with the ground
state species.

These are examples of some of the more interesting radia-
tion-induced electrode processes which have been studied. Much
of the interest has been stimulated recently by the prospects
for direct solar-to-electrical energy or solar-to-chemical energy conversion which might be possible with photoelectrochemical
cells.(1-3) The work reported here was designed to demonstrate
the utility of laser sources for these photoelectrochemical
studies; we have focused our attention on those phenomena uniquely related to the characteristics of laser irradiation.

In particular, we report here the results of our studies
of laser-induced photoemission processes and laser - induced
photolysis. The former study was undertaken to illustrate the
efforts of wavelength, source power, and intensity on photoemission-related process; whereas the latter study was designed
to illustrate the capabilities for photoelectrochemical quantum
yield measurements on transient photolytic species made possible
with a laser source.

' Current address: Department of Chemistry, Purdue University, West Lafayette,
IN 47907

Photoemission of electrons from mercury electrodes into electrolyte solutions has been studied extensively in recent years.(4-10) Occasionally other metals have been used as a source of photoemitted electrons,(11) but the dropping mercury electrode (DME) is generally recognized to have desirable characteristics.(12)

Interest in photo-related currents has not only been in characterizing the emission process but also in studying the reactions of the resulting hydrated electrons with various suitable scavengers.(13-16) Theoretical studies have also been initiated both with respect to the kinetics of scavenging itself(17-18) and transient effects in the electrochemical detection of the photorelated phenomena.(21)

Many previous experimental studies have been carried out with continuous or chopped radiaion sources, monitoring the steady state (DC)(22) or modulated(4,9,15,23) photocurrents under potentiostatic conditions. Most of the more recent work has used pulsed xenon flashlamps.(5,6,10,13,14,24,25) Detection of photo-related phenomena was by potentiostatic(10,24) or coulostatic(13,14,17) monitoring of the electrode process.

Very little work has involved the use of lasers as the radiaton source. The few laser-induced photoelectrochemistry studies which have appeared mostly used solid-state lasers (ruby or neodymium) with one or two lines and a slow repetition rate (sometimes single-shot only).(13,26-28) A recent report(29) used the nitrogen laser at 337.1 nm.

The work reported here had the general objective of studying the effects of very intense laser sources on electrode photoemission processes. Thus, the specific goals of this work were threefold: 1) to develop appropriate illumination and measurement instrumentation for both pulsed and cw laser sources in conjunction with a conventional DME assembly; 2) to determine the effect of source characteristics on electrode photoemission processes in the presence of suitable hydrated electron scavengers; 3) to evaluate the general utility of laser sources for photoelectrochemical studies.

In order to achieve the above goals we have used both a pulsed nitrogen pumped dye laser and a cw argon ion laser. The dye laser is continuously tunable from 258 to 750 nm, the output consisting of 10 nsec pulses at a repetition rate of 1 to 50 Hz and peak powers of several kilowatts. The argon ion laser was a cw source, usually chopped around 1 kHz. It was operated on one of four fixed wavelengths, with output powers up to 6 W.

A conventional DME polarographic assembly was illuminated under controlled potential conditions with capabilities for both polarographic steady state and transient (boxcar integrator and oscilloscope) current measurement capabilities. Scavengers used in these studies included $N_2O$, $NO_3^-$, several divalent cations (e.g., $Co^{2+}$, $Fe^{2+}$, $Mn^{2+}$, $Ni^{2+}$, $Cu^{2+}$, $Cd^{2+}$ and $Pb^{2+}$), and $Co(NH_3)_6^{3+}$.

The photo-related current was studied as a function of wavelength, electrode potential, and intensity for all the scavengers, using both sources and all three detection capabilities. Definite scavenging of electrons was not observed with the metal cations, in contrast to $NO_3^-$ and $N_2O$. A highly non-linear photo-effect was observed with the high peak-powered, pulsed laser system. This effect was particularly noticeable with the metal cations. To our knowledge such a pronounced effect has not been observed before. Our work illustrates some of the limitations as well as advantages of using laser sources with electrochemical detection of photoemission currents.

## Experimental

Laser Photolysis - Quantum Yield Studies. Electroactive species can be qualitatively and quantitatively characterized by chronoamperometric measurements at a microelectrode in the photolysis cell.(30-33) If the faradaic current for photolytic species is diffusion-controlled and uncomplicated by kinetic effects, the Cottrell equation applies:

$$i = nFAD^{1/2}C^o/(\pi t)^{1/2} \tag{1}$$

where $i$ is the faradaic current at time $t$, $n$ is the number od electrons transferred, $F$ is the Faraday, $A$ is the effective electrode area, and $D$ is the diffusion coefficient of the electroactive species. Thus, a plot of $i$ versus $1/t$ should be linear with a slope proportional to $C^o$, the bulk concentration of electroactive species in solution.

A theoretical expression has been derived(30) describing the initial concentration of intermediate, $R$, produced when a pulse of light is passed through a solution containing a photoreactive species, $O$,

$$C_R^o(b) = \Phi Q_o[\alpha C_0^o]\exp[-\alpha b C_0^o] \tag{2}$$

where $C_R^o$ is the concentration of intermediate as a function of pathlength (b), the quantum efficiency ($\Phi$), the instantaneous initial quanta of monochromatic light per unit area ($Q_o$), the absorption coefficient of the photoreactive species ($\alpha$), and the concentration of the reactant before the flash ($C_0^o$). This relationship assumes ideal conditons where $C_0^o$ does not change during the flash, the light pulse is collimated and monochromatic, and no other absorbing species are produced during the flash.

Replacement in this work of the previously used xenon flashlamp with a pulsed dye laser excitation source extends the validity and, consequently, the usefulness of this expression. The pulsed laser supplies collimated, monochromatic light pulses of high intensity and very short duration, and, therefore, allows measurements to be made at selected wavelengths and on shorter time scales.

The present study involved laser flash photolysis experiments using the Fe(III) oxalate system. Both the photochemistry(34-37) and the photoelectrochemistry(38,39) of the Fe(III) oxalate system have been studied. These studies have shown by spectroscopic and electrochemical techniques that Fe(III) can be photoreduced by both visible (blue) and uv light. Although a number of conflicting reaction mechanisms have been proposed for this system, it is known that the final product is Fe(II). Quantum yields for the production of Fe(II) have been reported for wavelengths less than 600 nm.(40-42) In addition, flash photoelectrochemical experiments have shown that the production of Fe(II) can be monitored at a potential where the Fe(II) is oxidized to Fe(III). Furthermore, when these oxidation currents are diffusion-controlled and follow Cottrell behavior, quantitative determinations of the Fe(II) produced by the flash can be made.(43)

In the studies reported here the concentration of Fe(II) produced from laser-induced photolysis was determined from Cottrell plots. The laser photolysis source used was a Xerox flash-lamp-pumped dye laser with ~ 0.5 μsec pulse width and ~ 1 joule output energy in the visible region. Because the laser pulse is monochromatic and collimated, the relationship between the concentration and the pathlength predicted by Equation 2 was observed. In addition, working at a known pathlength and measuring both the photon flux and the Fe(II) initially produced, quantum yields were determined at 442 and 457 nm.

Reagents. All inorganic salts used in this work were reagent grade and were used without further purification: NaOH, $NiCl_2$, $MnCl_2$, $CoCl_2$, $FeCl_2$, $FeNH_4(SO_4)_2 \cdot 12H_2O$, $K_2C_2O_4$, and $PbCl_2$ (Baker), $CuCl_2$, $CdCl_2$ and KCl (Mallinckrodt), $Co(NH_3)_6Cl_3$ (Kodak) and $NaNO_3$ (MCB). Nitrous oxide ($N_2O$) was obtained from Matheson and used without further purification. All solutions were made up in laboratory deionized water which had been further purified by a Corning demineralizer and water still.

Ferric oxalate solutions were made by disolving the appropriate amount of $FeNH_4(SO_4)_2 \cdot 12H_2O$ in an aqueous solution of $K_2C_2O_4 \cdot H_2O$. The pH of the solution was adjusted by the addition of dilute $H_2SO_4$ or KOH. All data reported here are for 0.853 x $10^{-2}$ M ferroxalate solutions at pH 6.0 and 0.25 M oxalate. The

Fe(III) concentration was determined spectro-photometrically with
thiocyanate reagent.(44)

Instrumentation for Photoemission Studies.  Two laser systems were used:  1) a nitrogen pumped dye laser, 2) an argon ion
laser.  A Molectron UV1000 nitrogen laser (1 MW peak power, 10
nanosecond pulse with 1-50 Hz repetition rate) was used to
transversely pump a Molectron dye laser operated in the DL200
configuration.  Doubling the fundamentals was accomplished by
using angle-tuned KDP crystals for second harmonic generation,
with a Corning 7-54 filter to block the fundamental.  The laser
was usually operated at 30 Hz.  Typical peak powers of fundamentals delivered to the electrochemical cell were 1-4 KW, corresponding to a maximum power density of ca. 0.5 MW/cm$^2$.  (The
actual peak power delivered out of the laser is more than an
order of magnitude greater than this, but there are considerable losses in steering and shaping the beam before it gets to
the DME.)  Peak powers of doubled wavelengths were approximately
5% that of the fundamental.  Average powers at the cell were
measured with a Scientech 362 power meter, and the relative
power monitored periodically with a Molectron J3 pyroelectric
joulemeter.

A Spectra-Physics 170-09 argon ion laser was used as the
cw source.  Four discrete wavelengths were used:  514.5, 488.0,
457.9 and 351/364 nm.  The cw output was modulated, usually at
1 kHz, with a 50% duty cycle using an Ithaco 383A variable
speed chopper.  For the visible lines the average power delivered to the cell was approximately 25% of the cw output power.
For the uv lines this figure dropped to 8%.

The laser output was directed into a sample chamber containing the DME.  Figure 1 is a schematic of the experimental
apparatus.

Figure 2 is a picture of the electrochemical cell mounted
in the sample chamber.  The cell itself is transparent, the
lower portion consisting of a 1 x 2 x 4 cm Suprasil curvette
(flurorescence type, Precision Cells) and the upper part Pyrex.
The total volume is approximately 40 ml.  The cell sits in a
nearly light tight sample chamber suitable for spectroscopic
studies.  A more detailed description of the spectroscopic
characteristics of the sample chamber has been published previously.(45)

The electrochemical cell consists of a three electrode
system:  a dropping mercury working electrode, a platinum wire
counter electrode which can be positioned very close to the DME,
and a saturated calomel reference electrode (SCE) which measures
the potential of the solution near the DME via a Teflon tube.
The cell is sealed with a Teflon cover.  Provision is made for
bubbling various gases through the solution, flowing gases over
the top of the solution (to exclude oxygen) and emptying, rin-
sing and filling the cell without disturbing the optical alignment.  The entire electrochemical cell can be finely positioned

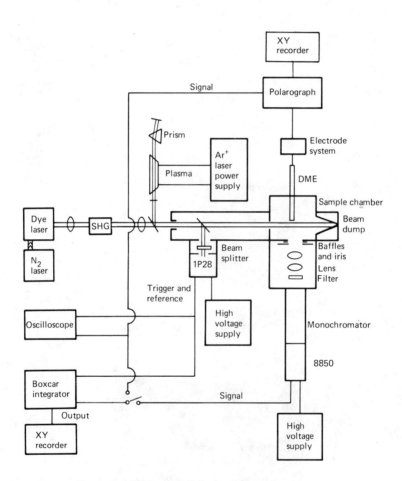

*Figure 1.   Schematic of the experimental apparatus*

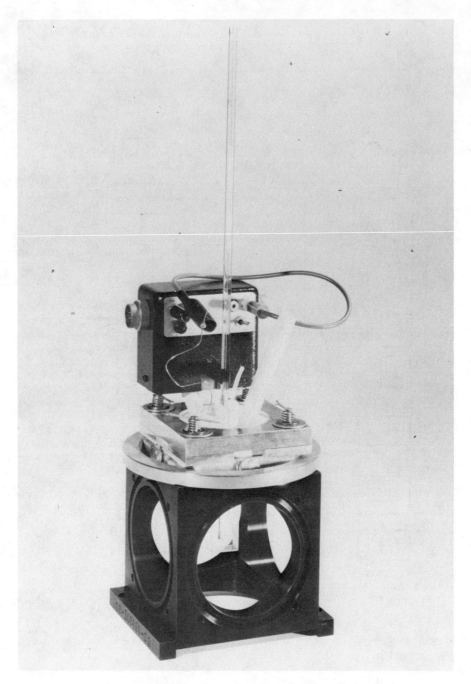

*Figure 2. Electrochemical cell and polarograph*
*interface mounted on sample chamber*

in the three xyz directions, thus enabling the mercury drop to
intersect the focused laser beam in line with the right angle
spectroscopic viewing assembling.

A Princeton Applied Research (PAR) model 174A polarographic
analyzer was used to control and scan the DME potential, control
the drop timer and monitor the current.

A Tektronix 7904 oscilloscope with 7A15A and 7A19 plug-in
amplifiers was used to observe the signal. The oscilloscope was
primarily used for alignment, single waveform monitoring and
other diagnostic purposes. The trigger was provided by the dye
laser pulse or modulated argon ion laser output.

A PAR 162/163/164 boxcar integrator was used for data acquisition and averaging. The AC coupling in the 164 gated in-
tregrator was modified to eliminate the large, slowly varying
DC component which was due to variation of the mercury drop
size. The boxcar was used for single point analysis primarily,
delaying the window (typically 50 $\mu$s) by an appropriate amount
to coincide with the signal maximum. Output from both the boxcar and the polarograph was displayed on x-y recorders.

Procedures for Photoemission Studies. The cell was rinsed
several times before the final salt solution was added. The
solution was deoxygenated for a least 10 minutes, usually with
scrubbed (chromous chloride and zinc amalgam) and water saturated argon. For the studies with $N_2O$ the gas was allowed to
bubble through for several minutes until a sufficient photoemission signal could be obtained. No attempt was made to determine
the $N_2O$ concentration. The majority of the other solutions
were 3 mM in the scavenging ion. The supporting electrolyte
solution was usually 0.1 M KCl. To reduce polarographic maxima
a dilute solution of Triton X-100 was added dropwise to the
electrochemical cell until no further apparent reduction in the
maxima was noted.

The polarograph was operated without any electronic filtering (i.e., no additional time constants). The hangtime of the
mercury drop was usually 5 seconds; typical sensitivities of the
polarograph were 0.5 to 75 $\mu$A full scale. The polarograph
drove the x-axis of both of the recorders, thus permitting simultaneous recording of both the DC polarograph and photoemission current vs potential. The laser beam was aligned with the
DME both visually and instrumentally (i.e., by monitoring the
photo-related signal on the oscilloscope). Preliminary spectroscopic scans were made by fixing the potential and scanning the
monochromator, viewing the luminescence at right angles to the
laser beam. The luminescence was detected by an RCA 8850 photomultiplier tube, processed by the boxcar and recorder. Occasionally the emission wavelength was fixed and the potential
scanned.

The nitrogen laser is well shielded electrically. In the
present experiments the transient current signal was monitored

many microseconds after the laser pulse, and no effect attributable to the laser discharge was detected. No electrical interference was noticeable from the cw argon ion laser.

Background signals from blank solutions (i.e., electrolyte
solution) were measured frequently as various conditons were
changed (e.g., laser intensity, wavelength, sensitivity, potential). Thus it was straightforward to compare any observed
photo-related phenomena in the presence and absence of scavenger.

Instrumentation for Laser Photolysis Studies. A Phase-R
model 2100B flashlamp-pumped tunable dye laser (Phase-R Co.,
New Durham, N.H.) was used as the photolysis light source.
When pumped with a model DL-18 coaxial flashlamp, with a triax
adapter diminishing the beam diameter to 12 mm, output pulses
with energies as high as 1 - 5 joules and widths as narrow as
0.5 μsec could be generated at a repetition rate of 20 ppm.
A commercial pyroelectric joulemeter (model J3-05DW, Molectron
Corp., Sunnyvale, CA) was used for light intensity measurements.

The photolysis cell was constructed from 1/4-inch thick
polyacrylic sheet cut to size and bonded together with chloroform. The cell held a total solution volume of approximately 7
ml. A quartz window was located in the bottom of the cell
through which the photolysis source was directed. The reference
and counter electrodes were mounted permanently in the cell wall
to eliminate any problems associated with reproducing their positions. Tubing connected the cell with a separate solution
reservoir, an aspirator for solution removal, and a scrubbed
nitrogen line.

The three-electrode monitoring system consisted of a hanging mercury drop working electrode (HMDE), a Pt counter electrode, and a saturated calomel reference electrode (SCE). The
mercury drop was suspended from a micrometer dispensing assembly
(Metrohm E410 Hanging Mercury Drop Electrode, Brinkman Instruments, Inc., Westbury, NY) for accurate control of drop size.
The entire HMDE assembly was positioned above the cell vertically and horizontally with a precision of + 0.1 mm using a
Vertical-Transverse Motion Mount (Ealing Corp., Cambridge, MA).
The counter electrode was constructed from copper metal covered
with a thin platinum sheet and sealed in the back wall of the
cell. The reference electrode was made of a three-compartment
cell with glass frits separating the compartments. The first
compartment contained the SCE, the second contained a 1 M KCl
solution, and the third contained a mixture of solvent, electrolyte, and buffer. The third compartment was connected to a
Luggin capillary mounted on the back wall of the cell with a
Teflon fitting.

The potentiostat, described in Ref. 46, had a control
unity-gain bandwidth of 900 kHz and a monitoring bandwidth of
100 kHz. The computerized data acquisition system has been
described.[31]

Procedures for Laser Photolysis Studies. The temperatures
of the laser dye and the water surrounding the triax adapter
were initially equilibrated to + 0.1°C. The absolute temperature varied between 18 and 20°C. These temperatures were
continuously monitored throughout each series of experiments
and adjusted if necessary. The laser was fired at 17 kV, which
corresponded to a charging energy of 289 joules. The laser dyes
used were Coumarin 440 in methanol ($\lambda_o$ = 442 nm) and Coumarin
460 in ethanol ($\lambda_o$ = 457 nm), (Phase-R Co., New Durham, NH).

Fe(III) oxalate solutions were deaerated for at least
thirty minutes before starting each experiment. Following
photolysis, the solution was aspirated from the cell and new
solution was obtained from the reservoir.

For each experiment, the cell containing the solution was
optically shielded from the laser by means of a removable shutter, and a blank was run to measure any amplifier drift and/or
any background current due to electronic disturbances. The
shutter was then removed, the $Fe(ox)_3^{-3}$ solution was photolyzed, and Fe(II) oxidation currents as a function of time were
monitored potentiostatically at -0.05V vs SCE. The current measured in the blank was then subtracted. This procedure was repeated a minimum of three times at each set of conditions, and
resulting current-time curves were averaged to give the net
result.

Each averaged current-time curve was corrected for faradaic-induced charging current before further analysis. The
data were corrected first by the "derivative method", based on
the following relationship:

$$i_F = i_T + R_u C_{DL} \frac{di_T}{dt} \tag{3}$$

where $i_F$ is the Faradaic current, $i_T$ is the total current,
$R_u$ is the uncompensated cell resistance, $C_{DL}$ is the capaci-
tance of the working electrode double layer, and ($di_T/dt$) is
the time derivative of the total current. The cell time constant ($R_u C_{DL}$), can be determined experimentally as outlined
previously.[31] If data show Cottrell behavior following this
correction, they can be assumed to be diffusion-controlled.

The derivative method tends to introduce a large amount of
noise into the calculated Faradaic current. If Cottrell behavior is observed, however, the raw data can be corrected by a
tabulated theoretical correction factor which does not introduce
noise.[47] As with the derivative correction method, knowledge
of the cell time constant is required. It has been pointed
out[31] that the "effective" RC ($RC_{eff}$) after light irradiation may differ significantly from the experimentally determined

RC because only part of the spherical electrode is exposed to photolyzed solution (~ 50-75%). Thus, the effective cell time constant may be less than that measured experimentally, where the total surface is involved. Fortunately, when Faradaic currents are diffusion-limited, the value of $RC_{eff}$ can be estimated from the raw data, as theory predicts that $t(i_{max}) = 0.85$ RC.([31]) Thus, the effective RC can be determined from the potentiostatic current-time curve following flash irradiation by observing the time at which the current goes through a maximum. It was this procedure that was followed in the work reported here.

## Results of Photoemission Studies

To evaluate the effects of laser source characteristics on electrode photoemission processes three different types of aqueous solutions were used. One of these contained inert electrolyte only (KCl or NaOH). The second contained inert electrolyte and a well characterized scavenger ($N_2O$ or $NO_3^-$). The third contained inert electrolyte and one of several divalent metal ions ($Fe^{2+}$, $Ni^{2+}$, $Mn^{2+}$, $Co^{2+}$, $Cu^{2+}$, $Pb^{2+}$, or $Cd^{2+}$. The first two types of solutions provided for direct comparison with previous studies using more conventional illumination sources. The third type of solution provided electroactive species for which distinct sensitivity to source characteristics was observed.

In all of the discussions below we will use the general terms "photo-related" currents or "photocurrents" to describe any current signals which are dependent on electrode illumination, regardless of whether photoemission of electrons is known to occur. The term "photoemission-related" currents will be used whenever the specific phenomenon of electron photoemission is to be considered.

The behavior of $N_2O$ as a scavenger is well known, and its photoelectrochemical characteristics have been previously described.([4,9,13,14,16,27,29]) It reacts very rapidly with hydrated electrons to form molecular nitrogen and hydroxyl radical. The latter species is reducible over the entire mercury electrode potential range. Thus, electrode photoemission in the presence of $N_2O$ yields a net cathodic current at all potentials negative to the photoemission threshold value for the particular wavelength of radiation.

When $NO_3^-$ is the scavenger the initial product is $NO_3^{-2}$, which reacts rapidly with water ($\tau_{1/2} < 15$ μs) to form $NO_2$. The $NO_2$ is easily reduced to nitrite ion at potentials negative of about -0.9 V vs SCE. Thus, cathodic photoemission-related currents are seen in the presence of $NO_3^-$ with substantial enhancement at sufficiently negative potentials.

The behavior of certain divalent transition metal ions as hydrated electron scavengers has been reported previously.([22,24,25])

The initial product postulated is the short-lived univalent cation.  In the absence of an oxidizable species the univalent
cation is reoxidized to the $2^+$ state at the electrode or by
reaction with the solvent.  A photoelectrochemical study[24]
with $Ni^{2+}$ as the scavenger described the effects of this type
of mechanism and observed photocurrents.  The following mechanism
was suggested to explain the current pulses that were observed
with pulsed irradiation of a DME in the polarographic plateau
region:[24]

$$e^-_{(aq)} + Ni^{+2} \rightarrow Ni^+ \tag{4}$$

$$Ni^+ + H_2O \rightarrow Ni^{+2} + H + OH^- \tag{5}$$

$$H \rightarrow H_{(ads)} \tag{6}$$

$$H_{(ads)} + H_2O + e^- \rightarrow H_2 + OH^- \tag{7}$$

Thus, it was suggested that the observed photocurrents were
photoemission-related and that reactions (2) and (3) in the
diffusion layer would result in enhanced currents.  Current
enhancement occurs because not only are photoemitted electrons
scavenged, but also the ultimate product, H atoms, is reducible
further.  Moreover, there is no net depletion of $Ni^{2+}$, as it is
regenerated by reaction of $Ni^+$ with solvent.  Although no
studies with other divalent metal ion scavengers have been reported, it is likely that the $Ni^{+2}$ electrode process provides
a model system.

The magnitudes of photoemission-related currents depend on
several factors.  Firstly, the quantum efficiency of the photoemission event itself increases with negative potential.  Secondly, if the scavenging reaction results in an electroinactive
product, electrons are permanently removed from the electrode,
and the net cathodic current will increase, up to a point, with
the scavenging rate constant.  Thirdly, if the scavenging reaction results in an electroreducible species, the net cathodic
current will be enhanced further.

The fundamental aspects of electrode photoemission and
subsequent scavenging processes have been discussed elsewhere[4,9,13,18,19] and will not be repeated here.  However, it
should be emphasized that the initial electron emission event
and subsequent scavenging of that electron must be complete in
less than about 1 μs after light absorption by the electrode.
Also, these events do not usually extend beyond 50-100 Å from
the electrode surface.

The studies reported here were conducted with the two laser sources described in the Experimental section. Various uv and visible wavelengths were used, and the beam characteristics were monitored and documented for each of the three studies reported below. In each case, photocurrents were monitored in three different ways: 1) conventional polarographic output; 2) an oscilliscope display of transient or modulated signals; and 3) boxcar averaging of transient or modulated currents synchronized with either laser source.

## $N_2O$ and $NO_3^-$ Solutions

Results with Chopped CW Laser Source. Figure 3 is a typical oscilloscope display of both the 1 kHz modulated laser radiation and the AC coupled synchronous photoemission current observed at -1.6 V vs SCE in the presence of $NO_3^-$ scavenger. In the absense of radiation there is no detectable current. Furthermore, while there was some small amount of photorelated current in the absence of scavenger, there was a tremendous enhancement of current attributable to photoemission after addition of $N_2O$ or $NO_3^-$. Figure 4 is a DC polarogram illustrating the large change in DC current upon irradiation. Figure 5 illustrates the AC coupled synchronously detected boxcar averaged signal. A small photorelated current (probably thermal in origin, vide infra) is seen even in the blank in the vicinity of -0.2 V; however, the photorelated current attributable to photoemission and scavenging easily dominates Figure 5B. Figure 5C illustrates the complete photoemission signal as a function of DME potential. The decrease in photoemission current at more negative potentials was consistently observed, coinciding with the potential at which solvent reduction commenced.

We investigated the dependence of photorelated current on both wavelength and light intensity using both $N_2O$ and $NO_3^-$ scavengers. Figure 6 illustrates the functional dependence of the photoemission current ($i_{PE}$) on DME potential; the theoretically expected(7,8,16,23) linearity of ($i_{PE}$)$^{0.4}$ with respect to potential is observed. The uv output is not strictly monochomatic (351/364 nm or 3.53/3.41 ev), which possibly accounts for the different slope observed. Also, $NO_3^{-2}$ (the initial product of $NO_3^{-2}$ scavenging) can be reoxidized positive of -1.1 V (vs SCE),(29) which would tend to lower the apparent photoemission current. All of the data represented by Figure 6 were obtained from boxcar signal-averaged plots such as Figure 5C. Different absolute vertical scales apply to each wavelength, but the relative dependence on wavelength and potential is apparent.

Figure 7 illustrates the dependence of the photorelated current on laser intensity. Once again, relative currents were obtained from the boxcar signal-averaged output as in Figure 5C. In Figure 7 the photoemission current was monitored at a fixed

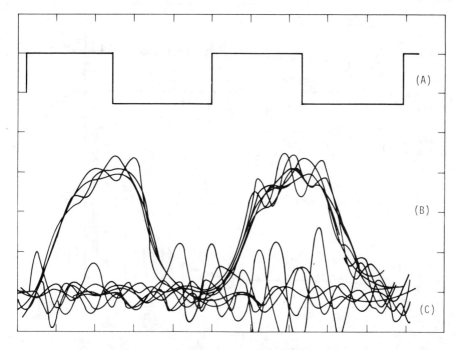

*Figure 3. Oscilloscope display of synchronous DC-coupled photoemission current with chopped cw-Kr⁺ laser (407 nm, 150 mW). (A) Reference signal, light on (5 V/division); (B) reference signal, light off; (C) polarographic signal, light off. Solution was 3 mM NaNO₃ in 0.1M KCl, E = −1.70 V (vs. SCE).*

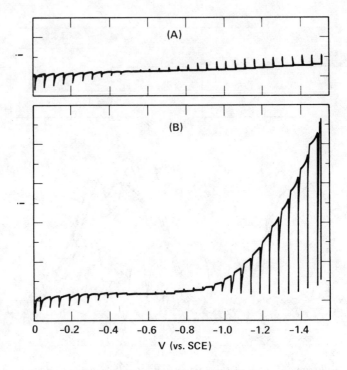

*Figure 4.  DC polarogram for chopped cw-laser irradiation with and without NO$_3^-$ scavenger, λ = 457.9 nm, laser output power = 0.5 W. (A) 0.1M KCl, 2.5 μA/division; (B) 3 mM NaNO$_3$ in 0.1M KCl, 2.5 μA/division.*

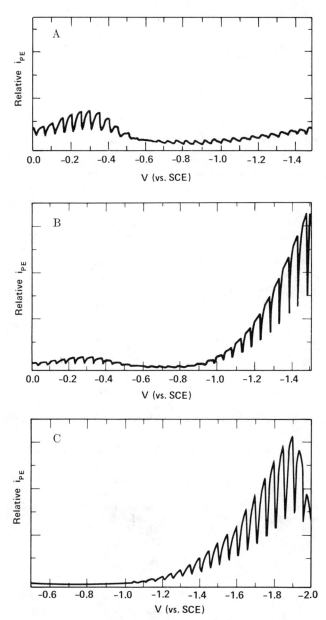

*Figure 5.  Boxcar-averaged photo-related current for chopped cw-laser irradiation with and without $NO_3^-$ scavenger, AC-coupled, synchronously-detected. $\lambda = 457.9$ nm, laser output power = 0.5 W. (A) 0.1M KCl, amplified 7.7×; (B) 3 mM $NaNO_3$ in 0.1M KCl, amplified 1.95×; (C) 3 mM $NaNO_3$ in 0.1M KCl, .77×.*

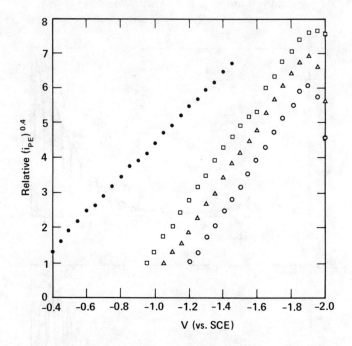

*Figure 6.    $(i_{PE})^{0.4}$ vs. DME potential for chopped cw-laser source,
supporting electrolyte was 0.1M KCl in all cases. (●) $N_2O$ 351/
364 nm (3.53/3.41 eV); (□) 3 nM $NaNO_3$, 457.9 nm (2.71 eV);
(△) 3 mM $NaNO_3$, 488.0 nm (2.54 eV); (○) 3 mM $NaNO_3$, 514.5
nm (2.41 eV).*

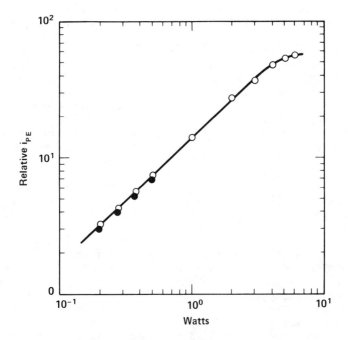

*Figure 7. Dependence of photo-related current on cw-laser intensity, 3 mM NaNO$_3$ in 0.1M KCl, λ = 514.5 nm, relative photoemission current vs. laser output. (○) E = 1.75 V; (●) E = −0.3 V.*

potential while the laser power was increased.  Beyond 4 W (or
ca. 2 W peak power actually focused onto the mercury drop) saturation occurs, corresponding to a maximum quantum efficiency for
photoemision of ca. 0.1% before saturation.  Figure 7 also illustrates the dependence on relative intensity at two different
potentials.  In this case neutral density filters (calibrated
for high energy pulsed lasers) were used to decrease the relative intensity at a potential where photoemission occurs (-1.75
V) and also at a potential where the photo-related current may
be due to thermal heating and perturbation of the double layer
(-0.3 V).  In each case a linear dependence on laser intensity
was observed (as indicated by unity slope on a log-log plot).

   Results with Pulsed Dye Laser Source.  Figure 8 illustrates
the temporal response of the photoemission current observed
with the pulsed laser.  The decay time observed essentially
reflects the cell time constant, since both the laser pulse
width (10 ns) and scavenging time constant (< 1 μs) are considerably less than the several hundred microseconds observed for
the current signal.

   Data taken with the high peak power pulsed laser were much
more ambiguous than those obtained with the cw or modulated argon ion laser.  For example there was a much more significant
transient photorelated current detectable at more negative potentials, even in the absence of scavenger.  This phenomenon is
illustrated in Figure 9A. With the addition of scavenger and
attenuation of the laser power (accomplished by adding neutral
density filters), a noticeable increase in transient current at
potentials near ~ -1.6 V and the appearance of transient
photo-related currents at less negative potentials were observed
(Figure 9B).  However, unattenuated laser radiation led to a
tremendous enhancement in photo-related current, extending far
positive of the photoemission threshold (Figure 9C).  No noticeable threshold could be observed in a DC polarogram.  However,
this is not surprising because of the low average power of the
pulsed laser (ca. 0.6 mW).  The phenomenon represented in Figure
9C was accompanied by visually observable disruption (streaming)
in the vicinity of the mercury drop.  This streaming would con-
tinue briefly after the light was blocked before once again be-
coming quiescent.  This phenomenon could only be observed with
light at 520 nm, the most intense and tightly focused wavelength
possible.  A slight attenuation in power, either by neutal density filters or tuning, eliminated this unusual streaming phenomenon, indicating a thermal or non-linear origin.

   Figure 10 illustrates the dependence of transient photo-related currents on pulsed laser intensity.  The residual background current shows an essentially linear dependence on laser
intensity whereas the data for $NaNO_3$ does not.  The total
photoemission current at -1.80 V (vs SCE) shows a non-linear
behavior, and represents a sum of at least two components:  1)
the background contribution which may reflect thermal effects,

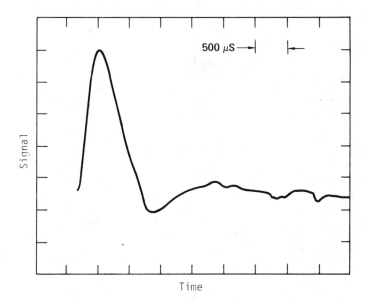

*Figure 8. Oscilloscope display of AC-coupled photoemission current synchronized to laser pulse. $\lambda = 580$ nm, $E = -1.5$ V, 5 mM $NaNO_3$ in 0.1M NaOH, 200 mV/division.*

impurities, multiphoton events, and $e^-_{(aq)}$-$e^-$(aq) annihilation reactions; and 2) the simple scavenging of hydrated electrons by nitrate ions. The photo-related current at -1.20 V (vs SCE) has a nearly linear but large slope on a log-log plot, indicating a very high but simple non-linear dependence on laser power.

Figure 11 illustrates the dependence of the transient photoemission current on potential using $N_2O$ scavenger and various wavelengths. Once again, data were obtained from boxcar averaged traces such as Figure 9B and a different absolute vertical scale was used for each wavelength. Several interesting points are represented in this figure. Firstly, the currents observed at fundamental (visible) frequencies show a nearly linear rise continuously over a very wide potential range, as expected for photoemission current. Currents of the two uv wavelengths do not, but show a more distinctly saturated effect within half a volt from the apparent threshold. Secondly, the shift in threshold is consistent with the shift in photon energy until reaching the uv lines. The thresholds for 260 nm and 305 nm are not at positive potentials (vs SCE) as they should be for photoemission. This effect is also noticeable but less pronounced with the argon ion laser data (Figure 6). Good agreement exists between the two sets of data (for cw and pulsed laser sources) when comparing the data for visible wavelengths; slight differences may be attributed to intensity differences and the previously mentioned effects using the high peak power laser.

In general, the enhancement of current over the background observed with the pulsed dye laser was only a factor of 2 to 7, whereas the enhancement observed with the argon ion laser was in excess of a factor of 100.

## Transition metal cations.

The following transition metal ions were investigated, usually with both the chopped cw argon ion laser and the pulsed dye laser: $Mn^{2+}$, $Fe^{2+}$, $Co^2$, $Ni^{2+}$, $Cu^{2+}$, $Cu^{2+}$, $Pb^{2+}$, $Cd^{2+}$ and $Co(NH_3)_6^{3+}$. The half-wave potentials $(E_{1/2})$ for the uncomplexed ions in 0.1 M KCl were -1.45 V, -1.30V, -1.25 V, -1.10 V, -0.20 V, -0.45 V, and -0.60 V, respectively. The two reduction potentials for $Co(NH_3)_6^{3+}$ were -0.35 V, and -1.35 V.

Results with Chopped CW Laser Source. The various metal cations may be categorized according to whether or not their reduction wave occurs well before, approximately coincident with or well after the expected photoemission threshold. For example, $Cu^{2+}$, $Pb^{2+}$ and $Cd^{2+}$ reduction potentials all fall more positive than the photoemission threshold for 514 nm radiation. A large DC component of the photo-related signal is observed. This effect appeared to be more significant for this group of metal cations which were more easily reduced, since similar results were

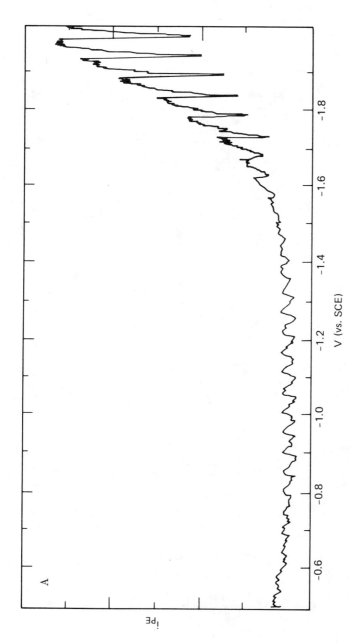

*Figure 9A.   Boxcar-signal-averaged, AC-coupled, synchronously detected photo-related currents using pulsed laser as radiation source. Supporting electrolyte was 0.1M KCl, $\lambda = 520$ nm. No scavenger, no neutral density filter, amplified 7.7×.*

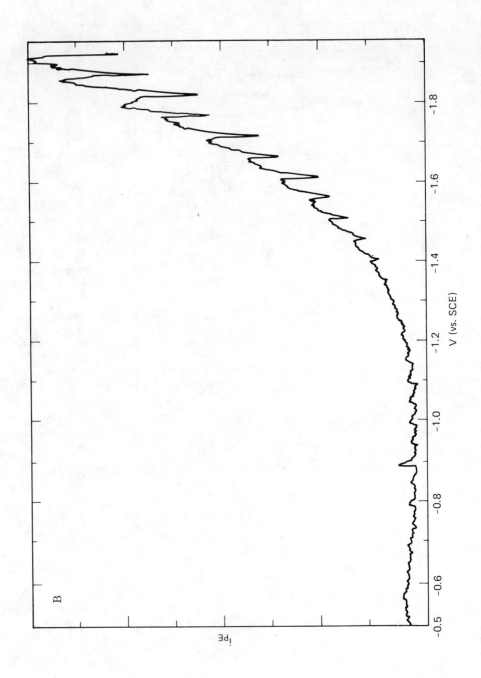

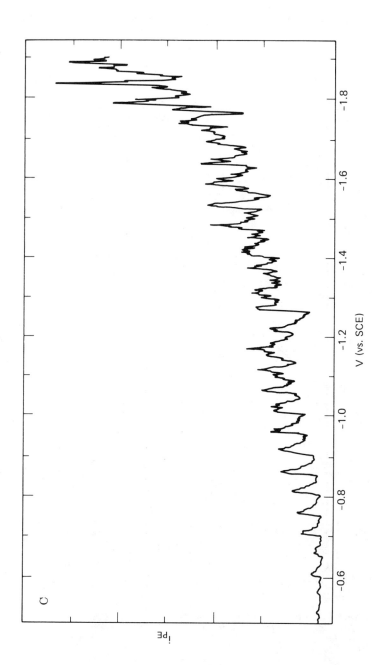

*Figure 9.  Boxcar-signal-averaged, AC-coupled, synchronously detected photo-related currents using pulsed laser as radiation source. Supporting electrolyte was 0.1M KCl, λ = 520 nm. (B) 3 mN NaNO₃, neutral density = 0.4, amplified 7.7×. (C) 3 mM NaNO₃, no neutral density filter, .77×.*

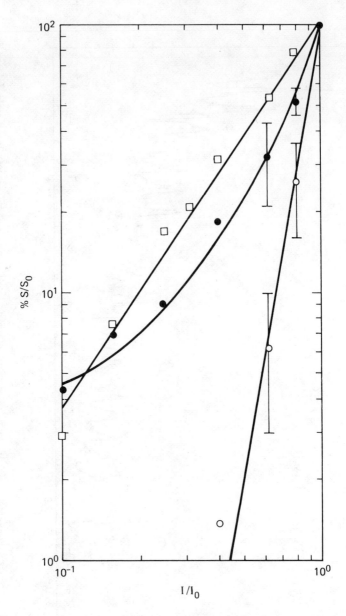

*Figure 10.  Relative transient photo-related current (% S/S₀)
vs. relative pulsed-laser intensity (I/I₀), λ = 520 nm, supporting
electrolyte was 0.1M KCl. (□) no scavenger, E = −1.8 V; (●)
3 mM NaNO₃, E = −1.8 V; (○) 3 mM NaNO₃, E = −1.2 V.*

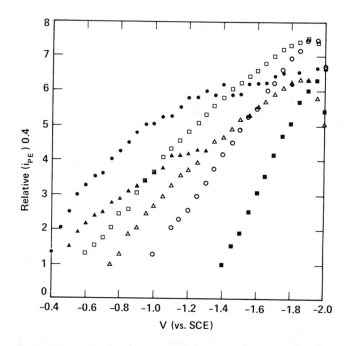

*Figure 11.    Dependence of transient photoemission-related current on DME potential and wavelength.   Supporting electrolyte was 0.1M KCl, scavenger was $N_2O$.  (●) 260 nm (4.77 eV); (▲) 305 nm (4.06 eV); (□) 386 nm (3.21 eV); (△) 406 nm (3.05 eV); (○) 520 nm (2.38 eV); (■) 610 nm (2.03 eV).*

obtained for $Cu^{2+}$ and $Pb^{2+}$. Because copper is several orders
of magnitude less soluble in mercury than is cadmium,(48) it
appears that the fate of the reduction product is irrelevant.
It is not clear why the photo-related current signal in Figure
12 is not completely modulated. This may be due to slow physical
or chemical steps involved in the photocurrent process acting
as a dampening factor.

No polarographic maximum was observed for $Cd^{2+}$, but a
maximum was observed for $Cu^{2+}$. A dilute solution of Triton
X-100 was added until no further reduction in the maximum was
obtained. However, except for a small shift in the apparent
threshold, the addition of maximum suppressor had no effect on
the photo-related current observed with chopped cw laser radiation (Figure 13). The unique potential dependence of photo-related current illustrated in Figure 13 was generally observed
for all the divalent cation solutions used here. Invariably
the rise in photo-related current corresponded to the rise in
polarographic current at $E_{1/2}$.

Figure 14 illustrates a similar phenomenon observed with
$CoCl_2$, which has a reduction potential just slightly more negative than any expected photoemision. Similar results were
obtained for $FeCl_2$, which also have reduction potentials approximately coincident with the photoemission threshold. Finally,
results similar to $CoCl_2$ were also obtained for $Mn^{2+}$, which
has a reduction potential much more negative than the photoemission threshold expected for 457.9 nm (ca. -0.9 V, see Figure 6).

Qualitatively all the photorelated currents observed with
chopped cw laser irradiation for the various metal cations were
similar, commencing at the onset of cation reduction and slowly
tapering off as the DME potential became more negative. It is
important to note that the onset of photo-related current is in
no way correlated with the photoemission threshold -- sometimes
commencing earlier, sometimes later. Any possible photoemission
was obscured by this other phenomenon. However, this photorelated current did not have an unusual dependence on laser power
intensity. The slope is nearly 1.0, in marked contrast to the
results obtained with the pulsed laser (Figures 10 and 15).

Results with Pulsed Laser Source. Data taken with the
pulsed dye laser also provided no definite evidence for additional photoemision related current beyond that observed with
the blank. With the exception of radiation at 520 nm, the only
distinction between the blank and the solution containing the
metal cation (when transient photo-related currents were monitored) corresponded to a discontinuity near the reduction potential wave, mostly seen when the reduction occured in a region
where photocurrents were observed. For example a discontinuity
was observed with $Mn^{2+}$ ($E_{1/2}$ = -1.45 V) but not with a $Cu^{2+}$ solution ($E_{1/2}$ = 0.20 V) when irradiating with 406 nm. The only
exception to this was $Co(NH_3)_6^{3+}$, which had reduction waves at

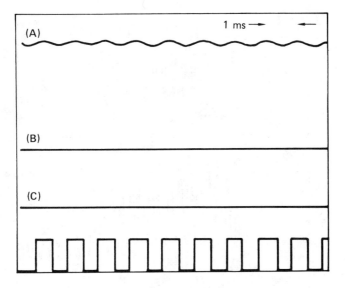

*Figure 12. Oscilloscope display of DC-coupled, photo-related current synchronized to square-wave-modulated argon-ion laser, λ = 514.5 nm, laser output power = 0.5 W, 3 mM CdCl₂ in 0.1M KCl, E = −0.7 V (vs. SCE). (A) Light on; (B) light off; (C) ground; lower trace is 1 kHz chopped argon-ion laser output. Curves (A), (B), and (C) were at the same vertical sensitivity and dc offset.*

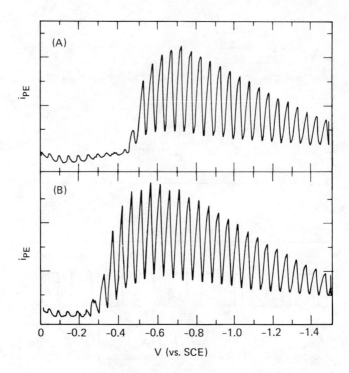

*Figure 13. Boxcar-averaged, photo-related current for chopped cw laser. AC-coupled, synchronously detected, laser output power = 2 W, 3 mM CuCl₂ in 0.1M KCl, λ = 514.5 nm, same vertical sensitivity. (A) Without Triton X-100; (B) with Triton X-100.*

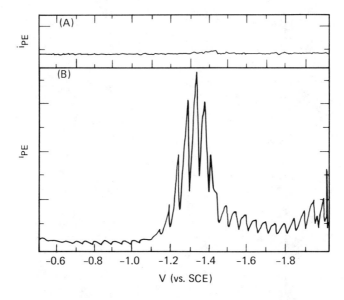

*Figure 14.   Boxcar-averaged, photo-related current for chopped cw laser, AC-coupled, synchronously detected, 3 mM CoCl$_2$ in 0.1M KCl. (A) No light, amplified 1.55×; (B) λ = 5.14.5 nm, laser output power = 3 W, .77×.*

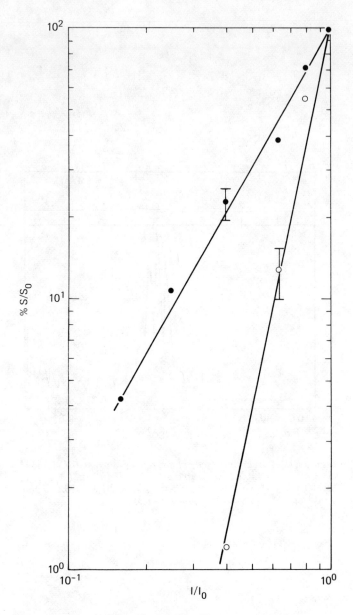

*Figure 15A.  Relative photo-related current (% $S/S_0$) vs. relative pulsed laser intensity ($I/I_0$), $\lambda = 520$ nm, 0.1M KCl was the supporting electrolyte.  3 mM $CoCl_2$, (●) E $= -1.75$ V, (○) E $= -1.41$ V.*

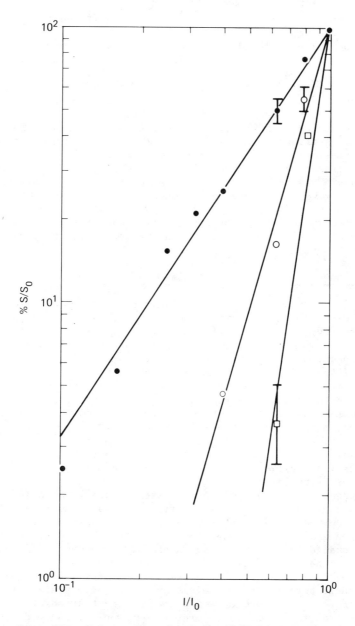

*Figure 15B. Relative photo-related current (% $S/S_0$) vs. relative pulsed laser intensity ($I/I_0$), $\lambda = 520$ nm, 0.1M KCl was the supporting electrolyte. 10 mM $CoCl_2$, (●) E = −1.8 V, (○) E = −1.35 V, (□) E = −0.9 V.*

-0.35 V and -1.35 V (vs SCE) but in no way differed from the
blank in its transient response to the laser pulse. Of all the
metal ions which had reduction waves in the photocurrent region,
$Co(NH_3)_6^{3+}$ alone did not exhibit a polarographic maximum.

The exceptional behavior observed with 520 nm radiation
included non-linear photocurrent dependence on laser intensity
and streaming phenomena (vida supra). Figure 15 represents the
dependence of the transient photo-related current on pulsed
laser intensity at 520 nm for two different solutions. The results are similar: a nearly linear dependence on intensity at
more negative potentials, increasing to a much higher-order process at less negative potentials. In the case of $Co^{2+}$ (Figure
15B) this higher order dependence is observed even before the
reduction wave. Interestingly enough this effect was nearly
absent in the $Co(NH_3)_6^{3+}$ solution. This result can probably be
attributed to absorption by the solution, as the extinction
coefficient at 520 nm is ~ 20 $cm^{-1}M^{-1}$ and the effect is very intensity dependent.

## Discussion of Photoemission Studies

This study illustrates the significant effect of compres-
sing a given amount of energy into a narrow pulse. Even under
the most favorable circumstances, barely discernible photoemission currents were obtained with the cw argon laser when its
output power was reduced to the average output power of the
pulsed laser (-0.6 mW). At higher average powers the photoemission currents seen with the cw argon laser far exceeded those
seen with the pulsed laser. On the other hand, even at 1.5 W
the unusual photorelated currents observed with the pulsed laser
were not observed with the cw argon laser.

The effect of polarization on photoemission currents is
still somewhat ambiguous.(8,18,28) In these studies the argon
ion laser was vertically polarized, but the pulsed laser was
essentially unpolarized.

Tunability in the pulsed dye laser proved to be a substantial asset. Our results are the first series of current vs potential curves obtained at several narrow bandwidth wavelengths.
The absence of a shift in photoemission threshold proportional
to the change in photon energy in the uv is noteworthy (Figure
11). This has been suggested before,(49) and can even be detected in earlier work.(4) There are several possibilities which
might contribute to this observation. Two factors are a lower
concentration of scavenger and a lower concentration of supporting electrolyte in our work. The former would tend to decrease
the observed photoemission current, due to an increased probability of the hydrated electron returning to the electrode. This
might lead to a more negative measured threshold. The latter
would tend to increase the mean distance from the electrode
where the electrons are solvated. The larger this distance, of

course, the harder it is for electrons to return to the electrode and hence the larger the photo-related current. This
effect would tend to shift the threshold to less negative potentials.(8,50) Also, a third factor to be considered is that the
uv data arose from doubling fundamental laser frequencies; with
the accompanying loss in photon flux there would be a decrease
in photoemission current, and hence a more negative measured
threshold.

Another interesting point, also not completely explained,
is the relatively large background photo-related signal observed
with the pulsed laser. Qualitatively our blanks resemble those
previously obtained using conventional sources;(6,10) the null
point was observed at about -0.6 volts (vs SCE). Some residual
photo-related current may have resulted from impurities in the
water or salts used. No particular effort, such as treatment
with $SO_3^{-2}$/uv irradiation,(5) was made to exclude this as
a possible contribution. However, the relatively large residual
current noted with the pulsed laser, both in comparison to other
workers using conventional radiation sources and our own concur-
rent work with the argon ion laser, makes it unlikely that impurities were playing a significant role. It is far more likely
that $e^-$(aq) - $e^-$(aq) annihilation reactions are significant in
pulsed laser studies. The relatively high flux would create a
correspondingly larger local concentration of $e^-$(aq). The slope
in Figure 10 is certainly greater than 1.0, although a slope of
2.0 would be expected for a strictly bimolecular $e^-$(aq) - $e^-$(aq)
which accounted for all of the photorelated current.(29)

Thermal perturbation is undoubtedly responsible for a
substantial portion of the photo-related current observed
here.(5,6,8,13) This is particularly true of the results with
the pulsed dye laser, where wavelength considerations eliminate
photoemission as a cause. Furthermore, compared to other laser
studies done using a mercury pool electrode;(26,28) one might
easily envision a greater thermal effect here using the much
smaller DME. It is even conceivable that the focused pulsed
laser led to disruption of the mercury or catalysis of hydrogen
reduction; such a possibility has been suggested(27) and is
consistent with our observations of a streaming from the mercury
surface. On the other hand, the limit for destruction of the
double layer has been estimated to be in excess of 10 MW
$cm^{-2}$,(29) and our power fluxes were considerably less than that.

Two-photon emission has not been conclusively shown.(18,27)
Our photon intensity vs current data does not unequivocally suggest a two-photon process to explain anomalous observations with
520 nm pulsed laser irradiation. In fact, the observed higher
order processes are consistent with what has been suggested
might occur under large thermal excursions.(27)

Photo-related currents observed in the presence of transition
metal ions pose difficult questions. Contrary to the conclusion
of other workers,(22,24) the observed photo-related currents do

not appear to be associated primarily with photoemission. Although transient photo-related currents are observed on the reduction plateau of each metal ion (just as reported earlier (24)), these signals do not differ appreciably from those observed with blank electrolyte solution. Moreover, the onset of photo-related currents is tied to the onset of polarographic reduction currents, but is not specifically related to the photoemission potential (vide supra). Thus, although photoemission and scavenging reactions must be occurring with transition metal ion solutions, the net effect on observed currents is relatively small compared to the primary phenomenon giving rise to photo-related currents.

Our explanation for the observed photo-related currents induced with the CW laser in the presence of metal ion reduction is simply that the chopped laser source perturbs the Nernstian equilibrium which exists at the electrode surface in a manner similar to that imposed by differential pulse polarography. This perturbation may be thermal in nature. In any event, the result is the generation of current pulses which go through a maximum near the $E_{1/2}$, yielding a plot of photo-related current vs potential which looks very similar to a differential pulse polarogram (Figures 13,14). As this result was highly dependent on laser power, these observations provide another example of the potential of laser irradiation to provide more detailed information about the electrode-solution interface. In this regard it is noteworthy that addition of Triton X-100 did not appreciably change the shape or magnitude of the photo-related current, but did shift the apparent threshold for $Cu^{2+}$ (Figure 15). Triton X-100, being a relatively large organic molecule, would be expected to have certain insulating properties, both electrochemically and from a diffusion standpoint.(8,50) However, it still is not easy to correlate this effect with a molecular model.

## Results and Discussion for Laser Photolysis Studies

Determination of Fe(II) Concentration from Flash Photoreduction - To accurately determine the Fe(II) concentration produced from the photoreduction of Fe(III) oxalate, the measured Fe(II) oxidation currents must be corrected for faradaic-induced charging current.(31,47) Because raw data corrected by the "Derivative method" (see Experimental) showed Cottrell behavior, the currents were subsequently corrected according to the "correction factor" procedure outlined above. Cottrell plots for the two current-time curves are shown in Figure 16. The corrected data clearly show more ideal Cottrell behavior. In order to calculate $C^o$ from the slope of the Cottrell plot, the effective electrode area and the diffusion coefficient of the electro-active species must be known. The total area of the working electrode was determined by collecting ten droplets, weighing, and back-calculating from the known density of mercury, assuming spherical drops. Since the light is collimated, the effective working area of the electrode,

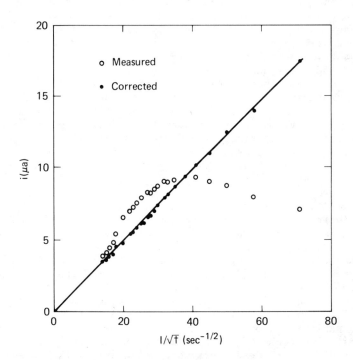

*Figure 16. Cottrell plot of current–time data for Fe(II) oxidation after laser flash irradiaion of ferric oxalate solution. E = −0.5 V vs. SCE; $RC_{eff}$ = 706 μsec; λ = 437 nm; b = 1 mm; $[Fe(Ox)_3{}^{3-}]$ = 0.853 × 10⁻²M.*

or the area irradiated, was assumed to be 50% of the total area or 1.07 x $10^{-2}$ cm$^2$. The diffusion coefficient of Fe(II) was assumed to equal that of Fe(III), which was experimentally determined to be 7.09 x $10^{-6}$ cm$^2$/sec by potential-step chronoamperometry.

The observation of diffusion-controlled currents over a time period of about 5 msec is significant in view of earlier Fe(III) oxalate studies conducted in this laboratory.(38,39) The earlier studies were based on chronoamperometric data obtained from time-delay potentiostatic electrolysis. Time-delay analysis(38) employs fast electroanalytical sampling of the photolyzed solution at various times after the flash. By varying the sampling time for consecutive experiments, the time-dependent behavior of the electroactive species can be followed. The Fe(II) oxidation current was found to change with time, passing through a minimum at about 10 msec and then increasing in magnitude at longer times.

Present results indicate that the amount of oxidizable species produced by the flash does not change with time. These findings raise valid questions about the previously proposed mechanism of the reaction. The present data imply that the Fe(II) concentration may not be changing with time, and that the final product concentration is being measured. Even if there is a reaction involving conversion of one oxidizable form to another, the net current should be proportional to final product as long as Cottrell behavior is observed at all times.

Identical results were obtained in a preliminary study of the Fe(III) oxalate system using a xenon flash lamp excitation source. Fe(II) oxidation currents were found to be diffusion-controlled over the entire time range (.3-250 msec). These results are significant because they reinforce the findings of the laser-induced photolysis study and eliminate the possibility that the "discrepancy" with the earlier studies is a wavelength-dependent phenomenon.

An explanation of the conflicting results is not obvious. The monitoring techniques are different - continuous versus time-delay, and the earlier workers were not aware of the faradaic-induced charging current contributions to the total current. It is possible that the apparent changes in Fe(II) concentration noted earlier may have been due to open-circuit depletion of Fe(II) due to double-layer charging after the flash.

## Concentration of Fe(II) vs. Pathlength

Birk and Perone(30) have developed the theoretical relation ship (Equation 2) describing the pathlength dependence of the initial concentration of intermediate produced by flash photolysis, based on a derivation similar to that by Hercules for optical flourescence.(51) Because of the complexity of this relationship and the necessary assumptions made in its derivation, Birk points out that it is more practical to examine a ratio of $C_R^o$ measurements made at two path lengths, b and b + $\Delta$b. From Equation 2, an expression relating the change in intermediate concentration to the change in pathlength follows

$$\frac{C_R^o \ (b)}{C_R^o \ (b+\Delta b)} = \exp(\alpha^{\prime} \Delta b C_0^o) \qquad (8)$$

where $\alpha^{\prime}$ is the effective absorption coefficient. The monochromatic, collimated, pulsed laser source makes the verification of Equation 8 feasible for the Fe(III) oxalate system.

The concentrations of Fe(II) produced by the photoreduction of Fe(III) oxalate at 442 nm and 457 nm are given in Table I for three pathlengths. As the pathlength increases the Fe(II) concentration decreases as expected.

Table I.  Dependence of Fe(II) Concentration on Pathlength in Photolysis Cell

All concentrations, x $10^4$M

| Data Set | Pathlength, b(mm) | $C_R^o(b)(\lambda_{442})$ | $C_R^o(b)(\lambda_{457})$ |
|----------|-------------------|---------------------------|---------------------------|
| 1        | 1                 | 1.58                      | .93                       |
| 2        | 5                 | 1.41                      | .65                       |
| 3        | 10                | 1.02                      | .47                       |

Table II compares the data with the theoretical relationship expressed in Equation 8. Literature values[52] of $\alpha_{442}$ and $\alpha_{457}$ were used to calculate the predicted concentration ratios. These values were $\alpha_{442} = 13.8$, $\alpha_{457} = 9.0$ $M^{-1}cm^{-1}$ (note: $\alpha = 2.3$ $\epsilon$). As can be seen there is considerable deviation from the predictions.

Table II.  Comparison of Fe(II) Concentration Dependence to
           Theory.  Calculation of $\alpha'$.

| $\lambda$(nm) | Measured concentration ratios from Table I | Predicted ratio using $\alpha_\lambda$ | $\alpha'_\lambda$ (cm$^2$M$^{-1}$) |
|---|---|---|---|
| 442 | $c_1/c_2$ = 1.12 | 1.05 | 3.33 x 10$^4$ |
|     | $c_2/c_3$ = 1.38 | 1.06 | 7.58 x 10$^4$ |
|     | $c_1/c_3$ = 1.54 | 1.11 | 5.64 x 10$^4$ |
| 457 | $c_1/c_2$ = 1.43 | 1.03 | 10.52 x 10$^4$ |
|     | $c_2/c_3$ = 1.38 | 1.04 | 7.58 x 10$^4$ |
|     | $c_1/c_3$ = 1.98 | 1.07 | 8.93 x 10$^4$ |

Average $\alpha'$ values:   5.52 x 10$^4$  ($\lambda$=442nm)

                          9.01 x 10$^4$  ($\lambda$=457nm)

The deviations from Equation 8 can be explained by two effects.  First, the intense laser pulse may cause some heating
of the solution.  This changes the refractive index of the liquid and the laser beam is dispersed by a "negative lens" effect.(53)  This decreases the amount of light available for
photolysis at the Hg drop, and, therefore, a smaller concentration of Fe(II) is produced than that predicted.  This beam dispersion increases with increased pathlength, which explains the
more pronounced deviations in Fe(II) concentration for larger
changes in b.  The second possible reason for poor agreement in
Table II is due to a transient inner filter effect; i.e., the
amount of available incident light at the mercury drop is being
reduced by a strongly absorbing intermediate species.  This effect would also be larger over longer pathlengths.  This latter
effect is probably the most significant.
     From the concentration ratios in Table II, it is possible
to calculate an effective absorption coefficient $\alpha'$, which
accounts for the absorption of all absorbing species produced
from the reactant as well as the reactant itself.  It may also
account for the "negative lens" effect.  Average values of $\alpha'$
for the two wavelengths are reported in Table II.  It is not
surprising that these absorption coefficients are larger than
the experimentally measured $\alpha$ values for Fe(III), because
previous workers have reported a photolytic intermediate which
is more strongly absorbing than the starting material in the
wavelength region of interest.(40,41)  The calculated $\alpha'$
values will be of subsequent use in determining $\phi_{442}$ and $\phi_{457}$
from Equation 2.

Estimates of $\phi_{442}$ and $\phi_{457}$

If $\alpha$, $C_o$, and b of Equation 2 are known and $C_R(b)$ and $Q_o$ can be measured, and estimate of $\phi_\lambda$, the quantum efficiency can be made. This is a measure of molecules of product formed per quantum of light absorbed and is an important concept for providing insight into photochemical processes. It is significant that the technique of electrochemical monitoring employed in this work enables one to monitor the concentration of intermediate produced as a function of pathlength, and, with knowledge of $Q_o$, to calculate a quantum efficiency for intermediates as well as final products.

The measurement of photon flux, $Q_o$, is not so straightforward. Actinometry is generally used for photon flux measurements; however, an appropriate actinometer and procedure have not yet been established for use with high energy pulsed lasers. As an alternative, a commercial power meter can be used for this measurement, and this was done in the work reported here. The reliability of the power meter measurement is probably only accurate to + 10%.

Following data acquisition for the concentration-pathlength studies at one wavelength, reproducibility of the initial pathlength current-time curve was checked to insure that the laser output efficiency had not diminished over the course of the experiment. The cell was replaced with the joulemeter, positioned so that the incident light at the cell window could be detected. The output peak voltage of the meter was converted to energy by means of a factory-supplied calibration curve. Energy per unit area was calculated by dividing the energy by the area of a 1 mm diameter beam. This was the "sampled" beam size for which the joulemeter with diffuser window was calibrated. A second energy measurement was obtained at approximately 1 cm above the first position to check the beam collimation. The two measurements were identical. This procedure was repeated for the second wavelength.

The uncertainty in this measurement $(Q_o)$ is due to several contributing factors. It is extremely difficult to place the joulemeter in such a position that the sensing element sees the same light intensity as the mercury drop. Only a small portion of the beam is sampled and this portion may not represent the actual energy at the electrtode surface. An independent experiment showed that the current monitored with flash at the mercury electrode varied by as much as ~ 30% over a distance of 6mm in the horizontal plane, emphasizing the uneven energy distribution of the laser beam. The meter was factory calibrated and the conversion factors supplied are probably inappropriate for larger beam measurements. No corrections were made for window reflection and absorption as the other sources of error mentioned were much larger. Table III gives the experimentally

determined $\phi_{442}$ and $\phi_{457}$, along with the previously reported values.(40,41)

Table III.   A Comparison of Experimentally Determined Quantum
             Yields to Those Previously Reported.

|  | Experimental | Previously Reported[a] |
|---|---|---|
| $\phi_{442}$ | ~.28 | ~.55 |
| $\phi_{457}$ | ~.16 | ~.52 |

[a]These values were graphically determined from a plot of $\phi$
versus $\lambda$.

The experimental values were calculated by rearranging Equation
2:

$$\Phi = \frac{C_R^o(b)}{Q_o[\alpha C_0^o]\exp[-\alpha b C_0^o]} \qquad (9)$$

The Fe(II) concentrations used were for b = 1 mm.  $Q_o$ values
were 3.08 x $10^{18}$ and 4.60 x $10^{19}$ quanta/cm$^2$ for $\lambda$ = 442 and 457
nm.   The exponential term was calculated using $\alpha'$ values from
Table II, whereas the pre-exponential term used the literature
values(52) for the Fe(III) absorption coefficient, $\alpha$, at 442
and 457 nm.   These are the manufacturer's specified lasing wavelengths for the dyes used at recommended concentrations in a
flat-flat cavity.
        The calculated values of $\phi_{442}$ and $\phi_{457}$ obtained here are
in reasonable agreement with the previously reported values, considering the many possible sources of error mentioned above.
These results bolster confidence in the concepts forming the
foundation of these measurements and suggest that it would be
worthwhile to pursue further studies aimed at minimizing sources
of error.   These should include an improved actinometry approach.
In addition, it would be worthwhile to choose a wave-length at an
absorption maximum, rather than near the foot as in the work here.
For ferric oxalate this would require setting up the laser source
for frequency doubling.

Conclusions

        Instrumentation and methodology necessary for examining

laser stimulated photoelectrochemistry has been established here.
The use of a boxcar integrator for data acquisition and signal-
averaging greatly improves the achievable signal-to-noise ratio,
particularly when using pulsed irradiation sources. Previous
workers usually examined only changes in the DC signal or single-
shot waveforms from an oscilloscope photograph. The use of a
tunable laser as the irradiation source also improves the flexibi-
lity of the photoelectrochemical instrumentation assembled here.
Photoemission experiments with previously well documented electron
scavengers by and large yielded the expected results, although
experiments with transition metal cations illustrated the increased
complexities of these systems the potential for obtaining quantitative measurements of photolytic intermediates appears progress-
ing from the results obtained here. As is usual when applying a
new technique to an established area of research, the use of
lasers in photoelectrochemistry appears to offer both advantages
and disadvantages. The higher photon fluxes stimulate many phenomena, some of them newly observed. However the tunability and
temporal resolution of lasers provide convenient means for studying photoelectrochemical processes in more depth than previously
possible.

## Acknowledgments

We would like to thank D. C. Johnson and H. E. Crampton for
design and construction of the electrochemical cell and mounting
apparatus, L.L. Steinmetz for discussions concerning the electronics, and B. W. Wallin, Ed Schniedlin, and Ed Neister for assistance with the lasers.

Work performed under the auspices
of the U. S. Department of Energy
under contract No. W-7405-ENG-48
(LLL) and No. EG-77-S-02-4263.A000 (Purdue).
Support was also provided by NSF
Contract CHE75-13444 (Purdue).

## Notice

References

1. F. K. Fong and N. Winograd, J. Am. Chem. Soc. 98, 2287 (1976).
2. A. Fujishima and K. Honda, Nature 238, 37 (1972).
3. A. B. Ellis, S. W. Kaiser and M. S. Wrighton, J. Am. Chem. Soc. 113, 1182 (1966).
4. G. C. Barker, A. W. Gardner and D. C. Sammon, J. Electrochem. Soc. 113, 1182 (1966).
5. G. C. Barker and D. McKeown, J. Electroanal. Chem. 62, 341 (1975).
6. G. C. Barker and G. Cloke, J. Electroanal. Chem. 52, 468 (1974).
7. L. I. Korshunov, Ya. M. Zolotovitskii and V. A. Benderskii, Elektrokhim. 4, 499 (1968).
8. A. M. Brodsky and Y. V. Pleskov in S. G. Davison (Ed.), Progress in Surface Science, Vol. 2, Part 1, Pergamon, Oxford, 1972, p. 1.
9. Y. V. Pleskov and Z. A. Rotenberg, J. Electroanal. Chem. 20, 1 (1969).
10. R. P. Baldwin and S. P. Perone, J. Electrochem. Soc. 123, 1647 (1976).
11. N. Basco, S. K. Vidyarthi and D. C. Walker, Can. J. Chem. 51, 305 (1974).
12. G. C. Barker, J. Electroanal. Chem. 39, 480 (1972).
13. G. C. Barker, Ber. Bunsenges. Phys. Chem. 75, 728 (1971).
14. G. C. Barker, B. Stringer and M. J. Williams, J. Electroanal. Chem. 51, 305 (1974).
15. G. C. Barker and G. Bottura, J. Electroanal. Chem. 47, 199 (1973).
16. Y. V. Pleskov, Z. A. Rotenberg and V. I. Lakomov, Elecktrokhim. 6, 1787 (1971).
17. G. C. Barker and A. W. Gardner, J. Electroanal. Chem. 47, 205 (1973).
18. V. A. Benderskii, S. D. Babenko, Y. M. Zolotovitskii, A. G. Krivnko and T. S. Rudenko, J. Electroanal. Chem. 56, 325 (1974).
19. V. A. Benderskii, J. Electroanal. Chem. 76, 327 (1977).
20. K. Yamashita and H. Imai, Bull. Chem. Soc. Japan 45, 628 (1972).
21. S. S. Fratoni, Jr. and S. P. Perone, Anal. Chem. 48, 287 (1976).
22. D. R. Crow and S. L. Ling, J. Chem. Soc. (Dalton), 698 (1972).
23. Z. A. Rotenberg, V. I. Lakomov and Y. V. Pleskov, Elektrokhim. 9, 11 (1973).
24. N. Martinus, D. M. Rayner and C. A. Vincent, Electrochim. Acta 18, 409 (1973).
25. N. Basco, S. K. Vidyarthi and D. C. Walker, Can. J. Chem. 52, 343 (1974).

26. G. C. Barker, D. McKeown, M. J. Williams, G. Bottura and V. Concialine, Faraday Soc. Disc. 56, 41 (1973).
27. G. C. Barker, A. W. Gardner and G. Bottura, J. Electroanal. Chem. 45, 21 (1973).
28. G. C. Barker, G. Bottura, G. Cloke, A. W. Gardner and M. J. Williams, J. Electroanal. Chem. 50, 323 (1974).
29. S. D. Babenko, V. A. Benderskii, Y. M. Zolotovitskii and A. G. Krivnko, J. Electroanal. Chem. 76, 347 (1977).
30. J. R. Birk and S. P. Perone, Anal. Chem., 40, 496 (1968).
31. K. F. Dahnke, S. S. Fratoni, Jr., and S. P. Perone, Anal. Chem., 48, 296 (1976).
32. K. F. Dahnke and S. P. Perone, J. Electrochem. Soc., 123, 1677 (1976).
33. Betty S. Hall, K. F. Dahnke, S. S. Fratoni, Jr., and S. P. Perone, J. Phys. Chem., 81, 866 (197).
34. C. A. Parker and C. G. Hatchard, J. Phys. Chem., 63, 22 (1959).
35. J. Lee and H. H. Seliger, J. Chem. Phys., 40, 519 (1964).
36. E. E. Wegner and A. W. Adamson, J. Amer. Chem. Soc., 394 (1966).
37. G. D. Cooper, B. A. DeGraff, J. Phys. Chem., 75, 2897 (1971).
38. R. A. Jamison and S. P. Perone, J. Phys. Chem., 76, 830 (1972).
39. J. I. H. Patterson and S. P. Perone, J. Phys. Chem., 77, 2437 (1973).
40. a)  C. A. Parker, Proc. Roy. Soc., Ser. A, 220, 104 (1953);
    b)  C. A. Parker, Trans. Faraday Soc., 50, 1213 (1954).
41. C. G. Hatchard and C. A. Parker, Proc. Roy. Soc., Ser. A, 235, 518 (1956).
42. J. H. Baxendale and N. K. Bridge, J. Phys. Chem., 59, 783 (1955).
43. J. I. H. Patterson and S. P. Perone, Anal. Chem., 44, 1978 (1972).
44. I. M. Kolthoff, et. al., "Quantitative Chemical Analysis", The Macmillan Company, New York, N.Y., 1069, Chapter 61.
45. J. H. Richardson and M. E. Ando, Anal. Chem. 49, 955 (1977).
46. S. S. Fratoni, Jr., Ph.D. Thesis, Purdue University, 1976.
47. S. S. Fratoni, Jr. and S. P. Perone, Anal. Chem., 48, 287 (1976).
48. N. F. Strachan and N. L. Harris, J. Inst. Metals 85, 17 (1956).
49. M. Heyrovsky and F. Pucciarelli, J. Electroanal. Chem. 27, 353 (1977).
50. Z. A. Rotenberg, V. I. Lakomov and Y. V. Pleskov, J. Electroanal. Chem. 27, 403 (1970).
51. D. M. Hercules, Anal. Chem., 38, 29A (1966).
52. G. B. Porter, J. G. W. Doering and S. Karanka, J. Amer. Chem. Soc., 84, j4027 (1962).

53.  F. H. Fry, "Analytical Photochemistry and Photochemical
     Analysis", J. M. Fitzgerald, Ed., Marcel Dekker, New York,
     N.Y., 1971, Chapter 2.

RECEIVED August 7, 1978.

# Coherent Anti-Stokes Raman Scattering Spectroscopy

BRUCE S. HUDSON[']

Department of Chemistry, Stanford University, Stanford, CA 94305

Coherent anti-Stokes Raman scattering (CARS) spectroscopy is the application of a nonlinear optical phenomenon known as three-wave mixing to obtain Raman spectral information. CARS has recently become an interesting technique because of developments in high power tunable lasers. The construction of a CARS spectrometer from commercial components is now routine. The spectra obtainable from such spectrometers have important advantages relative to spontaneous Raman scattering spectra in certain cases. In practice, the two most important advantages of CARS are its ability to completely reject fluorescence or other isotropic sample luminescence and its potential for very high resolution Raman spectroscopy of gases.

This article begins with a brief description of the three-wave mixing experiment. Several alternative descriptions of the phenomenon which forms the basis of a CARS experiment will be presented. Each of these descriptions is, by itself, incomplete but each provides an insight into a particular aspect of the experiment. It is hoped that at least one of these descriptions will prove satisfying to the reader. Emphasis will be placed on the aspects of the CARS experiment which lead to its advantages and disadvantages in an analytical sense.

CARS is subject to one-photon resonance enhancement similar to that observed for spontaneous Raman scattering. This situation is of interest because of the increased sensitivity and selectivity associated with the resonance condition. Furthermore, the fluorescence rejection capability of CARS becomes even more important when the excitation energy is in an absorption region. The analysis of CARS spectra is more complex under resonance conditions. The modifications of the basic expressions needed to include resonance enhancement will be given. Finally, the relationship between resonance CARS, resonance Raman and high resolution vibronic absorption spectra will be described, including the important effects of inhomogeneous broadening. Throughout this article emphasis is placed on dilute solution samples.

['] Current address: Department of Chemistry, University of Oregon, Eugene, OR 97403

0-8412-0459-4/78/47-085-171$05.50/0

CARS spectroscopy has been reviewed several times recently
(1-5). The semiclassical theory of CARS is discussed in some
detail in (1) where references are given to the original work of
Bloembergen and co-workers, Maker and Terhune and Butcher. A
recent review of the field of nonlinear optics in general has been
given by Flytzanis (6). Many examples of recent CARS experiments
are referred to in (1) and spectra are given in (2-4). A discussion of the analytical advantages of CARS relative to spontaneous Raman scattering has recently been presented (7).

## Description of the CARS Experiment

In the following discussion it will be assumed that the
sample is optically isotropic, e.g., a liquid or a gas. In a
CARS experiment two laser beams with frequencies $\omega_1$ and $\omega_2$ interact in the material to produce a collimated beam with the
frequency $\omega_3 = 2\omega_1 - \omega_2$. For given values of $\omega_1$ and $\omega_2$, the
coherent signals generated in the medium have frequencies $n\omega_1
+ m\omega_2$ where n and m are positive or negative integers and $n\omega_1
+ m\omega_2 > 0$. CARS is the case n = 2, m = -1. Suppose that the
intensity of the $\omega_3$ beam is measured with a suitably placed
detector. The intensity $I(\omega_3)$ is found to obey an expression of
the form

$$I(\omega_3) = \kappa \left| \chi^{CARS} \right|^2 I(\omega_1)^2 I(\omega_2) \tag{1}$$

where $I(\omega_1)$ and $I(\omega_2)$ are the intensities of the $\omega_1$ and $\omega_2$ beams,
$\chi^{CARS}$ is the effective third order susceptibility and $\kappa$ is a
collection of constants.

We now consider the frequency dependence of $I(\omega_3)$. Suppose
that $\omega_1$ is held fixed while $\omega_2$ is varied. It is found that
$I(\omega_3)$ varies very slowly with $\omega_2$ except when $\omega_1 - \omega_2 \approx \omega_r$ where
$\omega_r$ is a Raman active excitation of the sample (usually a vibra-
tional or rotational excitation). When $\omega_1 - \omega_2 = \omega_r$ there is an
increase in the value of $I(\omega_3)$ by as much as four orders of
magnitude. This is known as a CARS resonance. An alternative
designation of CARS is three-wave Raman mixing. A CARS spectrum
is obtained by measuring $I(\omega_3)$ as a function of $\omega_1 - \omega_2$.

Two other points of terminology should be mentioned. Three-
wave mixing ($\omega_3 = 2\omega_1 - \omega_2$) is a special case of four-wave mixing ($\omega_x = \omega_a + \omega_b - \omega_c$) where $\omega_a = \omega_b$. Second, the acronym CARS
refers to the process in which the generated signal $\omega_3 =
2\omega_1 - \omega_2$ has a higher frequency (anti-Stokes) than the "pump"
frequency ($\omega_1$). This implies that $\omega_1 > \omega_2$. When the frequencies
$\omega_1$ and $\omega_2$ are incident on the sample, there will be a simultaneous
generation of a signal at $\omega_3' = 2\omega_2 - \omega_1$ which will have a
frequency lower than the pump frequency. This is known as CSRS
(coherent Stokes Raman scattering, 'scissors').

Stimulated Raman scattering is also a kind of coherent Raman
scattering. It may be viewed as a case of spontaneous Raman

scattering where the signal generated at a frequency different
from the single incident frequency interacts with the applied
frequency and is amplified in a certain propagation direction.  It
shows a threshold behavior not observed with three-wave mixing.

## Coherence of the CARS Signal

The most important experimental aspect of a CARS experiment
is that the signal is generated as a coherent beam.  For liquid
samples this beam is directed at an angle with respect to the
incident $\omega_1$ and $\omega_2$ beams.  This $\omega_3$ beam may therefore be spatially
filtered from all other radiation from the sample and all of the
signal directed to the detector.  No filtering monochromator is
needed to analyze the radiation.  This results in a greater collection efficiency compared to the spontaneous Raman effect.  It
also means that the resolution of a CARS experiment is not
determined by monochromator resolution but rather by the degree
of monochromaticity of the laser excitation beams.  Furthermore,
since the fluorescence from a sample is isotropic, the spatial
filtering used to isolate the CARS beam reduces the sample
fluorescence by a factor of about $10^4$.  The anti-Stokes nature of
the CARS signal and the Stokes nature of the fluorescence can be
used to remove the fluorescence by optical filtering.  Also the
CARS signal is much stronger than the corresponding spontaneous
Raman signal.  Overall, this leads to a rejection of fluorescence
relative to spontaneous Raman scattering by a factor of $10^9$.

In a spontaneous Raman experiment an incident laser beam
with frequency $\omega_1$ is directed into a sample and the scattered
radiation is resolved into its frequency components including
those at $\omega_2 = \omega_1 \pm \omega_r$.  The plus sign corresponds to anti-Stokes
scattering and the minus sign to Stokes scattering.  The spon-
taneous Raman effect is inelastic light scattering:  both energy
and momentum are exchanged between the sample and the radiation
field.  The emitted radiation is isotropically distributed and all
frequency components are present at the same time.  They must be
analyzed with a large monochromator which determines the spectral
resolution and the signal collection efficiency.  The radiation
which is detected has no phase relationship with the incident
radiation.

An important aspect of spontaneous Raman scattering is that
its description in terms of the semiclassical approximation (i.e.,
a classical field interacting with a quantum mechanical medium)
requires extra assumptions involving fluctuations of the medium
(a normal mode dependent polarizability in a microscopic region)
or in the radiation field (zero-point fluctuations).  These
assumptions are discussed elsewhere (1).  The incoherent nature of
Raman scattering is related to these assumptions.  A fully quantum
mechanical description of Raman scattering includes a spontaneous
emission process which cannot be treated by the semiclassical
theory without some additional assumptions.

CARS (and its relatives) can be described in a fully semi-classical fashion without any additional assumptions. All that is required is the definition of a medium polarization written as a power series expansion in the strength of the applied electric fields:

$$\underline{P}(\underline{r},t) = \underline{P}^{(1)}(\underline{r},t) + \underline{P}^{(2)}(\underline{r},t) + \underline{P}^{(3)}(\underline{r},t) \tag{2}$$

where the first term is linear in the field, the second quadratic, etc. (Only electric field terms will be considered. Some of the magnetic terms are discussed by Terhune and Maker (8).) The first term is proportional to the usual linear polarizability ($\underline{\alpha}$ or $\underline{\chi}^{(1)}$) and is all that is needed for a description of the propagation and dispersion of light including absorption and the refractive index at low field intensities. The second term vanishes for isotropic media by symmetry. The third term describes CARS. The proportionality constant which appears in the $\underline{P}^{(3)}(\underline{r},t)$ term is $\underline{\chi}^{(3)}$, one third order susceptibility.

When a medium has a nonzero third order susceptibility, the application of fields at frequencies $\omega_1$ and $\omega_2$ will result in an induced polarization with frequency components $3\omega_1$, $2\omega_1 + \omega_2$, $2\omega_1 - \omega_2$, $\cdots$ $3\omega_2$, i.e., all combinations of the form $n\omega_1 \pm m\omega_2$. The induced polarization at a given frequency (e.g., $2\omega_1 - \omega_2$) will result in an emitted radiation field. Each volume element in the sample (at position $\underline{r}$) will produce this field with a particular phase. The key factor at this level of description is that the radiated fields may add in phase for particular propagation directions. The total field will be large for this direction.

This coherence also occurs for the first order polarization, $\underline{P}^{(1)}(\underline{r},t)$. The polarization induced by a single applied frequency, $\omega$, which is proportional to $\underline{E}(\omega)$ only has components at frequency $\omega$. The resulting total propagating electric field is particularly strong in a direction colinear with the propagation direction because the phase of the radiation produced in one volume element is in phase with the radiation of all other volume elements in that direction. For the first order (linear) polarization this effect gives rise to the ordinary refractive index. By analogy with the higher order phenomenon, this could be designated coherent Rayleigh scattering.

This linear (first order) case is important because it illustrates the relationship between the three aspects of the term "coherent" as it applies to experiments like CARS. First, there is the collimation aspect of the signal. The measured radiation is restricted to a particular direction. Second, there is the fact that the radiation in the detected beam has a phase relation to the applied radiation. This is due to the fact that the polarization in a particular volume element depends on $\underline{E}(\underline{r},t)$ in that element. Third, there is the fact that the detected radiation is the square of the sum of the fields from many volume elements rather than the sum of the squares of the fields from each element. The detected radiation is the square of the coherent superposition of the radiation from all scattering elements.

The relation between the collimation of the CARS signal and the extended nature of the scattering volume can be viewed as an expression of the uncertainty relation for the radiation. The uncertainty in the radiation wave vector $\underline{k}$ is small since its frequency and direction are defined. Therefore, the volume element giving rise to the radiation must be extended in space.

There is another sense in which the term coherent is often used. In this sense the term refers to interference effects between different resonances of the same molecule. Resonance Raman scattering shows this type of coherence in distinction to fluorescence. The coherence of CARS and coherent Rayleigh scattering is spatial coherence resulting from interference involving different molecules. On the other hand, one of the most important effects observed in CARS spectra involves the interference between different resonances on different molecules and thus the distinction between these two uses of the term is not usually made.

The coherence of the CARS signal is a property of the radiation field. It has a direct analogy in the linear phenomenon which gives rise to the refractive index. It is not related to any collective excitations of the material induced by the radiation field. The important factor is whether the radiation generated in one volume element is in phase with the radiation generated at a different volume element.

One way to interpret the special situation associated with the forward propagation of radiation in the linear polarization case is based on momentum conservation for the "absorbed" and "reemitted" photon. Reemission in the forward direction for a photon of the same frequency as the excitation frequency results in no net momentum transfer to the sample. This condition ($\Delta \underline{k} = 0$) is the condition which determines the direction for the propagation of the radiation in a three-wave mixing experiment. In this case the $\Delta \underline{k} = 0$ condition becomes

$$2\underline{k}_1 - \underline{k}_2 - \underline{k}_3 = 0 \tag{3}$$

where $\underline{k} = [n(\omega)\omega/c]\hat{k}$ where n is the refractive index. This is known as the phase matching condition.

Before discussing this aspect of CARS, we turn to a brief discussion of its quantum mechanical description. A general expression for the quantum mechanical scattering probability for any process described by the transition operator T between initial (I) and final (F) states of the matter is

$$S_T = \sum_F \sum_I \rho_I^{(N)} \langle I|T^\dagger|F\rangle\langle F|T|I\rangle \delta(E_F - E_I - \Delta E_{rad}) \tag{4}$$

where I and F refer to the entire N-particle system, $\rho_I{}^{(N)}$ is the N-particle density matrix element for the initial state and the delta function imposes the restriction that the change in energy of the matter $(E_F - E_I)$ must be balanced by a change in energy of the radiation field $(\Delta E_{rad})$. The states I and F refer only to the matter; the photon-state integration has been performed and the resulting factors are incorporated in the definition of the operator T along with the appropriate function of the matter coordinates. The summations are over all possible initial and final states consistent with energy conservation and an initial state population. This density matrix weighted summation is equivalent to an ensemble average. The scattering probability S is therefore a function of the thermodynamic quantities which determine the density matrix elements and of $\Delta E_{rad}$ which is measured.

The spatial and photon operators which appear in the operator T depend on the particular process involved. For absorption, the spatial part of the operator is the instantaneous electric dipole moment while for Raman scattering, it is the instantaneous polarizability. For these cases, and for CARS, this operator may be represented as a sum over individual operators each containing the coordinates of the particles in individual molecules. Thus,

$$S_T = \sum_F \sum_I \rho_I{}^{(N)} \sum_\alpha \langle I | t_\alpha^\dagger | F \rangle \sum_\beta \langle F | t_\beta | I \rangle \delta(E_F - E_I - \Delta E_{rad}). \tag{5}$$

We will assume that the N-particle density matrix element can be represented as a product of 1-particle density matrix elements $\rho_{\alpha i}{}^{(1)}$ for the initial state of molecule $\alpha$. We therefore exclude collective excitations of the matter.

For spontaneous Raman scattering, the experiment consists of measurement of the production of photons with frequency $\omega_2$ due to the presence of photons with frequency $\omega_1$. In this case, there must be a change in the energy of the radiation field (unless $\omega_1 = \omega_2$) and therefore there must be a change in the energy of the matter. This will generally be due to the excitation of one molecule in the sample. The final state depends on which molecule is excited. For a given pair of initial and final states, only one molecule and therefore one $t_\alpha$ will contribute. In this case we have

$$S_{RAM} = \sum_\alpha \sum_i \sum_f \rho_{\alpha i}{}^{(1)} | \langle f_\alpha | t_\alpha | i_\alpha \rangle |^2 \delta(\epsilon_f - \epsilon_i - \Delta E_{rad}) \tag{6}$$

where i and f refer to the initial and final states of molecule $\alpha$ with energies $\epsilon_f$ and $\epsilon_i$. Note that $S_{ram}$ is the sum over all molecules of the ensemble average of the transition probability for each molecule. There are no cross terms involving different molecules. Raman scattering is an incoherent process.

For CARS, the change in the energy of the radiation field is zero. This is because the operator T contains creation operators for $\omega_3$ and $\omega_2$ photons and destruction operators for two $\omega_1$ photons. Since $\omega_3 = 2\omega_1 - \omega_2$, the net energy change $\Delta E_{rad} = \omega_3 + \omega_2 - 2\omega_1$ is zero. This means that the final state can be the same as the initial state. In this case we have

$$S_{CARS} = \sum_\alpha \sum_\beta \sum_i \rho_{\alpha i}^{(1)} \rho_{\beta i}^{(1)} \langle i_\beta | t_\beta^+ | i_\beta \rangle \langle i_\alpha | t_\alpha | i_\alpha \rangle \delta(\Delta E_{rad})$$

$$= \left| \sum_\alpha \sum_i \rho_{\alpha i}^{(1)} \langle i_\alpha | t_\alpha | i_\alpha \rangle \right|^2 . \tag{7}$$

The overall transition probability is seen to be the absolute square of the ensemble average of the expectation value of the operator $t_\alpha$. The intensity contains all of the cross terms involving pairs of molecules including those which are very far apart. The scattering is spatially coherent.

The condition that the initial state is the same as the final state in a CARS experiment means that there is no change in the momentum of the material system. This means that there is also no change in the momentum of the radiation field. Since the momentum is $\hbar \underline{k}$ this leads to equation (3) which determines the direction of the emitted beam with frequency $\omega_3$. This phase matching condition can be used to derive an expression for the optimum angle between the incident $\omega_1$ and $\omega_2$ beams. The vector diagram corresponding to equation (3) is shown in figure (1). The length of each vector is determined by the associated frequency and the medium refractive index at that frequency, $k = n(\omega)\omega/c$. The vectors will only sum to zero if the angle between the two incident beams has the value $\theta_0$ given by

$$\cos\theta_0 = \frac{4n_1^2 \omega_1^2 + n_2^2 \omega_2^2 - n_3^2 \omega_3^2}{4n_1 n_2 \omega_1 \omega_2} \tag{8}$$

where $n_i$ is the refractive index at frequency $\omega_i$. For normal solvents which have a small dispersion and for small frequency shifts $\Delta \equiv \omega_1 - \omega_2$ we may assume that the refractive index is a linear function of the frequency so that

$$n_3 = n_1 + \delta$$
$$n_2 = n_1 - \delta \tag{9}$$

For CARS, $\omega_3 > \omega_2 > \omega_1$ and $\delta$ is positive for materials whose refractive index increases with frequency. Using the notation $\omega \equiv \omega_1$, $\omega + \Delta \equiv \omega_3$, and $\omega - \Delta \equiv \omega_2$ and neglecting terms second order in $\delta$ and fourth order or higher in $\theta_0$ we have

$$\theta_0 \approx \left[\left(\frac{2\delta}{n_1-\delta}\right)\left(\frac{\Delta}{\omega}\right)\left(\frac{\omega+\Delta}{\omega-\Delta}\right)\right]^{\frac{1}{2}} \approx \left[\frac{2}{n_1}\left(\frac{dn}{d\omega}\right)_\omega\left(\frac{\Delta^2}{\omega}\right)\right]^{\frac{1}{2}} \qquad (10)$$

For $\omega$ corresponding to 5000 Å and $\Delta/2\pi c = 1000$ cm$^{-1}$ the phase-matching angles for water, benzene and carbon disulfide are $0.5°$, $1°$ and $1.3°$, respectively. For dilute gases the dispersion of the refractive index is very small since $n \approx 1$ for all frequencies and hence the phase matching angle becomes zero.

The quantum mechanical description of the linear optical phenomena can be based on similar considerations. If one photon with frequency $\omega_1$ is destroyed and one with frequency $\omega_2$ is detected, then, if $\omega_1 \neq \omega_2$, the initial and final states must differ and momentum cannot be conserved by the radiation field alone. However, if $\omega_1 = \omega_2$ there will be a coherent effect corresponding to $\underline{k}_1 = \underline{k}_2$. This is propagation of the beam through the medium. There will also be incoherent terms with $\underline{k}_2 \neq \underline{k}_1$ (Rayleigh scattering). The intensity of the forward or propagating beam in an isotropic sample compared to the incoherent side scattered radiation gives an idea of the relative magnitude of these two types of phenomena.

There is therefore a common basis for the description of coherent linear and coherent nonlinear optical phenomena. In each case there is a possibility of no net change in the state of the matter because the process being monitored results in no net change in the energy or momentum of the radiation field. The simple quantum formalism outlined above shows that this corresponds to scattering from an extended region in space. Spontaneous Raman scattering is different in that it involves the incoherent summation of processes from individual molecules.

There are a number of other similarities between CARS and normal forward propagation. For instance, neither process results in a frequency distribution for the detected radiation under monochromatic excitation conditions. This is in contrast to Rayleigh and Raman scattering where excitation of the low frequency translational and rotational degrees of freedom of the matter leads to a continuous intensity distribution. The description of these incoherent phenomena requires the introduction of some fluctuation in either the matter or the radiation field. In the case of Rayleigh scattering, it is usual to consider that the polarizability in a small region of space is modulated by density fluctuations. The frequency spread of the scattered light is a measure of the time dependence of these fluctuations. In the case of coherent phenomena, such fluctuations must be averaged over the entire scattering volume which is macroscopic in size. For homogeneous media there are no macroscopic variations in the properties of the sample and thus no inelastic processes which are not compensated by radiation field changes.

When a linearly polarized beam of light traverses a symmetric isotropic medium it emerges with its polarization unaffected.

[Liquids and gases formed by asymmetric (chiral) molecules are said to be asymmetric isotropic materials. They have rotation symmetry but lack inversion symmetry. Such materials will not be considered.] If a CARS experiment is performed with $\omega_1$ and $\omega_2$ beams having parallel polarization, it is found that the $\omega_3$ beam is polarized parallel to the excitation beams. For the case where the $\omega_1$ and $\omega_2$ beams are polarized perpendicular to each other it is found that the $\omega_3$ beam is polarized parallel to the $\omega_2$ beam. In these two cases the $\omega_3$ beam is completely polarized. This differs from the spontaneous Raman case where the detected signal may be depolarized. The information obtained from a Raman polarization ratio measurement may be obtained in a CARS experiment by a comparison of the intensity observed for the two incident polarization conditions just described.

## The Frequency Dependence of the CARS Signal

We now turn to the theory of the dependence of the CARS signal on the values of the frequencies $\omega_1$ and $\omega_2$. This is most efficiently done by using a standard diagrammatic representation (9). First, consider the spontaneous Raman effect. This process is defined by the two diagrams in figure (2) and their associated perturbation theory expressions. These two terms represent scattering amplitudes. It is convenient to define the total scattering amplitude $\alpha$ as a function of the single incident frequency $\omega_1$ by using the fact that at a Raman peak $\omega_2 = \omega_1 - \omega_r$.

$$\alpha(\omega_1) \equiv \frac{1}{\hbar} \sum_a \left( \frac{M_{fa} M_{ai}}{\omega_a - \omega_1} + \frac{M_{fa} M_{ai}}{\omega_a - \omega_r + \omega_1} \right) \tag{11}$$

In this expression $\omega_r = \omega_1 - \omega_2$ and the $M_{ij}$ are electric dipole matrix elements. The frequency denominators are given as real quantities. Inclusion of damping (and therefore absorption) may be done by replacing the intermediate state frequencies by complex values. This is discussed in greater detail below. From equation (6) we see that the Raman intensity is related to the ensemble average of the absolute square of $\alpha(\omega_1)$.

$$S_{RAM} \alpha \langle\langle |\alpha(\omega_1)|^2 \rangle\rangle \tag{12}$$

The intensity of the Raman scattering process is large when the incident frequency is near one or more of the intermediate state excitation frequencies, i.e., $\omega_1 \approx \omega_a$. This is known as resonance enhancement.

The corresponding situation for CARS is shown in figure (3). Twelve diagrams and twelve amplitude contributions can be constructed subject to the conditions that two photons of frequency $\omega_1$ are destroyed, one new photon of frequency $\omega_2$ is created and

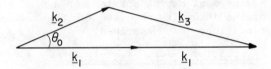

*Figure 1.   The phase-matching vector diagram for a CARS experiment. The length of each κ vector is nw/c where the refractive index is measured at frequency W at the subscripts on κ correspond to ω₁, ω₂, or ω₃.*

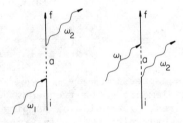

*Figure 2.   Time-ordered perturbation diagrams describing Raman ($\omega_1 \neq \omega_2$) and Rayleigh ($\omega_1 = \omega_2$) scattering*

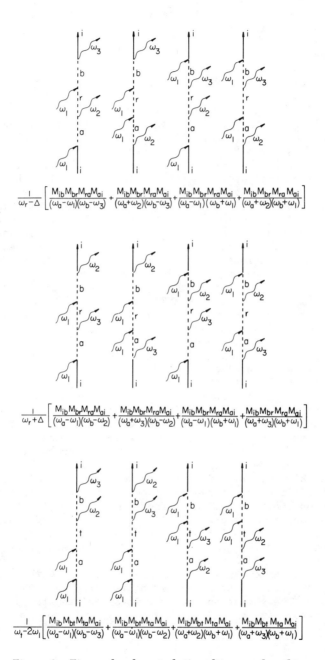

$$\frac{1}{\omega_r-\Delta}\left[\frac{M_{ib}M_{br}M_{ra}M_{ai}}{(\omega_a-\omega_1)(\omega_b-\omega_3)}+\frac{M_{ib}M_{br}M_{ra}M_{ai}}{(\omega_a+\omega_2)(\omega_b-\omega_3)}+\frac{M_{ib}M_{br}M_{ra}M_{ai}}{(\omega_a-\omega_1)(\omega_b+\omega_1)}+\frac{M_{ib}M_{br}M_{ra}M_{ai}}{(\omega_a+\omega_2)(\omega_b+\omega_1)}\right]$$

$$\frac{1}{\omega_r+\Delta}\left[\frac{M_{ib}M_{br}M_{ra}M_{ai}}{(\omega_a-\omega_1)(\omega_b-\omega_2)}+\frac{M_{ib}M_{br}M_{ra}M_{ai}}{(\omega_a+\omega_3)(\omega_b-\omega_2)}+\frac{M_{ib}M_{br}M_{ra}M_{ai}}{(\omega_a-\omega_1)(\omega_b+\omega_1)}+\frac{M_{ib}M_{br}M_{ra}M_{ai}}{(\omega_a+\omega_3)(\omega_b+\omega_1)}\right]$$

$$\frac{1}{\omega_1-2\omega_1}\left[\frac{M_{ib}M_{bt}M_{ta}M_{ai}}{(\omega_a-\omega_1)(\omega_b-\omega_3)}+\frac{M_{ib}M_{bt}M_{ta}M_{ai}}{(\omega_a-\omega_1)(\omega_b-\omega_2)}+\frac{M_{ib}M_{bt}M_{ta}M_{ai}}{(\omega_a+\omega_2)(\omega_b+\omega_1)}+\frac{M_{ib}M_{bt}M_{ta}M_{ai}}{(\omega_a+\omega_3)(\omega_b+\omega_1)}\right]$$

*Figure 3.   Time-ordered perturbation diagrams describing the third-order susceptibility*

one photon of frequency $\omega_3$ is created. Also, the initial state is
the same as the final state. The process leading to the creation
of a new $\omega_2$ photon is a stimulated process rather than a spontaneous process but that is not indicated by these diagrams. In
order to obtain the complete scattering amplitude it is necessary
to sum the expressions of figure (3) over all values of a, b and
r.

Consider the first diagram of figure (3) in more detail.
This particular contribution to the scattering process can also
be represented by transitions on an energy level diagram (figure
4a). The first step consists of the absorption of a photon of
frequency $\omega_1$ causing a virtual transition to the intermediate
state a. The most important intermediate states will be elec-
tronically excited states because of their large values of $M_{ai}$ and
the small values of $\omega_a - \omega_1$ when $\omega_1$ is in the visible region. The
next step is the stimulated emission of a photon of frequency $\omega_2$.
The energy absorbed from the radiation field at this point is
$\omega_1 - \omega_2 = \Delta$. Since $\Delta$ is on the order of a vibrational excitation,
the most important intermediate states r will be vibrationally
excited states of the ground state. The electric dipole matrix
element $M_{ra}$ will be large if the matrix element $M_{ai}$ is large and
if the vibrational state r is a Raman active vibration. The next
step is the transition from r to the intermediate state b due to
absorption of another $\omega_1$ photon. The energy absorbed from the
radiation field at this point is $2\omega_1 - \omega_2 = \omega_3$ and the energy
denominator will be small if $\omega_b \approx \omega_3$. The final step is the
spontaneous emission of an $\omega_3$ photon. For $\omega_3 = 2\omega_1 - \omega_2$ this will
take the matter back to the initial state energy. If the initial
state is in fact the ground state the emission of the $\omega_3$ photons
can proceed in a coherent fashion as discussed above.

It can be seen from figures (3) and (4) that CARS is an
excitation spectrum for a three-wave mixing process. The amplitude for this process is enhanced when the intermediate state r is
a real state of the matter.

The twelve contributions to the scattering amplitude can be
naturally divided into three groups of four each. The first group
has a common energy denominator factor of $(\omega_r - \Delta)^{-1}$, the second
group has the common factor $(\omega_r + \Delta)^{-1}$ and the third group has the
common factor $(\omega_t - 2\omega_1)^{-1}$. The frequencies $\omega_r$ and $\omega_t$ are the
excitation frequencies for the second intermediate state and
$\Delta = \omega_1 - \omega_2$. The first four terms describe the CARS process
per se, i.e., the enhanced scattering associated with the situa-
tion $\omega_r \approx \Delta$. These four terms may be factored into the product of
two terms. (The summation over the intermediate states a, b and
r is omitted.)

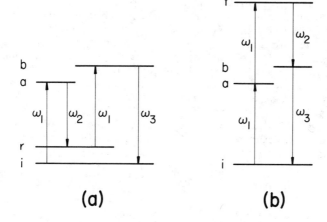

Figure 4. *An energy level diagram description of two of the terms contributing to the third-order susceptibility*

$$\frac{1}{(\omega_r - \Delta)} \left[ \frac{M_{ra} M_{ai}}{\omega_a - \omega_1} + \frac{M_{ra} M_{ai}}{\omega_a + \omega_2} \right] \left[ \frac{M_{ib} M_{br}}{\omega_b - \omega_3} + \frac{M_{ib} M_{br}}{\omega_b + \omega_1} \right]$$

$$= (\omega_r - \Delta)^{-1} \alpha(\omega_1) \alpha(\omega_3). \tag{13}$$

The second group of terms containing the factor $(\omega_r + \Delta)^{-1}$ leads to enhanced scattering when $\Delta = -\omega_r$. Since $\omega_r$ is positive this means that $\omega_2 > \omega_1$. These terms give rise to CSRS. For a CARS experiment their contribution is smaller than that of the first four terms by a factor of about $(\omega_r + \Delta)/\gamma_r$ where $\gamma_r$ is the line-width of the intermediate state r. For a Raman resonance $\omega_r \approx \Delta \approx 1000 \ cm^{-1}$ and $\gamma_r \approx 10 \ cm^{-1}$ this factor is about 200. The contribution from these CSRS terms is only a slowly varying function of $\omega_1 - \omega_2$ when $\omega_1 > \omega_2$. These terms therefore contribute to a background signal in a CARS experiment.

The third group of terms with the common factor $(\omega_t - 2\omega_1)^{-1}$ also contribute only a background signal to the CARS spectrum so long as $2\omega_1$ is not near any sharp two-photon electronic transitions. These terms are said to give rise to an electronic background signal in the sense that no vibrational excitations of the ground state are involved as intermediate states in the scattering process. The representation of one of these terms on the basis of an energy level diagram is given in figure (4b).

The scattering amplitude for the CARS process is the sum of the 12 terms of figure (3). If this amplitude is designated $A(\omega_1, \omega_2)$ we see from equation (7) that the signal intensity is given by the square of the ensemble average of $A(\omega_1, \omega_2)$.

$$S_{CARS} = |\langle\langle A(\omega_1, \omega_2) \rangle\rangle|^2 \tag{14}$$

It is important that the ensemble average be performed before the square is taken.

The quantum mechanical description of CARS outlined above does not use the concept of the third order susceptibility $\chi^{(3)}$ which is the starting point of the semiclassical theory. This is the essential difference between these two treatments. At this point, however, we revert to the semiclassical description primarily because there is an established procedure (1,10) for introduction of the resonance damping factors in this formalism. The expression corresponding to equation (14) in the semiclassical picture contains the fact that the intensity of the detected signal is proportional to the square of the ensemble averaged $\chi^{(3)}$, i.e., $|\langle\langle \chi^3 \rangle\rangle|^2$. The results of this averaging procedure depend on the nature of the polarization of the $\omega_1$ and $\omega_2$ beams and the thermodynamic parameters of the sample. Explicit expression will only be given below for special cases. The general results are given elsewhere (1).

The basic equation used to analyze CARS experiments may be written in the form

$$|\chi^{(3)}|^2 = |B + \mathcal{R}(\delta_r - i\gamma_r)^{-1}|^2$$

$$= B^2 + 2B\mathcal{R}\delta_r(\delta_r^2 + \gamma_r^2)^{-1} + \mathcal{R}^2(\delta_r^2 + \gamma_r^2)^{-1} \tag{15}$$

The background term B is the sum of the CSRS and electronic background contributions to $\chi^{(3)}$ plus all of the CARS terms except for the one associated with the resonance due to state r. B is only a slowly varying function of $\omega_1$ and $\omega_2$ and is usually dominated by its real part. Imaginary contributions to B can come from two-photon resonances (near $2\omega_1$). For the rest of this article we will assume that B is a real constant. The quantity $\delta_r$ is $\omega_r - \Delta = \omega_r - (\omega_1 - \omega_2)$. It is $\delta_r$ which is varied in order to obtain a CARS spectrum. The damping factor $\gamma_r$ has been introduced for the Raman resonance. This is the linewidth of the Raman resonance under investigation. $\mathcal{R}$ contains the matrix elements and one-photon resonance denominators given in equation (13). For future reference we will give an explicit expression for $\mathcal{R}$ for a special case namely that in which a molecule has a series of vibronic transitions (possibly to several different electronic states) all with the same molecule-fixed polarization (along the molecule X-axis). We assume that all of the other electronic transitions with different polarizations are at too high an energy to be important. Then (1)

$$\mathcal{R} = \frac{\rho\xi^4}{20\hbar^3} \sum_a \left[ \frac{(M_x)_{ra}(M_x)_{ai}}{\omega_a - \omega_1 - i\gamma_a} + \frac{(M_x)_{ra}(M_x)_{ai}}{\omega_a + \omega_2 - i\gamma_a} \right]$$

$$\times \sum_b \left[ \frac{(M_x)_{rb}(M_x)_{bi}}{\omega_b - \omega_3 - i\gamma_b} + \frac{(M_x)_{rb}(M_x)_{bi}}{\omega_b + \omega_1 + i\gamma_b} \right]$$

$$= (\rho\xi^4/20\hbar^3)\alpha(\omega_1)\alpha(\omega_3) \tag{16}$$

where $\rho$ is the number density, $\xi$ is a local field correction factor often approximated by $\xi = (n^2+2)/3$ and the factor of 20 comes from the orientation averaging. The imaginary damping factors $i\gamma_a$ and $i\gamma_b$ are related to the lifetimes of the intermediate states a and b. These will be discussed in detail below. This expression is valid for the case $\hat{\epsilon}_1 \cdot \hat{\epsilon}_2 = 1$ (parallel polarization). It should be multiplied by 1/3 for $\hat{\epsilon}_1 \cdot \hat{\epsilon}_2 = 0$ (perpendicular polarization).

From equation (16) we see that if $\omega_a - \omega_1 \gg \gamma_a$ and $\omega_b - \omega_3 \gg \gamma_b$ for all intermediate states a and b, then $\mathcal{R}$ is real. This fact was used in the expansion of equation (15). Furthermore, under these conditions $\alpha(\omega_1) \approx \alpha(\omega_3)$ so $\mathcal{R}$ is proportional to the total Raman cross section for this transition [see equation (12)].

The spectral shape described by equation (15) shows the interference behavior characteristic of coherent phenomena. The third term is a Lorentzian peak centered at $\delta_r = 0$ with a half width at half height of $\gamma_r$ and a peak intensity of $R^2/\gamma_r^2$. The first term is a constant. The second term results from the coherent interaction of the fields generated by the two kinds of contributions to the total third order susceptibility. It has a characteristic dispersion shape being zero at $\delta_r = 0$, positive for $\Delta < \omega_r$ and negative for $\Delta > \omega_r$. The kinds of curves obtained in CARS spectra are illustrated in references (2) and (4). For large values of $R/\gamma B$ the curve is dominated by the Lorentzian. The dispersion shape cross term can be revealed on logarithmic plots. For $R/\gamma B \approx 1$ both contributions to the spectrum are important. For $R/\gamma B \approx 0.1$ the curve is dominated by the dispersion term. For $R/\gamma B \ll 1$ the positive and negative maxima are at $\omega_r \pm \gamma$.

If there are two or more Raman resonances close together then it is necessary to sum the expression for $\chi^3$ over the various values of r and include the cross terms in the expansion of the absolute square.

## Analytical Problems Associated with the Background Contribution

The major problem with the use of CARS as a general analytical or spectroscopic technique is the high background level which arises from the electronic contribution to $\chi^3$ . For the strong Raman lines of pure liquids $R/\gamma B = 10$ to $100$ ($R/\gamma B \approx 100$ for the 992 $cm^{-1}$ mode of benzene). Neat liquids therefore present no problem since the peak intensity relative to the background level is $(R/\gamma B)^2$ or $10^2$ to $10^4$. However, for dilute solutions the background level is dominated by the contribution from the solvent while the Raman contribution of interest is proportional to the solute concentration. As a solution is diluted the shape of the CARS spectrum changes from one dominated by the Lorentzian peak to one dominated by the dispersion cross term. In the limit of great dilution the spectrum equals the background at $\Delta = \omega_r$ with positive and negative peaks on either side of the resonance.

By itself the change in spectral shape due to a high background level is not a particular problem although it complicates the interpretation of the spectra. The major problem is the decreased signal to noise ratio. The noise in a spontaneous Raman spectrum is usually determined by the shot noise of photon counting statistics and is therefore roughly the square root of the total signal. For the CARS case the typical photon flux levels in the signal beam provided by modern lasers is on the order of $10^{10}$ photons $sec^{-1}$. At these signal levels the shot noise contribution to the total noise is negligible in comparison to the shot to shot fluctuations of the laser. A complete discussion of the origin of noise in a CARS spectrum is beyond the scope of this article. Some of the important considerations have been outlined elsewhere (1) where references are given. The most important

aspect of the noise in a CARS spectrum is that since it is due to
laser fluctuations it can be largely removed by use of a reference
arm. For dilute solution studies, the best reference material is
the solvent. On the whole, however, it does not appear that CARS
offers any analytical advantages relative to spontaneous Raman
scattering for dilute solution applications unless the sample is
fluorescent.

Resonance CARS

   One of the most useful and interesting features of spontaneous Raman scattering is electronic resonance enhancement. When
the excitation frequency is near a strong electronic transition
the Raman scattering amplitude $\alpha(\omega)$ becomes very large. The
increase in the Raman cross section relative to excitation at
lower frequencies can be as large as $10^6$. As a result it is possible to study dilute solutions ($10^{-3}$ to $10^{-6}$ M). Furthermore,
this process is selective in two respects. First, only the Raman
transitions of the molecule or chromophore which has the electronic transition become enhanced. Second, only certain vibrations of the molecule are enhanced so that the resulting Raman
spectrum may be much simpler than that observed with excitation
away from the electronic transition. The Raman transitions which
are enhanced are generally those which appear in the high resolution vibronic absorption and fluorescence spectrum. These, in
turn, are the vibrations corresponding to normal modes which are
coupled to the electronic transition. Excitation of these modes
accompanies the electronic transition because the excited state
geometry is displaced along these normal mode directions (leading
to enhanced Franck-Condon factors) or because their excitation
mixes other electronic states with the state of interest resulting in vibronic intensity borrowing (Herzberg-Teller coupling).
Resonance Raman scattering is therefore useful in the interpretation of high resolution molecular electronic spectra, and, more
generally, in the study of the geometries of excited electronic
states.
   An important complication in the use of resonance Raman scattering in such studies is that fluorescence is also a very useful
tool for the study of excited electronic states. As a result, the
molecules for which we have the most detailed picture of their
excited states tend to be fluorescent. Furthermore, the low
temperature conditions which lead to well resolved electronic
absorption spectra, and thus well resolved resonance Raman excitation spectra, tend to favor fluorescence.
   CARS exhibits exactly the same resonance enhancement mechanisms as the spontaneous Raman effect but is not subject to the
complications of fluorescence. Therefore, resonance CARS appears
to be a promising technique in molecular spectroscopy.
   From equation (16) we see that when $\omega_1$ is near a resonance
$\omega_a$ or $\omega_3$ is near a resonance $\omega_b$ the quantity $R$ becomes complex.

In fact, the Raman amplitude $\alpha(\omega)$ also becomes complex under these conditions but since the Raman signal is proportional to the absolute square of $\alpha(\omega)$ this has no effect on the Raman intensity. For CARS, the complex nature of $R$ must be included in the expansion of equation (15). Letting

$$R = R + iI \tag{17}$$

we now have

$$|\chi^{(3)}|^2 = B^2 + \frac{2BR\delta_r}{(\delta_r^2+\gamma_r^2)} + \frac{R^2 + I^2 - 2BI\gamma_r}{(\delta_r^2+\gamma_r^2)} \tag{18}$$

R and I can be either positive or negative. Under certain conditions R can be very small while I is large. As a result a great variety of lineshapes is possible. For instance if $R \approx 0$ and $I > 0$ the Lorentzian peak centered at $\delta_r = 0$ will be negative if $R^2 + I^2 - 2BI\gamma_r$ is negative. R and I are proportional to the solute concentration while B is proportional to the solvent concentration (for dilute solutions) so if $I \geq 0$ there will, in principle, be some solute concentration at which the "peak" becomes "negative", i.e., below the asymptotic background level rather than above it.

Another characteristic feature of resonance CARS spectra is that R can be negative so the sense of the dispersion shaped cross term is reversed. From equation (16) we see that this happens when, for instance, $\omega_1 > \omega_a$ but $\omega_3 < \omega_b$ for two important vibronic resonances.

The complicating feature of resonance CARS spectroscopy is that since the vibrational resonances may be either "positive" or "negative" it is difficult to identify a feature as a vibrational resonance. Furthermore, the shape of a resonance CARS spectrum depends on the excitation wavelength, the concentration and the position of the electronic resonance which in turn may depend on the solvent and the sample temperature. However, if CARS spectra are obtained at various values of the concentration so that R and I are varied relative to B it is possible to use equation (18) to decompose the spectra in a unique fashion to obtain the resonance frequencies $\omega_r$.

From equation (18) we see that if B = 0 it is not possible to determine R and I separately since the only remaining term is $R^2 + I^2$. However, in the presence of a finite background ($B \neq 0$) both the sign and magnitude of R and I can be determined. When B = 0 the absolute square of $\chi^3$ reduces to the absolute square of $R(\delta_r - i\gamma_r)^{-1}$ and from equation (16) we see that $|R|^2 =$ (constant) $|\alpha(\omega_1)|^2|\alpha(\omega_3)|^2$. Thus, the CARS intensity for B = 0 is proportional to the Raman intensity measured at two excitation frequencies. For dilute solutions it is always possible to increase B relative to $R$ by further dilution and then R and I can be determined. The independent determination of R and I as a function of $\omega_1$ provides much more information than the determination of $R^2 + I^2$ provided by Raman scattering. This new information can be obtained because of the coherent nature of the scattering process.

Under resonance conditions, the most important terms in equation (16) are the resonant terms. Thus,

$$R = \frac{\rho \mathcal{E}^4}{20\hbar^3} \sum_a \left( \frac{(M_x)_{ra}(M_x)_{ai}}{\omega_a - \omega_1 - i\gamma_a} \right) \sum_b \left( \frac{(M_x)_{rb}(M_x)_{bi}}{\omega_b - \omega_3 - i\gamma_b} \right) \tag{19}$$

to a good approximation. A resolved electronic absorption spectrum provides values of $\omega_a$ and $|(M_x)_{ai}|^2$. The spectrum can be fit to a model for the excited electronic state such as a displaced harmonic oscillator model. The factors $(M_x)_{ra}$ can then be calculated from this model. (It is necessary to include all of the normal modes which are active in the absorption spectrum in this model and to make some assumption concerning the correspondence between the ground and excited electronic state normal modes.) In order to calculate the real and imaginary parts of $R$ from this model it is necessary to specify the values of $\gamma_a$ for each vibronic resonance. One procedure is to adjust $\gamma_a$ so that the absorption spectrum is reproduced.

However, the vibronic bandwidths of an absorption spectrum are normally determined by inhomogeneous broadening, i.e., the solute molecules are in a distribution of environments with each environment having a slightly different electronic spectrum. The observed linewidth is therefore not the homogeneous linewidth $\gamma_a^h$ but rather the sum of the homogeneous and inhomogeneous widths $\Gamma_a = \gamma_a^h + \gamma_a^i$. It is not immediately clear which linewidth should be used in equation (19).

This problem also occurs in the theory of resonance Raman scattering. A recent analysis for this case has been given by Penner and Siebrand (11). Their model is as follows. They assume that $\alpha(\omega)$ is given by

$$\alpha(\omega) = \sum_a \left( \frac{M_{ra} M_{ai}}{\omega_a - \omega - i\gamma^h} \right). \tag{20}$$

where $\gamma^h$ is the same for each vibronic resonance and is the homogeneous linewidth related to the vibronic state lifetime. They next assume that

$$\omega_a = \omega_0 + n\omega_r' \tag{21}$$

where $\omega_0$ is the vibrationless electronic excitation energy. This, of course, can be checked by comparison with the absorption spectrum and is not an essential feature of their model. They next assume that the inhomogeneous broadening results in a

Lorentzian distribution of values of $\omega_0$ with a distribution width $\gamma^i$. The assumption that this distribution is Lorentzian greatly simplifies the subsequent calculation but is probably not critical. The total Raman intensity as a function of $\omega$ is then obtained as the average of $|\alpha(\omega)|^2$ over the Lorentzian distribution [equation (12)]. The result of this calculation is that the resonance Raman excitation profile depends on both the homogeneous and inhomogeneous linewidth in such a way that each must be known in order to calculate the excitation profile. Penner and Siebrand propose that the homogeneous linewidth can be extracted from the excitation profile and the absorption spectrum.

The relevance of this calculation to the interpretation of resonance CARS spectra is that application of the same model leads to a different result. The reason for the difference is that in the Raman scattering case the quantity being averaged is $|\alpha(\omega)|^2$ so that the damping terms in the two factors of the product have opposite signs. In the CARS case the quantity being averaged is $\alpha(\omega_1)\alpha(\omega_3)$ [equations (14) and (16)]. In this case the signs of the damping terms in the two factors of the product are the same (both negative). This moves one of the poles of the contour integration related to the average over the Lorentzian distribution. The result is that the ensemble averaged value of $R$ is the same as equation (19) but with $\gamma_a$ replaced by $\Gamma_a = \gamma_a^h + \gamma_a^i$. Thus, in the CARS case the damping factor is to be interpreted as the total linewidth of the vibronic transition as observed in the absorption spectrum. This difference between resonance CARS and resonance Raman scattering results from the difference between a coherent and an incoherent phenomenon and the associated difference in the ensemble average used in their description. Although the specific form of the final results depends on the assumption of a Lorentzian inhomogeneous distribution, it is generally true that CARS and Raman scattering will lead to different expressions.

There is one further aspect to this problem. The expression for CSRS differs from that for CARS [equation (19)] in that the second sum has energy denominators of the form $\omega_b - \omega_2 + i\gamma_b$. This means that the average over the inhomogeneous distribution is very similar to the spontaneous Raman case since there are different signs for the two energy denominators. The resulting expression is the same as for the Raman case in that terms appear which depend individually on the homogeneous linewidth. This difference between CARS and CSRS depends on the prescription for introduction of the signs of the damping constants in the semi-classical theory (10). This prescription is based on the requirement that the third order susceptibility must be an analytic function of the applied fields which are at frequencies $\omega_1$ and $\omega_2$ for CARS and $\omega_1$ and $\omega_3$ for CSRS. The quantum theory of these third order susceptibilities (Hans C. Andersen, private communication) differs from the semiclassical theory with regard to the signs of the damping constants in the CSRS expression. The quantum theory predicts the same negative signs for CSRS as for CARS.  The identical form of the two expressions arises from the general feature of the quantum theory that states that the response of the matter must be calculated as if all fields are present including the generated field (12).  Thus, for CARS and CSRS the same expression is obtained since the same three fields are present.  This subtle difference has an easily measurable first order effect on resonance CSRS spectra since it changes the values of R and I calculated from equation (20).  It also affects the inhomogeneous average as discussed above such that in both CARS and CSRS the total linewidth should be used for $\gamma$.

The difference between the semiclassical and quantum theories of the third-order susceptibility has not yet been conclusively compared to an experimental result.  It seems likely that the semiclassical theory will be correct at high laser field intensities.

Conclusions

At the present stage of the development of CARS several conclusions can be made concerning the kinds of applications where it will be a useful method with advantages over the spontaneous Raman effect.  First, remote sensing applications can be very profitably done by CARS, i.e., detection of the signal at a large distance from the sample.  Second, high resolution gas phase, low temperature or molecular beam applications are clearly favored by the fact that the resolution is determined by the laser linewidth. For solution studies there are obvious advantages if the sample is fluorescent.  There may also be advantages when very small effects are of interest such as chirooptical effects.  Such applications require further optical engineering and laser development.  In the case of resonance enhancement new information is available from a CARS experiment particularly in relation to the mechanism of resonance enhancement and its relation to resolved electronic spectra.

Literature Cited

1. Andersen, Hans C. and Hudson, Bruce S., in "Molecular Spectroscopy, Vol. 5," Barrow, R. F., Long, D. A. and Sheridan, J., editors, pp. 142-201, The Chemical Society, London, 1978.

2. Tolles, W. M., Nibler, J. W., McDonald, J. R. and Harvey, A. B., Appl. Spectroscopy (1977) 20, 253.

3. Nibler, J. W. and Harvey, A. B., in "Analytical Raman Spectroscopy," Kiefer, W., editor, Wiley-Interscience, New York (in press).

4. Nibler, J. W., Shaub, W. M., McDonald, J. R. and Harvey, A. B., in "Vibrational Spectra and Structure, Vol. 6," Durig, J. R., editor, pp. 173-225, Elsevier, New York, 1977.

5. Hudson, B. S., Ann. Rev. Biophys. Bioeng. (1977) 6, 135.

6. Flytzanis, C., in "Quantum Electronics: A Treatise," Rabin, H. and Tang, C. L., Editors, pp. 9-207, Academic, New York, 1975.

7. Tolles, W. D. and Turner, R. D., Appl. Spectroscopy (1977) 31, 96.

8. Terhune, R. W. and Maker, P. D., in "Lasers: A Series of Advances," Levine, A. K., editor, pp. 295-372, Dekker, New York, 1968.

9. Peticolas, W. L., Ann. Rev. Phys. Chem. (1967) 18, 233.

10. Butcher, P. N., "Nonlinear Optical Phenomena," Ohio State University Engineering Publications, Columbus, Ohio, 1965.

11. Penner, A. P. and Siebrand, W., Chem. Phys. Lett. (1976) 39, 11.

12. Feynman, R. P., "Quantum Electrodynamics," p. 4, Benjamin, Reading, Massachusetts, 1962.

RECEIVED September 8, 1978.

# Spectroscopy by Inverse Raman Scattering

EDWARD S. YEUNG

Ames Laboratory—USDOE and Department of Chemistry, Iowa State University, Ames, IA 50011

Spectroscopy by inverse Raman scattering (SIRS) is one of many new techniques in molecular spectroscopy made possible by the development of high power lasers. Although SIRS was first demonstrated experimentally by Jones and Stoicheff in 1964 ($\underline{1}$), its growth was somewhat limited by certain technical difficulties. However, some of the properties inherent to SIRS show good potential for applications in chemistry, ranging from high resolution spectroscopy to chemical analysis.

## Theoretical Considerations

From a conceptual point of view, SIRS involves physical processes that may not be immediately obvious. The best way to appreciate the physical processes that lead to SIRS is to relate it to normal Raman scattering (RS). In Figure 1(a), we show the molecular transitions involved in RS. Molecules are excited by light at the frequency $\omega_L$ to some intermediate state, which can be real or vitual, and arrive at the Raman-active level with the emission of a photon of frequency $\omega_S$, the Stokes frequency. Energy conservation simply requires that $\omega_L - \omega_S$ be equal to the separation of the Raman levels. The conversion from $\omega_L$ to $\omega_S$ is an extremely inefficient process, and is of the order of $10^{-8}$ for the more favorable situations. This, in part, has prevented the development of RS as a trace analytical technique in typical situations, where the interaction is non-resonant. The conversion efficiency can be enhanced to the order of 75% ($\underline{2}$) by using stimulated Raman scattering (SRS). Figure 1(b) shows the transition scheme for SRS, which is nothing more than increasing the excitation until stimulated emission becomes important, thus further improving the transition probability. Because of the requirement for stimulated emission, there is a threshold in SRS. SIRS, as shown in Figure 1(c), is intermediate between the first two cases. Both photons, at $\omega_L$ and at $\omega_S$, are supplied to the sample. The

0-8412-0459-4/78/47-085-193$05.50/0
© 1978 American Chemical Society

intense radiation at $\omega_S$ guarantees that the system is in the stimulated emission regime. Such stimulated emission, however, must be accompanied by the absorption of photons at $\omega_L$. One therefore simply monitors the depletion of the laser beam at $\omega_L$ in the presence of the intense laser at $\omega_S$. The measurement of absorption rather than emission leads to the term "inverse Raman".

The quantum mechanical description of the SIRS process is quite straightforward. Following the treatment of Placzek (3), one finds that the probability of a Raman transition can be expressed as

$$|a|^2 \propto N_L(N_S + 1)|S|^2 \tag{1}$$

where S is the normal Raman scattering tensor, and $N_L$ and $N_S$ are the photon number densities at the excitation and the Stokes frequencies, respectively. In RS, $N_S \ll 1$ so that the transition probability is directly proportional to the intensity of excitation. In SRS and in SIRS, $N_S \gg 1$, so that the transition probability is proportional to the product of the intensities of the two radiation fields. In effect, the presence of the Stokes photons enhances the conversion efficiency of the photons at $\omega_L$ to photons at $\omega_S$. The monitoring of the absorption at $\omega_L$ is equivalent to measuring this conversion efficiency.

We note that in all three cases, the molecular scattering tensor, S, remains the same. This means that the same molecular properties contribute to RS, SRS and SIRS. In principle, one should be able to obtain identical molecular information using any of these processes. In practice, however, the presence of a threshold and the presence of higher-order mixing of the light waves in SRS make the corresponding spectra look quite different. The higher laser powers in SRS and SIRS can further perturb the molecules so that other nonlinear processes can become important. We further note that resonance enhancement of Raman scattering is an effect associated with the scattering tensor, S, when some real molecular state participates strongly in the scattering process because of a near-match to the photon energy. One thus expects to have the same kind of resonance enhancement in SRS and in SIRS.

The explicit relation among the three processes can be derived (4) from the conversion efficiency, $\eta$, of the Raman process.

$$\eta = \frac{\text{number of Stokes photons}}{\text{number of exciting photons}} = \left(\frac{d\sigma}{d\Omega}\right)(4\pi N\ell) \tag{2}$$

where $(d\sigma/d\Omega)$ is the absolute Raman scattering cross section per polarization ($\underline{5}$) in $cm^2 sr^{-1}$, N is the number density of the molecules per unit volume and $\ell$ is the total interaction length. One can define a quantity $\gamma$, which is the relative enhancement of the Raman transition probability under the influence of the laser at $\omega_S$. This is simply the ratio of the two terms in parentheses in Eq. (1). Converting to common units in laser experiments:

$$\gamma = \frac{10^7 P_S}{n_S^2 8\pi hc^2 \Delta\omega\omega_S^3} \tag{3}$$

where $P_S$ is the power per unit area $(W/cm^2)$ of the photons at $\omega_S(cm^{-1})$, $n_S$ is the refractive index of the medium at $\omega_S$, $\Delta\omega$ is the frequency spread of the transition, and all other physical constants are in cgs units.

One can now relate the observed inverse Raman absorption coefficient, $g(cm^{-1})$, and the stimulated Raman gain coefficient, $G(cm^{-1})$, to the ordinary Raman scattering cross section. The first two are simply related by:

$$g = (\omega_L/\omega_S)G \tag{4}$$

Combining Eq. (2) and (3), we have for the probe beam intensity, $I_L$:

$$I_L(\ell) = I_L(0)e^{-g\ell} \tag{5}$$

$$g = \frac{10^7 P_S \omega_L N(d\sigma/d\Omega)}{n_S^2 2hc^2 \Delta\omega\omega_S^4} \tag{6}$$

A related type of Raman process is coherent Raman gain spectroscopy ($\underline{6}$). There, the beam at $\omega_S$ is monitored. In the presence of an intense beam at $\omega_L$, a condition similar to SRS exists. The gain, G, at $\omega_S$ can therefore be measured and related back to ordinary Raman cross sections using Eq. (4) and (6). The measurements are usually made with two identical beams at $\omega_S$, one interacting with the intense beam at $\omega_L$ and the other acting as a reference. This has the added advantage that the interference between the two beams can be recorded. Hence both the real and the imaginary part of the nonlinear susceptibility ($\underline{7}$) can be determined simultaneously.

We can now estimate the degree of enhancement of the Raman effect under typical experimental conditions. A giant-pulse laser, e.g. the ruby laser, can give 100 MW/cm$^2$ of power without focusing. $CCl_4$, a typical strong Raman scatterer, has a line at 459 cm$^{-1}$ and $n_S = 1.46$ at 694 nm. Equation (3) gives an enhancement factor of $10^6$ for a linewidth of 1 cm$^{-1}$. Conventional Raman spectrometers do not collect scattering over all $4\pi$ sr, so that the effective enhancement is much larger than this value. This is somewhat compensated by the inherently more sensitive detection by photon counting in RS over absorption measurements in SIRS. For a noticeable enhancement in the conversion efficiency, $\gamma > 1$. This gives a power of 94 W/cm$^2$ for $P_S$, certainly within reach for most lasers. However, enhancement with such low power is not directly useful because of the smallness of g in that case.

One can in principle operate at as low values of $P_S$ as one wishes, the ultimate limit being determined by the minimum amount of absorption one can record. There is, however, a restriction on the power of the beam at $\omega_L$. For a given $P_S$, there will be normal anti-Stokes Raman scattering which also reaches the detector. $P_L$ must therefore be larger than this scattered intensity for any absorption to be detectable. This limit can be shown to be:

$$P_L = P_S (d\sigma/d\Omega) NB\Phi/g \qquad (7)$$

where $\Phi$ is the beam divergence of the beam at $\omega_L$ and B is the Boltzmann factor of occupation of the excited Raman level. For room temperature experiments involving Raman shifts of 1000 cm$^{-1}$, this limit is 0.6 mW/cm$^2$, certainly easily attainable using lasers. For large values of $P_S$, one may have SRS at the corresponding Stokes positions and stimulated anti-Stokes scattering at $\omega_L$. This produces a decrease in $P_S$ and an increase in $P_L$, and must be controlled to make the SIRS measurements meaningful. The same precaution must also be observed for large values of $P_L$.

A totally different type of interference in SIRS is two-photon absorption (TPA). The experimental arrangement for both SIRS and TPA involve the use of two interacting laser beams. The only difference is that in SIRS one beam is depleted while the other gains intensity, and in TPA both beams lose intensity. We can roughly compare the relative magnitudes of the two effects.

The TPA coefficient is $\delta FN$ ($\underline{8}$), where F is the photon flux per unit time and $\delta$ is the TPA parameter. For a typical $\delta$ of $10^{-50}$ $cm^4$ sec (anthracene) and a typical $N(d\sigma/d\Omega)$ in Raman of $5 \times 10^{-8}$ $cm^2 sr^{-1}$, one finds that TPA is two orders of magnitude smaller an effect. However, some Raman transitions have a $N(d\sigma/d\Omega)$ of much less than $5 \times 10^{-8}$ $cm^2 sr^{-1}$ and some TPA transitions ($\underline{9}$) may have $\delta$ as large as $10^{-48}$ $cm^4$ sec. Under these conditions, interference effects between the two processes will be appreciable.

One may be able to distinguish between TPA and SIRS because the former is typically broad ( a few hundred $cm^{-1}$) and the latter is typically narrow (a few $cm^{-1}$), at least in condensed phases at room temperature. For low pressure gases ($\underline{10}$) or low temperature crystals ($\underline{11}$), TPA can be sharp and indistinguishable from SIRS. TPA can occur at $2\omega_L$, at $2\omega_S$, or at $\omega_L + \omega_S$. In the first case, one can record the intensity $I_L$ with and without the presence of the beam at $\omega_S$ to sort out the effect. In the second case, $P_S$ becomes smaller, but should not affect the measurement significantly since the amount of TPA is usually small. In the third case, one has to change $\omega_S$ and look for the change in the spectrum. As $\omega_S$ is moved to higher energy, the corresponding SIRS spectrum moves to higher energy whereas the TPA spectrum moves to lower energy.

## Experimental Methods

From the above discussion, it is clear that SIRS requires two radiation fields, overlapping in both time and space. The light beam at $\omega_S$ should be of reasonable power, and should be monochromatic relative to the width of the Raman transition. The light beam at $\omega_L$ must have a certain minimum power, but can be spectrally broad as long as it includes the corresponding $\omega_L$ for the Raman transition of interest. Many experimental arrangements are therefore possible for SIRS.

One of the most convenient sources of high power, mono-chromatic photons is the Q-switched ruby laser, and it is not surprising that many SIRS experiments are based on this laser. With this laser, one needs the second kind of photons to be in the range of 537 nm to 694 nm to cover the entire range of interest in Raman spectroscopy. Perhaps the easiest way to obtain this second kind of photons is to use the relatively broad stimulated anti-Stokes emission from a strong Raman scatterer generated by the same laser. Stimulated anti-Stokes emission is normally sharp when the exciting laser contains only a single line, but degrades to a relatively broad (up to a few hundred $cm^{-1}$) "continuum" when the laser contains several frequency components ($\underline{12}$). The very first demonstration of SIRS ($\underline{1}$) is based on this experimental arrangement. A Q-switched ruby laser is simply focused into a cell containing toluene to generate the stimulated anti-Stokes "continuum" centered around $\omega_S + 1003$ $cm^{-1}$, which is then focused into a cell containing the sample. Absorption is detected by collecting the emerging light onto a spectrograph and by recording on a photographic plate. Because of the energy-conserving restriction, only the part in the "continuum" corresponding to $\omega_L$, such that $\omega_L - \omega_S$ is equal to the Raman energy level separation, will be absorbed. Using this arrangement, the authors were able to record the inverse Raman absorption of benzene at 992 $cm^{-1}$, pyridine at 990 $cm^{-1}$, and nitromethane at 918 $cm^{-1}$. In the last case, the "continuum" was weak so that many laser pulses were needed to recorded the spectrum, even though the absorption itself was very strong. This further confirms that SIRS does not depend on having an intense laser at $\omega_L$.

The use of the anti-Stokes "continuum" was extended by Duardo and coworkers ($\underline{13}$), where they made use of the stimulated emission of one Raman transition as a source of $\omega_L$ to probe the absorption of another Raman transition in the same molecule. The C-H mode in acetonitrile at 2940 $cm^{-1}$ has a high Raman cross-section as well as a broad stimulated emission spectrum. The inverse Raman absorption of the C≡N mode at 2250 $cm^{-1}$ can therefore be conveniently recorded in this liquid. The usefulness of this one-cell concept is greatly enhanced when two liquids rather than one are used ($\underline{14}$). There, the proximity of the two Raman lines can be guaranteed by the proper choice of the mixture. The absorbing species can thus be present as a minor component and still be detected.

A different type of source for the "continuum" is the short-lived spontaneous fluorescence of dyes. The typical arrangement ($\underline{15}$) involves the ruby laser for $\omega_S$, which is frequency doubled by a KDP crystal so that the dye can be excited. A dispersive element (prism) is used to separate the second harmonic of the ruby to illuminate a dye cell. The fluorescence is collected by a lens and is combined with the ruby fundamental in the sample cell, and then into a spectrograph. With the proper choice of dyes, selected regions of the Raman spectrum can be covered. The only requirement is that the fluorescence must be short-lived, so that temporal overlap with the laser pulse is significant.

A much more versatile type of continuum is the type generated by self-focusing and self-phase modulation in solids and
liquids at very high laser intensities (16). For example, a
picosecond pulse at 530 nm can generate a continuum covering
290-800 nm in a 22 cm long sample of supracil quartz. In principle, the entire Raman spectrum can be covered with the same
experimental arrangement. The only problems are that the
exciting laser is broad compared to typical Raman lines, and that
the "continuum" is weak and may require multiple laser pulses for
proper exposure on a photographic plate.

To avoid the difficulties associated with these weak continuum sources, Yeung (4) used instead a dye laser pumped by the
second harmonic of the laser pulse at $\omega_S$. The optical system is
shown in Figure 2. A Q-switched ruby laser produces 50-100 MW
of 694 nm radiation in a 25 ns pulse. The ruby fundamental output ($\omega_S$) passes through a KDP crystal and generates second harmonic radiation in a 15 ns pulse, which is separated from the
ruby fundamental by M1 and proceeds via M2 and M3 into the dye
cell to pump the dye laser. The dye laser cavity consists of an
output mirror M3 and a totally reflecting back mirror M6. Mean-
while, the ruby fundamental is guided by M4 and M5 to combine
with the dye laser and to excite the sample. The broad dye laser
output is then recorded on a photographic plate. Photoelectric
detectors can be used if the mirror M6 in the dye laser is replaced with a diffraction grating to select out $\omega_L$ for the Raman
transition under investigation.

Dye lasers pumped by the second harmonic of ruby do not allow modes with small Raman shifts to be studied because of the
limited lasing region. To overcome this problem, one can use a
different optical arrangement (4) as shown in Figure 3. A
Q-switched ruby laser goes through a liquid cell containing a
strong Raman scatterer, e.g. nitrobenzene. The resulting stimulated Stokes emission is used as $\omega_S$. The ruby laser continues
through M7 to pump an infrared dye such as DTTC. The dye laser
cavity consists of totally reflecting mirrors M8 and M9, and the
output coupler M7. This way, modes with small Raman shifts can
be studied by SIRS.

Various variations of the use of ruby laser and laser-pumped
dye laser have been tried (17,18,19). The most unique is an
intracavity arrangement (19). Because of the dependence of the
dye laser intensity on the gain of the cavity, one expects to
magnify the effect of the inverse Raman absorption. It was found
that thermal gradients caused by the ruby laser in the dye solution, inverse Raman absorption from the dye solvent, and nonlinear dependence of the laser intensity are serious problems in
the intracavity arrangement (4).

All of the above experimental arrangements are based on
detection using a photographic plate. The obvious advantage is
that the Raman spectrum is obtained in the time scale of the

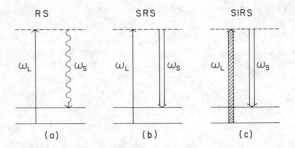

Figure 1. *Comparison of transition schemes in normal Raman scattering (RS), stimulated Raman scattering (SRS), and inverse Raman scattering (SIRS). (⟶) Excitation, (⤳) spontaneous scattering, (⟹) stimulated scattering, and (⟹) absorption.*

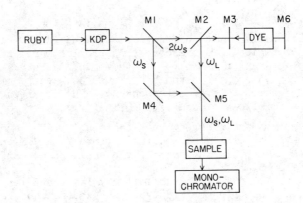

Figure 2. *Experimental arrangement for SIRS using two pulsed lasers*

laser pulse.  On the other hand, it is extremely difficult to
obtain quantitative information because of the nature of photographic response.  Tsunoda (20) used a photoelectric detection
scheme to follow the events in SIRS.  However, the broad spectral
output of the dye fluorescence used as the "continuum" still does
not allow truly quantitative results to be obtained.  If one
modifies one of the schemes using dye lasers by spectrally narrowing the output at $\omega_L$, one should be able to detect the absorption photoelectrically by using part of the dye laser output
as a reference intensity.  Still, one might find it difficult to
determine $P_S$ because of the pulsed nature of the two beams.  A

vidicon can be used instead of the photographic plate to record
SIRS over a wide range of Raman shifts.  By using a double-beam
arrangement (e.g. imaging the reference portion of the dye laser
on a different part of the vidicon) one should be able to do
quite a bit better than photographic detection.

The major problem with laser-pumped pulsed dye lasers as a
source of the "continuum" is the unreliable mode output of these
systems.  The optical elements in the dye laser cavity (cell
windows, mirrors) create standing waves that are wavelength
dependent.  These interference effects can cause lower dye laser
output at selected wavelengths which can be confused with inverse
Raman absorption.  Lytle (21) suggested that index matching of
the solvent and off-angle dye cell geometry can be used to minimize these effects.  One can also use a double-beam arrangement
to account for laser inhomogeneities.

A totally different concept for SIRS is based on a Q-
switched ruby laser and a cw dye laser (22).  The optical arrangement is shown in Figure 4.  A giant-pulse ruby laser, R,
is directed by M2 into the sample cell, C, and then into a
factory-calibrated ballistic thermopile, B, so that the energy
of each laser pulse can be measured.  The losses of the ruby
laser from the cell windows and the two mirrors, M2, are empirically determined so that the energy in the cell is obtained.
Since the power is always lower than the stimulated Raman threshold for the sample, depletion within the cell is neglected.  The
ruby laser is plane polarized, and can be arranged to have parallel or perpendicular polarization to the dye laser.  A commercial cw dye laser, D, having a spectral output of less than

$1 \text{ cm}^{-1}$ is beam-expanded ten times so that it is completely
covered by the larger ruby laser beam but still samples a major
portion of the ruby laser.  The dye laser is directed into the
sample cell by M1 after passing through an optical delay line,
ODL, and eventually enters a double grating monochromator, S.
The optical delay line is used to isolate the dye laser from the
ruby laser pulse during the inverse Raman event.  Otherwise, the
disturbance can cause large fluctuations in the dye laser intensity.  The dye laser is controlled by a Pockels cell, PC, and
is switched on just shortly before the ruby laser pulse.  This is

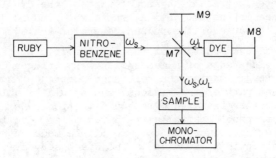

*Figure 3.   Experimental arrangement for SIRS for
small Raman shifts*

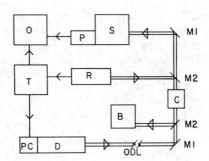

*Figure 4.   Experimental arrangment
for SIRS based on one pulsed and one
cw laser*

necessary to avoid saturating the photomultiplier tube, P, which can handle large currents, but only for short times. This way, good signal-to-noise ratios can be achieved. The monochromator is set at the dye laser frequency, $\omega_L$, with a spectral slit width of 2 nm so that most of the stray ruby radiation is rejected. The actual tuning of SIRS is determined by the dye laser and not by the spectrometer, which is just roughly synchronized with the tuning. The events are initiated by the firing of the ruby laser, and a trigger generator, T, in turn controls the Pockels cell and the oscilloscope, O. The inverse Raman event is recorded in a single trace on the oscilloscope (500 MHz bandwidth).

A typical signal trace is shown in Figure 5. The dot at the upper left-hand corner represents the zero-intensity level, i.e. when the dye laser is off. The early part of the trace gives the dye laser intensity before interacting with the ruby pulse. The first decrease in intensity is synchronous with the ruby pulse, and is the inverse Raman absorption. The second, much larger, decrease in intensity is from the disturbance of the ruby pulse in the dye laser cavity, and has no significance in SIRS. The degree of absorption can be derived directly from this trace.

The pulsed + cw arrangement in SIRs gives more readily quantitative information about the process. It also can provide spectral information at higher resolution. However, one does not have the advantage of obtaining a large portion of the Raman spectrum, as is typical of using more "continuum" type sources for $\omega_L$.

What are some other optical arrangements that may be developed for SIRS in the future? For pulsed type measurements, one is faced with the difficulty of spanning the complete spectral region of Raman fundamental transitions using a single dye, either in fluorescence or in a dye laser. A possible alternative is a laser-pumped optical parametric oscillator (OPO). Such an arrangement may be similar to that in Figure 2 where the dye laser is replaced by an OPO. A single nonlinear crystal pumped by the second harmonic of the ruby laser should be able to span the region $100 \text{ cm}^{-1}$ to $4500 \text{ cm}^{-1}$ for Raman transitions. One expects to be able to minimize the effects of standing wave interferences mentioned above in dye laser systems. The spectral output of the OPO is broad enough ($\sim 10 \text{ cm}^{-1}$) to allow individual Raman lines to be recorded photographically, and can be further narrowed to allow higher resolution studies.

The question that remains is whether or not SIRS can be done in a cw mode. This quickly reduces to a question about the power densities available in common cw lasers. In argon ion systems, one can have the order of 100 W in a single line inside the cavity. By focusing down to a spot size of $8\mu$, one will achieve a $P_S$ of 50 MW/cm$^2$ with a Rayleigh range of 0.4 mm. For pure

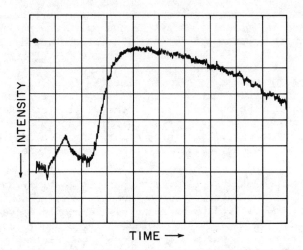

*Figure 5.   Inverse Raman absorption as recorded on an oscilloscope.  Horizontal scale = 50 nsec/division.*

liquids of strong Raman scatterers, Eq. (6) predicts an inverse
Raman absorption of 0.1%. Such an experiment is certainly possible, but is not straightforward. In fact, we note that since
the power density is inversely proportional to the area of the
beam waist and the Rayleigh range is directly proportional to
the same, there is no advantage in increasing the degree of
focusing.

## Applications

Analysis of Fluorescing samples. One of the most attractive
features of SIRS is the possibility of rejecting fluorescence in
the recording of a Raman spectrum. The first mechanism for this
discrimination comes from the fact that one is monitoring at the
anti-Stokes side of the exciting laser. Fluorescence is from hot
band absorption in this case and should be weaker than normal
Stokes fluorescence. The second, and the most important, mechanism is from the spatial distribution of the two processes.
Fluorescence is over $4\pi$ steradians whereas in SIRS only the laser
(the order of milliradians in divergence) is detected. In principle, therefore, one can use spatial filtering to discriminate
against fluorescence.

An actual application of this nature has been reported by
Lau et al. (23). There, they observed SIRS for rhodamine B and
rhodamine 6G in ethanol solution. Normal Raman spectroscopy on
these using visible light sources is virtually impossible because of the high fluorescence background. Using SIRS, they have
been able to record the Raman spectrum over a 1000 cm$^{-1}$ range
with good signal-to noise ratio. Because of the proximity of the
electronic absorption bands, the spectrum is resonantly enhanced
and is very pronounced. Similar degrees of discrimination
against fluorescence can be expected in mixtures where species
other than the analyte fluoresce. The only real difficulty in
the case of fluorescing samples is that they can show significant
absorption at $\omega_L$ and at $\omega_S$. In the first case, an electronic
absorption may be mistaken for SIRS. The remedy for this is to
also record $\omega_L$ in the absence of the photons at $\omega_S$ to obtain a
reference. In the second case, the exciting power will be depleted and the quantitative information is lost.

Trace Determinations. Even though SIRS can give an enhancement over normal Raman scattering of the order of $10^6$, it does
not mean that the limit of detection will be improved by that
same amount. Photon-counting in normal RS is inherently more
sensitive than the absorption measurement in SIRS. In principle,
one can use extremely long pathlengths to compensate for the
low concentration of the analyte. However, maintaining the high
power densities over such long paths and keeping the two lasers

spatially overlapping may be technically difficult.  In general,
one can expect to be able to use SIRS for the determination of
minor components in mixtures, but probably not for ultratrace
analysis.

We can use Eq. (6) to estimate the detection limits that can
be achieved in SIRS for typical Raman scatterers.  For a strong
Raman scatterer, e.g. $CCl_4$ described above, one can expect a
limit of detection of 0.1% concentration in solution for a 10 cm
cell and a power density, $P_S$, of 15 $MW/cm^2$, if the detector is
sensitive enough to record a 0.1% absorption.  For atmospheric
pressure gases, 3 $MW/cm^2$ is sufficient to produce the same amount
of absorption.  Lower concentrations can obviously be compensated
for by using longer absorption pathlengths and/or using higher
laser powers.  The limit on the useful laser power is determined
by the effect of self-focusing (24), which destroys the quantitative nature of SIRS, the breakdown of the material (25), and
the onset of other nonlinear processes.

A study of SIRS in a mixture, particularly the minor component, was reported by Gadow et al. (14).  They tried using the
mode-locked ruby laser in an arrangement similar to McQuillan
et al. (26) and found that the detection limit is 15-20 mole percent for the minor component in toluene, which is roughly the
same as that found in SRS (27).  Much better performance was
achieved in a one-cell arrangement.  The detectability of the
minor component in toluene solution was found to be 5 m$\underline{M}$ for
pyridine and 1 $\underline{M}$ for aniline.  The difference in these can be
attributed to the differences in g in each case.  The authors
noted that the detectability is partly limited by the decrease in
$P_S$ as the major component reaches threshold for SRS.  They suggest that by introducing a selective absorber to prevent SRS in
the major component, a factor of seven improvement can be obtained.

An obvious way to try to improve the detection limit in SIRS
is to have the sample inside the dye laser cavity.  In conventional absorption spectroscopy, the intracavity method can generally provide two to three orders of magnitude enhancement in
the sensitivity (28).  The main problem in transferring this
technique to SIRS is that the dye laser can be seriously perturbed
by the intense laser at $\omega_S$.  Also, SIRS lines from the solvent
and the dye may interfere.  Werncke et al. (19) reported such an
intracavity study.  They were able to isolate the ruby laser from
the dye cell to a degree to overcome the problem mentioned above.
A lens-mirror combination focuses both lasers inside the sample,
and is found to reduce greatly the interference effects common
in broadband dye lasers.  Using this experimental arrangement,
they were able to establish a limit of detection for benzene in
carbon tetrachloride of 1 m$\underline{M}$, which is two orders of magnitude

better than the corresponding value outside the dye laser cavity. A somewhat puzzling result is the fact that the Raman inactive line of benzene at 1190 cm$^{-1}$ is not detected even though the detectability is higher here than in earlier experiments involving picosecond pulses (29). For all of the above intracavity experiments, the sensitivity obviously depends on the gain of the dye laser (which depends on the degree of pumping), and nonlinear behavior can generally be expected. The ideal situation is one where the dye laser is barely lasing, so that any loss from the inverse Raman effect will be greatly magnified in the laser output.

Yet another method for enhancing the detection limit is to make use of the resonance Raman effect (30). When $\omega_L$ is resonant or nearly resonant with an electronic transition of the molecule, the Raman transition probability, $|a|^2$ in Eq. (1) can become a few orders of magnitude larger. This then can be used to increase the signal to compensate for the low concentrations in samples. It has been shown (31) that in the resonant regime:

$$g \ \alpha \ \frac{1}{(\omega_L - \omega_o)^2 + \Gamma^2} \tag{8}$$

where $\omega_o$ and $\Gamma$ are the frequency and the linewidth of the electronic transition, respectively. The important point is that the electronic absorption must not be confused with the induced absorption in SIRS. Werncke et al. (31) note that there is a minimum detectable concentration determined by $g$, and a maximum concentration limit determined by the linear absorption coefficient of the sample at $\omega_L$ and at $\omega_S$. This is clearly demonstrated in the resonant SIRS in the dye DTDC, where a spectrum can only be obtained in the range of $1 - 5 \times 10^{-6}$ M. With photoelectric detectors, they predict a detectability of $10^{-6}$ M for SIRS of typical compounds.

A particularly interesting effect in resonant SIRS is the abnormal distribution of intensities in the Raman spectrum. Since $\omega_S$ is normally fixed, different modes (different Raman shifts, $\omega_R$) will either be resonantly enhanced or not enhanced depending on the value of $\omega_L$, which is equal to $\omega_S + \omega_R$. However, if one fixes $\omega_L$ and tunes $\omega_S$ instead, the degree of enhancement will be constant for modes with the same symmetry.

The only reported study in gases deals with molecular nitrogen in air (32). There, a 30 cm focal length lens is used to

focus a Q-switched ruby laser to 1 GW/cm$^2$. The IV-F photographic
plates register an absorbance of 0.025. Gases at concentrations
much lower than this will be very difficult to detect.

Determination of Raman Cross-sections. The measurement of
absorption in SIRS does not rely on absolute intensity calibration, which is necessary in the determination of absolute Raman
cross-sections using conventional techniques. It has been suggested (4) that SIRS is superior to normal RS for this purpose.

In the pre-laser era of Raman spectroscopy, it was almost
impossible to measure absolute Raman cross-sections. This is
because the intensity of the excitation is usually difficult to
determine and because the interaction volume is difficult to define. The only real alternative is to measure relative scattering
intensities and relate these to some theoretical prediction. The
relative strengths of Raman to Rayleigh scattering can be calculated (33) in principle, but the presence of intermolecular
forces and short-range ordering in liquids makes such relative
measurements unreliable. It has also been suggested that the
J=1 to J=3 transition in molecular hydrogen be used as a standard
for Raman intensities (34). Again, this cannot be used in
liquids.

There are difficulties in absolute Raman cross-section
measurements in laser Raman methods as well. (i) The detector
must be calibrated so that the signal can be converted into a
measure of the absolute photon flux reaching the detector.
Typically a standard intensity source (black-body radiator) is
used. Such calibration procedures are subject to various systematic errors. (ii) The throughput of the spectrometer must be
determined accurately. Particularly serious are problems associated with polarization effects and varying spectral slit
widths. (iii) The solid angle of collection is very difficult to
define properly. Also, the magnification factor in forming the
image of the interaction region onto the slit and the relation of
the image size to the mechanical slit width must be known precisely. (iv) The Raman scattering intensity has an angular
dependence that is normally neglected. In a typical spectrometer,
one collects scattering from a cone around the 90$^o$ axis and assumes that the measured intensity corresponds to 90$^o$ scattering.
In actual fact, an integration over the distribution of angles
actually collected is appropriate. (v) The temperature dependence
of the scattering is normally neglected. It has been shown (35)
that Raman intensities can change by as much as a factor of two
over a 150$^o$ temperature range. In using high laser powers to obtain good signal-to-noise ratios, the sample may be heated significantly to produce such errors.

The best attempt in the determination of absolute Raman
cross-sections to date is probably the one by Kato and Takuma
(36). The scattering from the sample is collected in a symmetric
arrangement with a black-body radiator and the two signals are

compared side by side.  This optical arrangement effectively
eliminates errors due to (i) and (ii), minimizes errors from
(iii), but still suffers from the contributions of (iv) and (v).
The large discrepancies in the reported cross-sections from the
various laboratories clearly show the difficulties in such measurements.  For example, for the benzene line at 992 cm$^{-1}$,
Skinner et al. (37) obtained a value that is twice as large as
the one reported by McClung et al. (38), even though the precision of the individual measurements is much better than this.
Table II in Ref. (39) again shows discrepancies much larger than
the individual precisions for five independent published values
of the same Raman line.

   Yeung (4) measured the absolute Raman cross-section of the
3062 cm$^{-1}$ line in benzene using SIRS.  There, a photographic
plate was calibrated using standard procedures so that the amount
of absorption can be determined.  The most difficult part was to
measure the power, $P_S$, of the ruby laser.  This was accomplished
by monitoring the pulse shape with an oscilloscope and the pulse
energy with a thermopile simultaneously.  Because the dye laser
pulse was roughly 7 ns and the ruby laser was roughly 25 ns in
duration, $P_S$ can be taken to be the peak power of the ruby laser
pulse.  Temporal overlap of the two laser pulses was empirically
confirmed.  Spatial overlap, however, was not guaranteed because
of the multimode structure of these lasers.  The far-field pattern of the dye laser showed that the dye laser was less inhomogeneous than the ruby laser.  This gave a smoothing effect so
that the average power of the ruby laser over the cross section
of the beam can be used as $P_S$.

   To see that there is an averaging effect whenever one laser
beam is spatially more homogeneous than the other, one can sub-
divide the cross section of the laser beams into small segments
each with well-defined intensities, $A_i$ and $B_j$ respectively.  The
"average" powers experimentally determined are $A = 1/i\Sigma A_i$ and
$B = 1/j\Sigma B_j$, with the inverse Raman absorption being the product
of these two.  If B is more homogeneous than A, one can average
over all $A_i$ within each segment j of B, so that the interaction
is given by $1/j\Sigma A_j B_j$.  As long as j is a much larger region than
i, and as long as $A_j$ and $B_j$ are not correlated, $A_j$ will be approximately equal to the true average power of the entire laser
beam, A.  Thus, the total interaction becomes $A(1/j\Sigma B_j)$, or
simply AB.

   The results in Ref. (4) are shown in Table I.  It can be seen
that there is close agreement between the values obtained using
SIRS and those obtained using normal RS.

<u>Table I</u>

Raman Parameters for the 3065 cm$^{-1}$ Line of Benzene

|  | Ordinary Raman | Inverse Raman |
|---|---|---|
| Raman Shift (cm$^{-1}$) | 3062.0[a] | 3065.5[b] |
| FWHM Bandwidth (cm$^{-1}$) | 7.5[b] | 7.1[b] |
| Peak SIRS Absorption[d] ($\times 10^{-4}$ cm MW$^{-1}$) | 7.4[c] | 8.0[b] |
| Absolute Raman (d$\sigma$/d$\Omega$)[d] ($\times 10^{-30}$ cm$^2$ sr$^{-1}$) | 8.5[b] | 8.7[b,c] |

[a] reported in Ref. (5)
[b] measured in Ref. (4)
[c] calculated from Eq. (6)
[d] for $\omega_S = 14403$ cm$^{-1}$

A more refined method for the determination of Raman cross-sections using SIRS is given in Ref. (22), which is based on a giant-pulse ruby laser and a cw dye laser. For a typical signal trace shown in Figure 5, one can determine both $I_L(0)$ and $I_L(\ell)$ in Eq. (5) for the inverse Raman absorption. It is most convenient to use the absorption maximum, although in principle any part of the peak can be used. The corresponding power in the ruby laser, $P_S$, can be derived from the measured energy in the pulse and the width and shape of the pulse. The latter information is contained in the same oscilloscope trace because at every point in time the absorption is proportional to the intensity. Alternatively, a second oscilloscope can be used to record the pulse duration.

There are certain clear advantages in using SIRS for determining Raman cross-sections. Because of the low beam divergence and the reliable alignment of the laser beams relative to each other, the angular dependence of the scattering process is properly accounted for. The short pulse durations and the larger beam cross-sectional areas reduce the extent of heating of the sample, so that temperature effects on the scattering intensity are minimized. The spectral resolution of the lasers in SIRS can be much higher than that of the spectrometer in normal RS.

Compared to earlier attempts for such application of SIRS
($\underline{4}$), the pulsed ruby + cw laser arrangement is superior.  Spatial
overlap of the two beams is more satisfactory because of the
single ($TEM_{00}$) mode nature of the dye laser.  The multimode output of the ruby laser can be effectively averaged to determine
the power density.  Any effect from self-focusing will also be
minimized.  Temporal overlap of the two lasers is guaranteed because one laser is cw.  There may in fact be some high-frequency
modulation in the dye laser intensity from the beating of the
longitudinal modes whenever more than one such mode is present.
Simple mathematical modeling shows that as long as the temporal
characteristics of the two lasers are uncorrelated, these
fluctuations will be averaged out and will not affect the measurements.  Alternatively, one can use a single longitudinal mode
laser for these experiments.  We note also that the photoelectric
detector need not be extremely fast in response.  As long as the
amount of absorption is small, one can approximate the exponential
term in Eq. (5) with the first two terms in the expansion.  The
Raman cross-section is then determined by the ratio of $\{I_L(\ell)$
$- I_L(0)\}$ and $P_S$.  If the time response of the photodetector causes
it to underestimate the quantity in parentheses, our determination
of $P_S$ from the same oscilloscope trace will be low by the same
relative amount.  In this way, the time response of the detector
is not a critical requirement.

Using this procedure, the absolute Raman cross-section of the
nitrobenzene line at $1345$ cm$^{-1}$ is found to be $1.38 \pm 0.27 \times 10^{-29}$
cm$^2$ sr$^{-1}$.  This is to be compared with published values of $1.56$
($\underline{37}$) and $1.93$ ($\underline{38}$), in the same units.  It is expected that
further refinement in the experimental method, e.g. independent
pulse width measurements and scale expansion on the photodetector
signal, can reduce the uncertainties even more.

Study of Polaritons.  Because of the well-defined polarization directions and the propagation directions of the two photons
in SIRS, the study of polaritons in crystals has been particularly fruitful ($\underline{18}$).  With the absence of a threshold in SIRS,
the nearly complete polariton and phonon spectra can be observed.
For photons with parallel polarization planes, the results are
the same as for normal Raman scattering.  For photons with different directions of polarizations, one can show ($\underline{18}$) that in
uniaxial crystals SIRS and SRS result in complementary polariton
frequencies.

One such study was performed in a hexagonal $LiIO_3$ crystal
($\underline{18}$).  To enhance the sensitivity of the experiment, the crystal
was placed inside the cavity of the dye laser.  The polarization
directions of the ruby and the dye lasers were independently
controllable.  It was possible to observe the $A(z)$ phonons by

180° scattering because of reflections at the crystal faces. All
of the observed phonon and polariton absorptions can be assigned
and compared to the corresponding RS and SRS spectra. Only directions of propagation parallel or perpendicular to the optical
axes were used because of the large diviations of the beams at
other directions. In principle, one would like to span all these
directions to form a more complete picture. Such experiments will
have to wait until higher sensitivity can be achieved to compensate for the small interaction regions.

Study of Reaction Transients. It has been pointed out very
early on (1) that SIRS can be used for studying free raducals and
other short-lived species. The time resolution of the technique
is determined only by the pulse duration of the lasers. In
principle, therefore, one can obtain time-resolved Raman spectra
of reaction transients down to the 30 ps range and still maintain
a spectral resolution of 1 cm$^{-1}$. The obvious advantage of SIRS
over other picosecond methods based on electronic absorption is
that more detailed structural information can be obtained. To
this date, however, there has been no report of such studies.
This is mainly due to technical difficulties in detecting inverse
Raman absorption from species at low concentrations. In the next
few years, it may be reasonable to expect some of these studies
to reach fruition.

High Resolution Spectroscopy. The spectral resolution of
SIRS is determined by the two lasers used, so that typically
higher resolution can be achieved compared to normal RS, where the
monochromator slits cannot be too narrow and the f-number cannot
be too unfavorable for proper light collection. For studies in
gas samples, the normal 90° collection geometry in RS inherently
limits the resolution to a Doppler width determined by the Stokes
frequency of the Raman scattering. For colinear SIRS with co-
propagating laser beams (0° scattering), it can be readily shown
that the residual Doppler width is that corresponding to the
frequency of the Raman transition itself, and is one order-of-
magnitude less than that in typical RS experiments. Similarly,
for colinear counter-propagating laser beams, the residual Doppler
width is roughly two times that in normal RS. The high resolution
potential of SIRS has not been explored to date, but is certainly
one of the most useful features inherent to the technique.

Summary

Spectroscopy by inverse Raman scattering offers many unique
advantages in the study of molecules, such as the rejection of
fluorescence in Raman spectra, the ease for obtaining quantitative
information, the high speed at which a Raman spectrum can be
recorded, the high spectral resolution achievable, and the
simplicity in performing polarization studies. One can anticipate

rapid growth in this field as laser technology becomes better and better developed.

## Acknowledgement

The author wishes to thank the U.S. Department of Energy, Office of Basic Energy Sciences, Chemical Sciences Division, for research support that led to part of this work.

## References

(1)  Jones, W. J., and Stoicheff, B. P., Phys. Rev. Letters, (1964), 13, 657.
(2)  Grun, J. B., McQuillan, A. K., and Stoicheff, B. P., Phys. Rev., (1969), 180, 61.
(3)  Placzek, G., Handbuch der Radiologie, (1934), 6, (No. 2).
(4)  Yeung, E. S., J. Mol. Spectrosc., (1974), 53, 379.
(5)  Fenner, W. R., Hyatt, H. A., Kellam, J. M., and Porto, S. P. S., J. Opt. Soc. Am., (1973), 63, 73.
(6)  Owyoung, A., IEEE J. Quantum Elect., (1978), QE-14, 192.
(7)  Maker, P. D., and Terhune, R. W., Phys. Rev., (1965), 137 A801.
(8)  Peticolas, W. L., Ann. Rev. Phys. Chem., (1967), 18, 233.
(9)  Honig, B., Jortner, J. and Szoke, A., J. Chem. Phys., (1967) 46, 2714.
(10) Yeung, E. S., and Moore, C. B., in "Fundamental and Applied Laser Physics," Ed. Feld, Kurnit and Javan, p. 223, Wiley-Interscience, New York, 1972.
(11) Hochstrasser, R. M., Sung, H. N., and Wessel, J. E., J. Chem. Phys., (1973), 58, 4694.
(12) Stoicheff, B. P., Phys. Letters, (1963), 7, 186.
(13) Duardo, J. A., Johnson, F. M., and El-Sayed, M. A., Phys. Letters, (1966), 21, 168.
(14) Gadow, P., Lau, A., Thuy, Ch. T., Weigmann, H. J., Werncke, W., Lenz, K. and Pfeiffer, M., Optics Comm., (1971), 4, 226.
(15) McLaren, R. A., and Stoicheff, B. P., Appl. Phys. Letters, (1970), 16, 140.
(16) Alfano, R. R., and Shapiro, S. L., Phys. Rev. Letters, (1970), 24, 592.
(17) Klein, J., Werncke, W., Lau, A., Hunsalz, G., and Lenz, K., Exp. Technik der Phys., (1974), 22, 565.
(18) Kneipp, K., Werncke, W., Ponath, H. E., Klein, J., Lau, A., and Thuy, C. D., Phys. Stat. Sol. (1974), 64, 589.
(19) Werncke, W., Klein, J., Lau, A., Lenz, K., and Hunsalz, G., Optics Comm., (1974), 11, 159.
(20) Tsunoda, Y., Jap. J. Appl. Phys., (1972), 11, 1293.
(21) Lytle, F. E., "Inverse Raman Studies of Chemical Lasers," UCRL-13557 Technical Report, (1972), 8.
(22) Hughes, L. J., Steenhoek, L. E., and Yeung, E. S., Chem. Phys. Letters, (1978), to be published.

(23)  Lau, A., Werncke, W., Pfeiffer, M., Lenz, K., and Weigmann, H. J., _Sov. J. Quant. Electron._, (1976), $\underline{6}$, 402.
(24)  Kelley, P. L., _Phys. Rev. Letters_, (1965), 15, 1005.
(25)  Dowley, M. W., Eisenthal, K. B., and Peticolas, W. L., _Phys. Rev. Letters_, (1967), $\underline{18}$, 531.
(26)  McQuillan, R. A., and Stoicheff, B. P., _Appl. Phys. Letters_, (1970), $\underline{16}$, 140.
(27)  Weigmann, H. J., Lenz, K., Werncke, W., Lau, A., Pfeiffer, M., and Gadow, P., _Z. Chem._, (1971), $\underline{11}$, 36.
(28)  Peterson, N. C., Kurylo, M. J., Braun, W., Bass, A. M., and Keller, R. A., _J. Opt. Soc. Am._, (1971), $\underline{61}$, 746.
(29)  Werncke, W., Lau, A., Pfeiffer, M., Lenz, K., Weigmann, H. J., and Thuy, C. D., _Optics Comm._, (1972), $\underline{4}$, 413.
(30)  Behringer, J., and Brandmuller, J., _Z. Elektrochem_, (1956), $\underline{60}$, 643.
(31)  Werncke, W., Lau, A., Pfeiffer, M., Weigmann, H. J., Hunsalz, G., and Lenz, K., _Optics Comm._, (1976), $\underline{16}$, 128.
(32)  VonHolle, W., _U.S. Ballistic Research Laboratories Memorandum Report No. 2607_, (1976).
(33)  Brandmuller, J., and Schrotter, H., _Z. Physik_, (1957), $\underline{149}$, 131.
(34)  Udagawa, Y., Mikami, N., Kaya, K., and Ito, M., _J. Raman Spectrosc._, (1973), $\underline{1}$, 341.
(35)  Kondilenko, I. I., and Babich, I. L., _Ukrains'kii Fizichnii Zhurnal_, (1960), $\underline{5}$, 532.
(36)  Kato, Y., and Takuma, H., _J. Opt. Soc. Am._, (1971), $\underline{61}$, 347.
(37)  Skinner, J. G., and Nilsen, W. G., _J. Opt. Soc. Am._, (1968), $\underline{58}$, 113.
(38)  McClung, F. J., and Weiner, D., _J. Opt. Soc. Am._, (1964), $\underline{54}$, 641.
(39)  Owyoung, A., and Peercy, P. S., _J. Appl. Phys._, (1977), $\underline{48}$ 674.

RECEIVED August 25, 1978.

# Time-Resolved Resonance Raman Spectroscopy (TR³) and Related Vidicon Raman Spectrography: Vibrational Spectra in Nanoseconds

WILLIAM H. WOODRUFF' and STUART FARQUHARSON

Department of Chemistry, University of Texas at Austin, Austin, TX 78712

Vibrational Raman spectroscopy is a rich source of structural information, which is particularly valuable as a probe for structures of species in solution. Raman scattering can easily be observed under experimental conditions, such as aqueous solutions or low vibrational frequency, wherein the observation of direct infrared absorption is difficult or impossible. Although normal Raman scattering is a weak effect, requiring relatively high concentrations of scattering species, the resonance Raman effect can enormously increase the sensitivity of Raman spectroscopy. In the resonance Raman case (laser excitation within an electronic transition of a scattering chromophore) detection limits lower than $10^{-7}$ $\underline{M}$ can be attained, and spectra can commonly be obtained in the $10^{-6}$ – $10^{-5}$ $\underline{M}$ concentration range. The resonance Raman effect has been the subject of numerous recent reviews (e.g., Reference [1]).

Raman scattering occurs on an extremely short timescale ($10^{-14}$s or less). By virtue of this property combined with the sensitivity and selectivity for a given chromophore of the resonance Raman effect, resonance Raman spectroscopy offers an attractive probe for structural information on transient chemical species such as reaction intermediates or excited states. In practice, however, the resonance Raman effect has seldom been applied to chemical transients. This is due to two factors: primarily, the long (minutes to hours) instrumentally-imposed time required to obtain a Raman spectrum using conventional techniques; and, secondarily, the special optical requirements of the resonance Raman experiment wherein the sample typically absorbs 90% of the incident laser light within the Raman scattering volume. The few studies which have used essentially conventional instrumentation to record resonance Raman spectra of transients have employed either continuous-flow techniques ([2,3]) or repetitive (electrochemical) reaction initiation plus lockin or boxcar detection ([4]).

'Author to whom correspondence should be addressed.

0-8412-0459-4/78/47-085-215$05.25/0

Recently, a few groups have applied image-intensified vidicon detectors or related devices to Raman spectroscopy, with the objective of drastically reducing the time required to obtain Raman spectra (5-11). These detectors are employed in the same manner as a photographic plate, in conjunction with spectrographic dispersion of the Raman spectrum. This results in a multiplex advantage in spectral acquisition time analogous to the Fellgett advantage of a Fourier transform spectrometer.

In addition to the spectral multiplex advantage, vidicon Raman spectrography offers the potential for acquisition of Raman spectra in extremely short times. This possibility exists when the vidicon spectrograph is used in conjunction with pulsed-laser excitation of Raman scattering. Under these conditions, the time resolution of a Raman experiment becomes in principle the same as the duration of the laser pulses. Due to the multiplex nature of the vidicon spectrograph, it is possible to record a sizable segment of a Raman spectrum within the timespan of a single laser pulse. This combination of pulsed-laser excitation (whether single-pulse or repetitive-pulse) and vidicon spectrographic detection is the approach which has generally been taken in the acquisition of time-resolved Raman spectra (5,7-11).

Formidable experimental difficulties, in addition to those encountered in normal Raman spectroscopy, are encountered in the time-resolved resonance Raman (TR[3]) case. In the normal Raman case the sample generally does not absorb light at the laser wavelength, while in the resonance Raman case it is typical for virtually all of the light at the laser wavelength to be absorbed within the scattering volume of the sample. When pulsed-laser excitation is employed with an absorbing sample, which is the usual TR[3] requirement, complications can be expected from sample heating and photochemistry. Furthermore, optical requirements coupled with high peak laser power can lead to damage to sample and cell material. The two previous reports of time-resolved resonance Raman spectra minimized these problems either by employing many repetitive excitation pulses at rather low per-pulse energy to gain 5 ns time resolution (4), or by using a relatively long-duration (0.6 µs) single-pulse excitation to minimize peak pulse power at relatively high per-pulse energy. One of our objectives has been to obtain TR[3] spectra with time resolution of a few nanoseconds while retaining the ability to acquire a spectrum excited by a single laser pulse. Preliminary communication of this work has appeared elsewhere (12).

In the process of developing the basic TR[3] instrumentation and techniques, we have demonstrated that the vidicon Raman spectrograph is entirely superior to a conventional scanning spectrometer as a detection system for most routine Raman spectroscopy. In addition, we have identified certain conditions of pulsed-laser excitation under which interferences from non-linear Raman effects, particularly stimulated Raman emission,

may be expected.  A range of commonly encountered types of
resonant and nonresonant Raman samples are investigated, and a
systematic comparison of the capabilities of the vidicon Raman
spectrograph and the conventional scanning spectrometer are
presented.  Our single-pulse TR$^3$ spectra represent a <u>ten order of
magnitude</u> improvement over scanning spectrometry in the time
required to obtain comparable spectra, and a two order of magnitude improvement in time resolution over previously reported
single-pulse TR$^3$ spectra (<u>9</u>).

Experimental Section

Figure 1 shows a schematic diagram of the apparatus used in
the present study.  The vidicon spectrograph consists of a
standard SPEX 1870 0.5 m spectrograph with the camera attachment
removed.  An adapter for the camera port was machined to position
the photosensitive surface of the vidicon detector in the
spectrographic image plane.  The vidicon detector was a Princeton
Applied Research 1205I two-stage image intensified (ISIT)
detector head, with a vacuum-deposited ultraviolet scintillator
for adequate response below 400 nm.  The diffraction grating in
the spectrograph is a 1800 groove/mm holographically recorded
diffraction grating (HRDG) instead of the standard 1200 groove/
mm conventionally ruled grating.  This substitution is necessary
to eliminate grating ghosts (<u>6</u>).  In some cases, it was necessary
to employ a cutoff filter (Schott OG-550) in front of the
entrance slits to reduce stray light at the laser wavelength.
The sample stage and collection optics were a modified version of
the Nestor design (<u>13</u>).  Translation of the sample stage in X,Y,Z
coordinates was accomplished with Ardel T-50 micrometer transla-
tor modules.  The optical bench and lens translators were Ealing
components.  Optical components were suprasil or quartz throughout.  The lenses (ESCO Products, S1UV) were 2 1/2" diameter,
the collection lens being f/1 and the matching lens f/7.  The
objective lens was translatable in the X,Y,Z directions <u>via</u>
Ealing vertical and transverse motions.  The polarizing filter
was an Ealing ultraviolet polarizer, and the scrambler was a
quartz wedge from Lambda/Airtron.

The lasers employed to excite Raman scattering in this study
included Spectra-Physics 164 Argon ion and Krypton ion lasers for
C.W. excitation and, for TR$^3$ studies, a Quanta-Ray DCR-1 Q-
switched Nd:YAG oscillator.  The gas laser beams were rid of
plasma emission lines by a Burke filter (dispersive direct-
viewing prism) assembly, and were directed and focussed using
conventional Raman illuminator optics.  The 9 nsec pulses at
the Nd:YAG fundamental wavelength (1.064 μm) required special
handling.  To provide a suitable Raman excitation wavelength
in the visible region, the beam was passed through a second
harmonic generator (type 2 potassium dideuterium phosphate, KD*P,
from Quanta-Ray).  This arrangement produced a maximum of 75 mJ

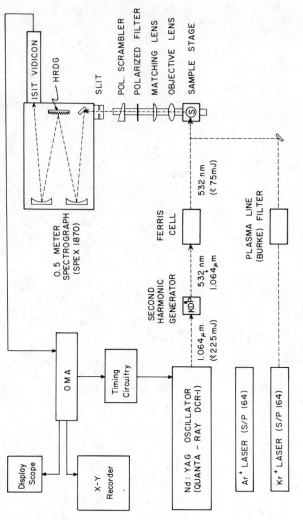

*Figure 1. Diagram of the TR³ apparatus. The abbreviation HRDG denotes holographically recorded diffraction grating.*

of laser energy in seven-nanosecond pulses at 5318 Å.  However, after frequency doubling the Nd:YAG beam still contains sub-stantial (>50%) residual 1.064 μm radiation.  This is insuf-ferable from a spectroscopic point of view, and also increases the technical difficulty of handling the Nd:YAG pulses, inasmuch as the infrared radiation is much more damaging to optical components than the visible.  We solve this problem by using, literally, a chemist's solution to remove the 1.064 μm radiation from the desired 5318 Å.  This we denote the Ferris cell (to acknowledge the contributions of N.S. Ferris), which is a cylindrical cell of 20 cm pathlength filled with a 10% w/w solution of $Fe(NH_4)_2(SO_4)_2 \cdot 6H_2O$ in 1 $\underline{M}$ degassed, aqueous $HNO_3$. This solution has an absorbance of approximately unity per cm at 1.064 μm and zero at 5318 Å.  Thus the Ferris cell transmits virtually all of the 5318 Å component of the frequency-doubled Nd:YAG beam and none of the 1.064 μm.  Analogous absorbing solutions can be devised to eliminate or transmit the other Nd: YAG harmonics.

Samples were contained in 1 mm inside diameter melting point capillaries for C.W. experiments.  However, these capillaries were destroyed by the tightly focussed Nd:YAG beam, thus for the pulsed experiments 3 mm inside diameter, 1 mm wall thickness quartz capillaries were generally used.  For pure liquids or colorless solutions, a long pathlength cylindrical cell was sometimes used, with the laser beam incident upon the flat window, its focal point several centimeters inside the liquid. The Raman-scattered light was collected perpendicular to the axis of the cylinder.

The vidicon-detected spectra were processed by the standard PAR OMA console, and displayed on an oscilloscope for immediate viewing and on a X-Y plotter for a permanent copy.  For single-pulse experiments, the scanning function of the OMA detector was synchronized with the laser pulse via the OMA console such that the laser pulse arrived at the sample within the 600 μs retrace time of the vidicon's electron beam.  This was done by using the DELINHDI signal from the OMA to trigger appropriate timing and level conversion circuitry, and ultimately to fire the laser via the laser's remote triggering inputs.  For repeti-tive-pulse or C.W.-excited spectra using the vidicon spectrograph no attempt was made to synchronize the vidicon scans and the laser operation.

In several cases, conventionally scanned spectra were obtained for comparison to the performance of the vidicon spectrograph.  These conventional spectra were obtained using either a SPEX 1401 spectrometer as described elsewhere (14) or a Cary 82 with a cooled ITT FW-130 photomultiplier and photon counting detection.  Laser excitation for the conventional spectra was provided by the C.W. $Ar^+$ or $Kr^+$ lasers described above.  Visible and ultraviolet absorption spectra of sample solutions were obtained using Cary 14, 15, or 118 spectrophotometers.

## Results and Discussion

Pure Liquids. Figure 2 shows Raman spectra of carbon
tetrachloride obtained using the vidicon spectrograph with both
C.W. (Figure 2A) and pulsed (Figure 2, B-E) excitation. The
two C.W. excited spectra show the signal-to-noise ratio (S/N)
attainable using both maximum signal accumulation with the OMA
and a single vidicon exposure of 33 milliseconds. The spectral
range shown is that which is detectable simultaneously with the
vidicon spectrograph, 381 $cm^{-1}$ using 5145 Å excitation. The
spectra clearly show the superior speed due to the spectral
multiplex advantage of the vidicon spectrograph: the 33 msec
vidicon exposure in Figure 2(A) corresponds to a conventional
scan speed of greater than 11,500 $cm^{-1}$ per second!

The carbon tetrachloride spectra also illustrate the performance of the vidicon spectrograph near the laser excitation
frequency. These spectra were obtained without any attempt to
suppress laser light entering the spectrograph, because any
such suppression (step filters of fore-monochromators) will
limit the spectral range of the spectrograph. It can be seen
that, even though the sample geometry was a transverse
capillary, which is a notorious source of excessive stray light,
the 218 $cm^{-1}$ peak of $CCl_4$ is observed with essentially the same
S/N as would be seen in a conventional double spectrometer.
Furthermore, peaks at just slightly above 100 $cm^{-1}$, if present,
could easily be observed.

Figure 2(B-D) shows the effect of increasing laser pulse
energy upon the pulsed-laser excited spectrum of carbon tetrachloride. These spectra were observed using the cylindrical
cell described above. The normal intensity pattern of the $CCl_4$
spectrum may be seen by comparing the $\nu_2$ (218 $cm^{-1}$), $\nu_4$ (314 $cm^{-1}$),
and $\nu_1$ (459 $cm^{-1}$) peaks in the C.W. spectrum, 1(A). Essentially
the same intensity pattern is observed when pulsed excitation
is employed at an energy of 5 mJ/pulse, Figure 1(B). In Figure
1(C), however, obtained using 16 mJ pulses, the $\nu_1$ $CCl_4$ peak is
significantly intensified relative to $\nu_2$ and $\nu_4$, compared to
the C.W. and 5 mJ/pulse spectra. When the per-pulse energy is
increased to 27 mJ, $\nu_1$ is still more strongly enhanced and
the peak has begun to narrow relative to the spontaneous Raman
linewidth. These characteristics; definite energy threshold
for intensity enhancement, threshold dependent upon cross-
section for spontaneous Raman (i.e., the strongest spontaneous
Raman mode in a given spectrum will become enhanced at the
lowest energy threshold), nonlinear dependence of Raman intensity
upon excitation energy, and narrowing of the enhanced peak, are
all characteristic of the stimulated Raman effect (15,16).
However, our observations were made at 90° to the laser beam,
whereas stimulated Raman emission is propagated in a cone whose

axis is colinear with the laser beam. Thus we are observing
90° <u>Rayleigh</u> scattering of <u>stimulated</u> Raman emission. This
is a reflection of the potential sensitivity (when observed
directly) of stimulated Raman emission and related effects
such as CARS, which may be exploited in $TR^3$-like experiments.
Figure 2(E) shows a spectrum of $CCl_4$ obtained with a <u>single, 7
nanosecond</u> laser pulse, showing stimulated Raman enhancement of
$\nu_1$.

   In view of the stimulated Raman emission observed in the
spectra in Figure 1, and similar effects observed in pulsed-
excited spectra of other pure liquids, it is fair to ask
whether single-pulse excitation will ever result in a spectrum
exhibiting normal, spontaneous Raman intensity patterns. Figure
3 shows the spectrum of nitrobenzene obtained using repetitive-
pulse, 2(A), and single-pulse, 2(B), excitation. Although both
the 1344 $cm^{-1}$ and 1004 $cm^{-1}$ modes of nitrobenzene have very low
thresholds for stimulated Raman emission (16), the relative
intensities of all of the modes are the same as one observes
when C.W. excitation is employed. This is achieved by avoiding
tight focussing of the pulsed laser beam, and thus remaining
below the energy density threshold for nonlinear Raman effects.
This scattering arrangement has the additional advantage of
minimizing laser damage to sample cell materials. Figure 3(B)
demonstrates that time-resolved normal Raman spectra can be
obtained with good S/N and without nonlinear Raman effects.

   <u>Nonresonant Solutes: Lysozyme.</u>  As a more challenging test
of the performance of the vidicon spectrograph with nonresonant
Raman samples, C.W. excitation was used to obtain the spectrum
of a biomolecule in aqueous solution and in the absence of
resonance enhancement. We wished to establish the ability of
the vidicon spectrograph to handle high light levels, both at
the laser frequency (stray light) and at frequencies shifted
from that of the laser (background due to featureless scattering
or luminescence), and still detect weak Raman peaks. These
sample characteristics are amply met by solutions of macromolecules (e.g., proteins, DNA). We chose a 30% solution of the
nonchromophoric protein lysozyme as a test sample. In addition
to intense Rayleigh scattering expected of a large molecule,
lysozyme exhibits background scattering levels almost ten times
as high as the Raman peaks, as shown on the vertical axis of
the conventionally scanned spectrum, Figure 4(A). Both Figures
4(A) and 4(B) were obtained using C.W. laser excitation at
4880 Å, but Figure 3(B) was obtained using the vidicon spectrograph. It can be seen that all of the major features in the
scanned spectrum are visible in the vidicon spectrum, even
though the vidicon spectrum was obtained 100 times faster per
vidicon frame than the scanned spectrum. Longer accumulation
times would have improved the S/N in the vidicon spectrum, but
this is not possible without an external signal averager due to

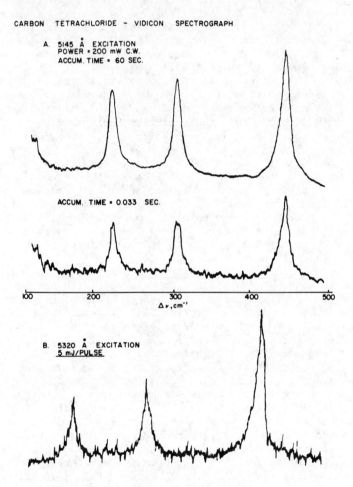

*Figure 2. Raman spectra of the 100–500 cm⁻¹ region of carbon tetrachloride taken using the vidicon spectrograph. (A) (above) Top two traces; cw excitation, Ar⁺ laser, 5145 Å. (B, above; C, D, E, right)*

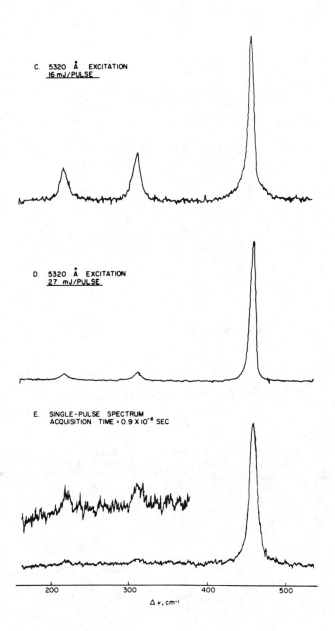

C.  5320 Å  EXCITATION
    16 mJ/PULSE

D.  5320 Å  EXCITATION
    27 mJ/PULSE

E.  SINGLE-PULSE  SPECTRUM
    ACQUISITION  TIME = 0.9 X 10⁻⁸ SEC

Δ ν, cm⁻¹

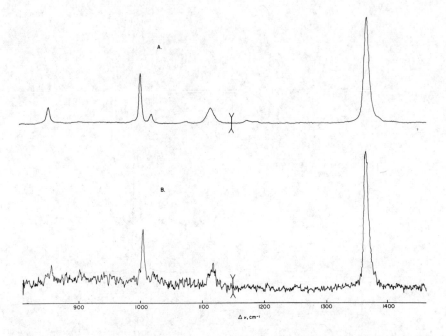

*Figure 3.   Pulse-excited Raman spectra of nitrobenzene, ND:YAG laser, 5318 Å.  (A)
Full-scale OMA signal accumulation; 10 nsec pulses, 10 pulses/sec.; 90 mW ave.
power; 140 sec accumulation time; 1.4 × 10⁻⁶ sec exposure time. (B) Single laser
pulse, 7 × 10⁻⁹ sec; 0.9 × 10⁻⁸ sec acquisition time.  The double-ended arrows denote the point where adjacent vidicon exposures were joined.  This notation is used
throughout.*

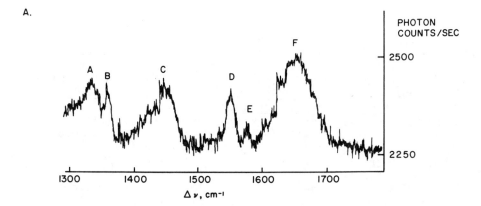

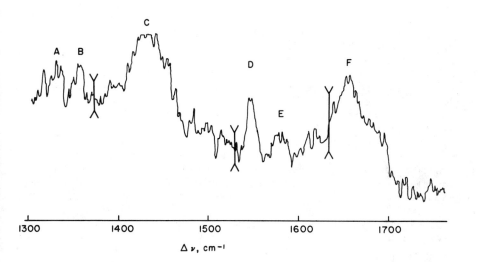

*Figure 4.   Comparison of scanned and vidicon-detected normal Raman spectra of lysozyme, 30% lysozyme in H₂O. (A) Scanning double monochromator (SPEX 1401), photomultipler detection; conventional scan, 4880 Å excitation, 85 mW cw, 4800 sec scan time. (B) Vidicon spectrograph, ISIT detection, full-scale OMA signal accumulation; 4880 Å excitation; 500 mW cw, 44 sec accumulation time.*

the high background light level of the lysozyme sample and
the limited count range (100,000 counts full scale) of the
memories of the OMA.

### C.W. Excitation of Resonant Solutes:  Cytochrome c.

Figure 5 shows the conventionally scanned (5A) and vidicon-
detected (5B) resonance Raman spectra of the heme protein
cytochrome c, concentration 5.5 x $10^{-4}$ M, excited with the 5145 Å
line of the $Ar^+$ laser.  It is evident from comparison of Figures
5(A) and 5(B) that the vidicon spectrograph is an entirely
superior Raman detection system, yielding both faster spectral
acquisition and better S/N than the conventional double spectrometer under similar conditions.  The potential spectral multiplex
advantage of the vidicon spectrograph over the double monochromator, roughly a factor of 100 depending upon natural line-
widths of the sample and parameters of the spectrometer, trans-
lates into approximately a factor of 10 actual improvement in
acquisition time for comparable S/N.  The factor of 10 difference
between the potential and actual advantage of the vidicon
spectrograph is due in part to lower per-detection-element
sensitivity of the ISIT vidicon compared to a photomultiplier,
which amounts to a factor of between 1.5 and 2.  The remainder
of the difference may be ascribed to the obviously poorer stray
light rejection of the spectrograph.  Again, no attempt was
made to suppress stray light for these measurements.

We wished to establish using C.W. excitation the minimum
laser energy required to record a resonance Raman spectrum with
the vidicon spectrograph, and also to establish the best time
resolution attainable using the internal timing of the OMA
detection system.  The results are shown in Figure 5(C), wherein
the resonance Raman spectrum of cytochrome c was recorded in a
single, 33 millisecond scan of the vidicon's electron beam across
its photodiode array.  This is the electronically-imposed limit
on time resolution which can be obtained using any PAR OMA
system's response to continuous illumination, without gating
the electron optics of the image intensifier stages.  Most of
the features of the cytochrome c spectrum are clearly discernible
in Figure 5(C), although only 1.8 millijoules of laser energy
excited the scattering.  Comparison of Figures 5(A) and 5(C)
shows an improvement of almost five orders of magnitude in the
temporal acquisition of resonance Raman spectra in the vidicon
spectrograph compared to conventional scanning under similar
excitation conditions, albeit with a considerable sacrifice in
S/N in the vidicon case.

### $TR^3$ Detection of Nonreacting Solutes:  Cytochrome c.

Figure 6 shows spectra of cytochrome c recorded using conventional scanning with 5309 Å C.W. excitation, and using the $TR^3$
apparatus with 5318 Å pulsed excitation in both repetitive and
single-pulse modes.  Comparing the C.W. spectrum to the

repetitive-pulsed one, several points can be made.  First, the spectra are essentially the same feature for feature, indicating that the per-pulse energy which we employ, 11 mJ in the present case, does not degrade or significantly perturb the photolytically-stable heme chromophore of this protein. The shoulder on the low-frequency side of peak C is an artifact in the vidicon spectrograph, and the difference in relative areas of peaks D and E is due to a polarization anomaly in the Cary 82 spectrometer.  Second, considering the improved S/N in the pulse-excited spectrum and the laser powers employed in each case, the vidicon Raman spectrograph realizes approximately a factor of 14 improvement over conventional scanning in spectral acquisition time due to the multiplex advantage, without regard to whether the Raman experiment is C.W. or time-resolved.  Third, the repetitive-pulse TR$^3$ spectrum was obtained by excitation from 1300 pulses of 7 ns duration, at a repetition rate of 10 Hz. Thus the sample was exposed to laser radiation for only 1.3 x $10^{-5}$ s out of a total spectral acquisition time of 130 s, and time resolution of 7 ns is possible for any process which can be repetitively initiated the required number of times.

To obtain TR$^3$ spectra in processes which cannot be repetitively initiated, single-shot acquisition of TR$^3$ spectra is required.  The bottom spectrum in Figure 6 was obtained using a single excitation pulse from the Nd:YAG oscillator, delivered during the 0.6 µs retrace time of the OMA detector. Otherwise the conditions were identical to those employed for the repetitive-pulse spectrum.  The S/N of the single shot spectrum, 3.5 for peaks C and H, is the expected factor of 36 poorer than for the repetitive-pulse spectrum, and approximately a factor of 8 poorer than the C.W., scanned spectrum.  Neverthe-less, the main features, peaks C, E, H, and perhaps F, are visible in the single-shot spectrum.  The acquisition time for the single-shot spectrum is a flat factor of 7 x $10^{11}$ shorter than that for the C.W., scanned spectrum in Figure 1.  The S/N deficit suffered by the single-shot spectrum would allow the C.W. spectrum to be acquired 64 times faster than that in Figure 1 to give S/N equal to the single-shot spectrum. Considering this S/N difference, the single-shot spectrum represents a real improvement of ten orders of magnitude over the conventional Cary 82 spectrometer in the temporal acquisition of comparable spectra.  Compared to the previous TR$^3$ studies (8,9), these results represent a conspicuous improvement in S/N for repetitive-pulse TR$^3$ for comparable time resolution, and an improvement of two orders of magnitude in time resolution over the only previously reported single-shot TR$^3$ spectra (9).

TR$^3$ Detection of Transients:  The Photodissociation of CO-Hemoglobin.  The cooperative binding of four ligands such as dioxygen or carbon monoxide by the hemoglobin tetramer is a well-known and physiologically vital phenomenon (17).  Conformational

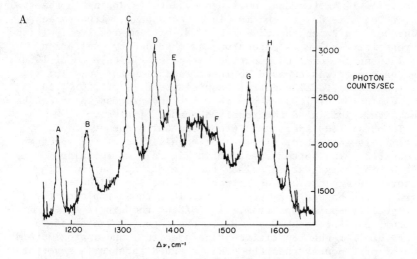

*Figure 5. Comparison of scanned and vidicon-detected, cw-excited reso-nance Raman spectra of cytochrome* c; *5.5 × 10⁻⁴M. (A) (above) Scanning double monochromator (SPEX 1401), photomultiplier detection; conventional scan, 5145 Å excitation, 40 mW cw, 2550 sec scan. (B) (top right) Vidicon spectrograph, ISIT detection, full-scale OMA signal accumulation; 5145 Å excitation, 55 mW cw, 147 sec accumulation time/frame. (C) (bottom right) Single OMA frame scan, 33 msec spectral acquisition time; 5145 Å excitation, total energy = 1.8 mJ.*

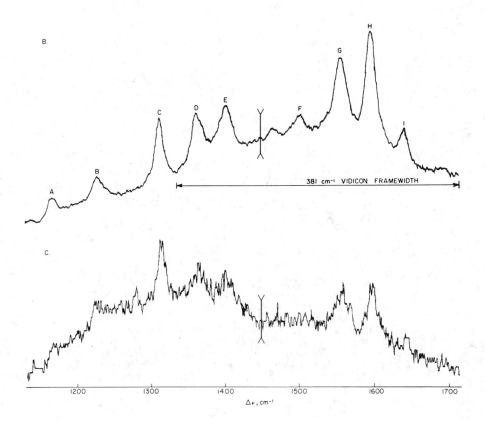

381 cm⁻¹ VIDICON FRAMEWIDTH

$\Delta \nu$, cm⁻¹

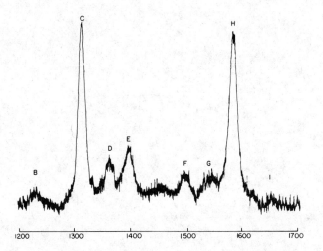

*Figure 6. Conventional (cw scanned) and time-resolved resonance Raman spectra of cytochrome c.(Top) cw excitation by 5309 Å Kr⁺ laser line, scanning spectral detection by Cary 82 spectrometer, 80 mW cw, 5000 sec scan time.(Top right) 5318 Å repetitive-pulse TR³ spectrum, vidicon spectrographic detection; 10 nsec pulses, 10 pulses/sec, 110 mW ave. power, 130 sec accumulation time, $1.3 \times 10^{-5}$ sec exposure time.(Bottom right) single-pulse, 7 nsec TR³ spectrum, 5320 Å excitation, $0.9 \times 10^{-8}$ sec acquisition time.*

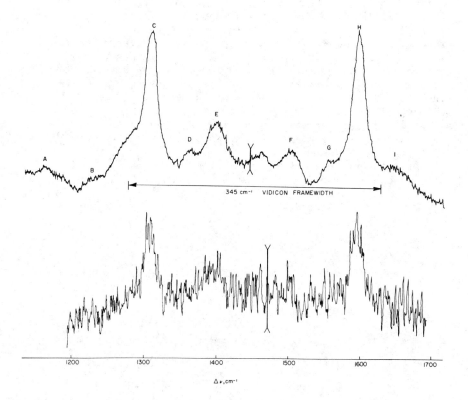

345 cm⁻¹   VIDICON FRAMEWIDTH

1200    1300    1400    1500    1600    1700

$\Delta\nu$, cm⁻¹

interplay between the heme and protein structures is thought
to be responsible for this cooperativity.  The most generally
accepted model proposes that the "stereochemical trigger" for
the ligated (oxy tertiary, "Relaxed" quaternary) to unligated
(deoxy tertiary, "Tense" quaternary) protein conformational
change is the spin-state change of the iron atom upon deligation
at the axial site trans to the proximal histidine (18,19).  This
spin-state change is accompanied (or followed) by displacement
of the iron atom out of the heme plane toward the proximal
histidine, and probably by appreciable lengthening of the iron-
imidazole bond.  The heme structure change is transmitted to the
protein tertiary and quaternary structures, effecting the
observed cooperativity of ligand binding in the tetrameric
protein.  The temporal relationships among the events of heme
deligation, spin-state change, heme structure change, and
protein structure change are of obvious importance in understanding the relationships between heme structure and protein
function.  Inasmuch as C.W. resonance Raman spectroscopy is a
well-established probe for equilibrium heme electronic states
and structures (1), time-resolved resonance Raman spectroscopy
may be expected to provide similar information on heme transients
and their temporal behavior.

Present evidence on the dynamics of the photolysis of
carbonmonoxy hemoglobin (COHb) suggests that the following events
occur:

| Reaction | | Reference |
|---|---|---|
| 1.  $COHb \xrightarrow[t_{1/2} < 0.5 \text{ ps}]{h\nu, \ \emptyset \ \sim \ 0.5} CO + Hb^{3°Oxy}_{4°R}$ | | (20) |
| 2.  $Hb^{3°Oxy}_{4°R}$ (Fe in-plane) $\xrightarrow[t_{1/2} << 7 \text{ ns}]{} Hb^{3°Oxy}_{4°R}$ (Fe out-of-plane) | | (21) |
| 3.  $Hb^{3°Oxy}_{4°R} \xrightarrow[40 \text{ ns} < t_{1/2} < 90 \text{ ns}]{} Hb^{3°Deoxy}_{4°R}$ | | (22) |
| 4.  $Hb^{3°Deoxy}_{4°R} \xrightarrow[t_{1/2} < 1 \text{ ms}]{} Hb^{3°Deoxy}_{4°T}$ | | (23,24) |
| 5.  $Hb + CO(1 \text{ atm}) \xrightarrow[<< 100 \text{ ms}]{\text{complete in}} COHb$ | | (17) |

where 3° and 4° refer to the tertiary and quaternary structures
of the protein.  In a typical experiment, we illuminate the
Raman scattering volume of our sample with 7 ns laser pulses of
5318 Å wavelength, 10 mJ energy, and 10 Hz repetition rate.
Each pulse is sufficiently intense to photodissociate all of the
COHb within the scattering volume in approximately 300 ps.  The
remaining 6.7 ns of the laser pulse "sees" only the product of

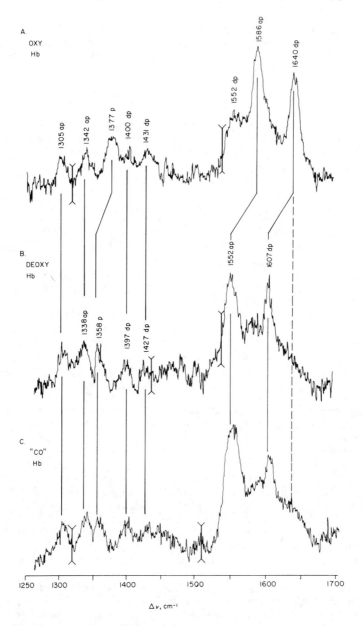

*Figure 7. Time-resolved resonance Raman spectra of (A) oxy-hemoglobin, (B) deoxyhemoglobin, and (C) photodissociated car-bonmonoxyhemoglobin (see text), in the frequency region of the structure-sensitive "indicator bands."*

*Abbreviations: p = polarized, dp = depolarized, ap = anomolously (in-versely) polarized. Conditions: 5318 Å excitation, 7 sec pulses, pulse repetition frequency 10 Hz, pulse energy 10 mJ, accumulation time 165 sec.*

reaction (1) or (2) plus any $Hb_{4°R}^{3°}$Deoxy which has been produced
by reaction (3). Our time-resolved resonance Raman spectra
of "COHb", therefore, are at least 86% $Hb_{4°R}^{3°}$Oxy, less than 10%
$Hb_{4°R}^{3°}$Deoxy, and approximately 4% COHb. Additionally, since
COHb is completely reformed in less than 0.1 s, 10 Hz laser
pulses can be repeated indefinitely in order to improve spectral
signal-to-noise ratio by signal accumulation.

Figure 7 shows the time-resolved resonance Raman spectra of
the structure-sensitive 1300-1700 cm$^{-1}$ spectral regions of $O_2$Hb,
Deoxy Hb, and "COHb" (photodissociated as noted above). In
these experiments, $O_2$Hb remains ligated due to its relatively
low quantum yield for photodissociation. The spectra of $O_2$Hb
and Deoxy Hb appear insignificantly different from the respective
C.W. spectra excited at similar laser wavelengths. The three
indicator bands which reflect heme electronic and/or geometrical
structure shift from 1377, 1586, and 1640 cm$^{-1}$ in $O_2$Hb to 1358,
1552, and 1607 cm$^{-1}$ in Deoxy Hb, as expected (1,25). The two
highest-frequency vibrations are thought to be sensitive
primarily to displacement of the iron atom in or out of the heme
plane, particularly when the iron atom and the heme are far from
coplanar (as in Deoxy Hb) (25-27).

The spectrum of photodissociated COHb in Figure 7 is
essentially the same as that of Deoxy Hb. This suggests that
the structural relaxations of the heme group following photodissociation of COHb are complete in much less than 7 nsec,
despite the evidence that the protein structural relaxations
take place in longer times (vide supra, equations 2,3). Two
points are clear from this result: first, the proposed stereochemical trigger for cooperativity in hemoglobin (the heme
structure change) is temporally decoupled from the protein
reorganizations which it purportedly triggers; and, second, the
nonequilibrium globin structure in photodissociated $Hb_{4°R}^{3°}$Oxy
apparently exerts no significant transient constraint upon the
heme structure (at least, on the timescale which we are able to
observe). Concerning the second point, it has been clearly
demonstrated (26) that static globin constraints result in no
resonance Raman-detectable distortion of the heme group of carp
hemoglobin (which can exist in the T or R protein conformations,
independent of the ligation state of its hemes). It was
conceivable, however, that such an effect of globin constraint
might be observed in an experiment sensitive to the dynamics of
the structural reorganizations. Our results indicate that no
such dynamic effect occurs. The implications of these results
in questions of hemoglobin cooperativity are discussed elsewhere
(21). For the present purposes, our results clearly demonstrate
the power of TR$^3$ as a structure probe for transients.

Acknowledgement. This work was supported by NSF Grants
CHE77-15220 and CHE78-09338.

## Literature Cited

1. Spiro, T.G. and Loehr, T.M. in "Advances in Infrared and Raman Spectroscopy", Vol. 1, Clark, R.J.H. and Hester, R.E., Eds., Heyden, London, 1975, Chapter 3.

2. Woodruff, W.H. and Spiro, T.G., Appl. Spectrosc., (1974) 28 576.

3. Hester, R.E., Grossman, W.E.L., and Ernstbrummer, E. in "Proceedings of the 5th International Conference on Raman Spectroscopy", p. 13, Schmid, E.D., et al., Eds., Schulz Verlag, Freiburg, 1976.

4. Jeanmarie, D.L., Suchanski, M.R., and Van Duyne, R.P., J. Am. Chem. Soc., (1975) 97 1699; Jeanmarie, D.L. and Van Duyne, R.P., ibid., (1976) 98 4029; ibid., 4034; See also more recent reports in this series by Van Duyne and co-workers.

5. Delhaye, M. in "Proceedings of the Fifth International Conference on Raman Spectroscopy", p. 747, Schmid, E.D., et al., Eds., Schulz Verlag, Freiburg (1976).

6. Woodruff, W.H. and Atkinson, G.H., Anal. Chem., (1976) 48 186.

7. Bridoux, M., Deffontaine, A., and Reiss, C., Compt. Rend. C., (1976) 282 771.

8. Campion, A., Terner, J., and El-Sayed, M.A., Nature, (1977) 265 659.

9. (a) Wilbrandt, R., Pagsberg, P., Hansen, K.B., and Weisberg, C.V., Chem. Phys. Lett., (1975) 36 76; (b) Pagsberg, P., Wilbrandt, R., Hansen, K.B., and Weisberg, K.V., ibid., (1976) 39 538.

10. Peticolas, W.L. in "Proceedings of the Fifth International Conference on Raman Spectroscopy", p. 163, Schmid, E.D., et al., Eds., Schulz Verlag, Freiburg, 1976; Peticolas, W.L., personal communication, 1978.

11. Lyons, K.B., Carter, H. L., and Fleury, P.A. in "Light Scattering in Solids", Balkanski, M., Leite, R.C.C., and Porto, S.P., Eds., p. 244, Flammarion, Paris, 1976.

12. Woodruff, W.H. and Farquharson, S., Anal. Chem., (1978) 50 1389.

13. Nestor, J.R., Princeton University, personal communication, 1974.

14. Woodruff, W.H., Pastor, R.W., and Dabrowiak, J.C., J. Am. Chem. Soc., (1976) 98 7999.

15. Bloembergen, N., Amer. J. Phys., (1967) 35 989.

16. Maier, M., Appl. Phys., (1976) 11 209.

17. Antonini, E. and Brunori, M., "Hemoglobin and Myoglobin in their Reactions with Ligands", North-Holland, Amsterdam, 1971.

18. Hoard, J.L. in "Hemes and Hemoproteins", Chance, B., Estabrook, R.W., and Yonetani, T., Eds., Academic Press, New York, 1966, pp. 9-24; Hoard, J.L., Hamor, M.J., Hamor, T.Z., and Caughey, W.S., J. Am. Chem. Soc., (1965) 87 2312.

19. Perutz, M.F., Nature, (1970) 228 726.

20. Shank, C.V. and Ippen, E.P., and Bersohn, R., Science, (1976) 193 50.

21. Woodruff, W.H. and Farquharson, S., Science, (1978) 201 831.

22. Alpert, B., Banerjee, R., and Lindqvist, L., Proc. Nat. Acad. Sci. USA, 71, 558 (1974).

23. Sawicki, C.A. and Gibson, Q.H., J. Biol. Chem., (1976) 251 1533.

24. Ferrone, F.A. and Hopfield, J.J., Proc. Nat. Acad. Sci. USA, (1976) 73 4497.

25. Spiro, T.G. and Strekas, T.C., J. Am. Chem. Soc., (1974) 96 338.

26. Scholler, D.M. and Hoffman, B.M. in "Porphyrin Chemistry", Longo, F.R., Ed., 1978, Ann Arbor Sciences.

27. Spiro, T.G. and Burke, J.M., J. Am. Chem. Soc., (1976) 98 5482.

RECEIVED September 11, 1978.

# INDEX

# INDEX